DRINK, DEAR BOY?

Drink, Dear Boy?

Alwyne Chappell

JANUS PUBLISHING COMPANY
London, England

First published in Great Britain 2010
by Janus Publishing Company Ltd,
105–107 Gloucester Place,
London W1U 6BY

www.januspublishing.co.uk

British Library Cataloguing-in-Publication Data
A catalogue record for this book is available from the British Library

ISBN 978-1-85756-706-9

Cover Design: Janus Publishing

Printed and bound in Great Britain

Dedication

I dedicate this book to Jean.

Without whose total support, my dreamed of adventure would never have happened.
Nor, without Jean's encouragement, would I have completed *Drink, Dear Boy?*

Acknowledgement

Many thanks to my supporters club who read the original unwieldy manuscript
double-spaced on one-sided A4 paper. All found errors but none found all errors.
Your enthusiasm for my project is much appreciated.

Ian Chappell
Stuart Chappell
Amanda Chappell
Mary Chappell
John Fairfoot
Janet Fairfoot
Jean Baum
Brian Black
Peter Black
Charmian Perkins
Colin Geddes
Birgitta Dammann
Nick Ellerby
John Wood

My last thank you is to Jeannie Leung, Managing Director of Janus Publishing.
For taking the stress out of the publishing process and accepting with humour
my constant (annoying) telephone requests for progress reports.

Contents

Chapter One

Better make a plan, build a boat and sell the house. The hard bit is saying goodbye.

The yacht, a 10m sloop, lay serenely at anchor; the water was so clear you could see the anchor chain snaked out on the weed-free seabed. The bay's near-perfect circle was framed with lush vegetation, forming a cool backdrop to the deserted white sandy beach and through the opening to the Mediterranean, the sea colour changed to dark blue.

I felt the boat lurch and heard the warps groan; I put down the August edition of the yachting magazine. Peering through the porthole I could see that the barnacle-encrusted timber post – part of the Blyth Harbour jetty – was nicely scraping the paint from the topsides of our yacht *Delphenus*. The rusty freighter – the cause of our erratic movement – was disappearing into the misty rain, leaving its muddy wake slapping against our hull. I studied the photograph on the cover of the glossy magazine again.

'That's where we're going to sail one day' I announced, prodding the front cover.

Jean nodded; she had heard such statements many times before and mouthed in unison as I completed my proclamation, 'When the children are old enough to look after themselves we're off to the Med.'

I struggled into my waterproofs, trying not to knock the table on which our children were playing Monopoly, and climbed out of the hatch. As I repositioned the fenders between *Delphenus* and the abrasive jetty timbers the rain intensified; large drops of dirty water fell from the jetty 5m above and splashed onto my new varnish work.

Most sailors are dreamers. They crave something different from the everyday norm and those who sail England's north-eastern coastal waters probably dream more than most. Whitby is the only haven between the Humber and Tyneside that offers entry for boats whatever the state of the tide. The Humber's shoal waters at low tide are unkind to the unwary; Tyneside is fine, but your boat is apt to get covered in coal dust.

Safe, idyllic bays are non-existent and consequently, the north-eastern yachting scene doesn't hog the front cover of glossy sailing magazines.

I pulled my waterproof hood tighter as the rain intensified and I watched the rising tide slopping darkly and ominously around the jetty supports: another typical summer sailing holiday for the Chappell family.

'Yes,' I said to myself, 'one day we're going to sail off to the Med.'

When you have 11 and 12-year-old children, planning a lifestyle change for the time when they reach maturity is a project that falls into the long-term planning category. In our case, my wife Jean and I decided that we had ten years to wait before my dream of sailing off to the Med could be realised. I specify my dream, rather than our dream, for it has to be said that Jean went along with it, rather than enthusiastically embracing it.

Jean's great loves were her family and her home, her family being two sons, a daughter and me; home was three small stone cottages converted into one. It was now known as The Cottage and was set in a quiet cul-de-sac in the centre of Boston Spa, a small Yorkshire village midway between Leeds and York.

Why should I want to sail away from all this? Well, I didn't particularly want to leave everything we had, for I was well aware of all our blessings. Had I the funds to enable me to scratch every itch without changing anything … well, that's a different dream altogether. As I didn't have sufficient money to enable me to retire, there were a few gaps in the sailing-away-from-it-all feasibility assessment. I told myself that to sail away with total financial security would remove any sense of achievement that sailing into the unknown would provide; I was probably overtired at the time.

Whilst the eighteenth birthday seems to be the popular coming-of-age choice in many families, Jean and I preferred the traditional 21 years. It was out of the question to leave our children whilst in their teens; even leaving them when they reached the age of twenty-one wouldn't be much easier. To leave at the later time fitted in with my feeling that we should set off on our adventure before I reached the age of fifty. If we didn't leave before then, I believed that we would become too comfortable and that we would keep finding reasons to delay the whole project.

We had ten years to go, which was surely long enough for any project, but there was much to do and ten years would probably seem little enough as time went by. Planning would be the key, for which there is no substitute. The strange thing about planning is that the required level of it seems to be proportional to the amount of money available. We would require a new boat for our adventure and based on the above simplistic rule we would require some seriously detailed planning.

Delphenus was our 8m Stella class sailing boat with a clinker-built mahogany hull: that is each timber plank overlapping the edge of the plank below. She had a single-cylinder petrol engine and, with luck, it sometimes came to life when the starting handle was turned. There were no electrics, so the lighting was courtesy of gimballed brass oil lamps. Space was at a premium for two adults and three rapidly growing children. I forgot to mention that she was beautiful.

Regretfully, however, she wasn't the right craft for our planned project. We required a bigger, modern and more comfortable vessel with a reliable auxiliary diesel engine. Buying a new boat would be extremely costly, so the answer was simple enough: I built *Spindrift*; sounds good said quickly. But I wasn't quick enough; had I started the project a year earlier I would have avoided the newly introduced VAT.

I sold *Delphenus* and bought the glass fibre deck and hull mouldings of a Mirage 28, along with a separate cast iron keel; the rest would be up to me. Fortunately, the manufacturer offered an advice service for those brave or foolish enough to attempt home boatbuilding; unfortunately, they went into liquidation. I heard that another company bought them out, but that didn't help me at the time.

I built *Spindrift*, with the help of all my family, in a timber storage shed attached to the joinery shop of the company I worked for. Throughout the build, every weekend was spent in the draughty and often bitterly cold shed. If the work required extra hands the whole family would be there, but generally just the two whose turn it was on the roster would accompany me with never a complaint.

The final fitting out took place in our front garden, which was next to my workshop. Jean wasn't too happy about my workshop, for under normal circumstances it was our dining room. However, I assured her that when I had finished, there would be no sign that the room had been used for anything other than dining.

Regrettably, the protective covering placed over our polished oak dining table proved to be not man enough for the job. Acetone had done its worst and the table was never the same again. Jean has a habit of resurrecting this unfortunate incident during totally unrelated discussions; there seems to be no statute of limitation with regard to this particular crime that really should be long forgotten.

I would say just one word to those who would have you believe that the sense of achievement and satisfaction gained from sailing a self-built boat is worth all the hard work: taradiddle. Such a theory is akin to suggesting that you would enjoy cricket all the more had you made your own bat. If sailing is what you want to do, then two years of boat building is less than satisfying.

I therefore salute all home boatbuilders and particularly those who manage to complete their projects. I have never seen any statistics related to DIY boatbuilding, but judging by the number of partly built crafts for sale in the late 1970s, I wouldn't be surprised to learn that more than half of all home-built boat projects ended in failure.

I was fortunate to have covered facilities with woodworking machinery and equipment to hand, yet even with this considerable advantage it took two years of dedicated hard slog to complete *Spindrift*. I'm sure that had I attempted to carry out all the work in my garden, I would have done well to complete the project in five years.

Spindrift was launched in the late seventies and I have to say that the event was something of an anticlimax. For two years I had looked up at her shiny dark blue-green hull dwarfing everything in the joiner's shop. Then followed a period of her looking massive on our front lawn; garden gnomes couldn't compete with *Spindrift*. Consequently, I was totally unprepared for the shock of seeing how small she looked from the quayside as she floated in her natural environment.

For two years I had dreamed of sailing *Spindrift*, always safe in the knowledge that she would cope with anything the sea could throw at her. Now, here she was, rocking in the wake of a passing outboard-propelled rubber dinghy: I experienced that rush of adrenaline commonly known as panic.

Each member of the family had their own private feelings at the launch ceremony; I suspect that the most common emotion was relief. Jean's relief was almost certainly linked to the restoration of her dining room and its slowly diminishing workroom fragrance of acetone and epoxy resin.

For my eldest son, Ian, his strongest emotion I suspect would be the relief of seeing the end of the obligatory "help Dad" weekend work roster; regrettably marred by the knowledge that hotel holidays would be a thing of the past. Ian wasn't alone in the sailing fraternity to have friends who asked the question, 'Are you having a holiday this year or are you sailing with your dad?'

My younger sony, Stuart – who actually enjoyed working on the boat, but like me is both a pessimist and a sailing enthusiast – would have been relieved to note that *Spindrift* was actually floating but mostly he would be excited at the prospect of taking her out to sea.

My daughter, Lynne – blithe to a degree – whose cup is always half full and never half empty, would be looking forward to having lunch on board.

Spindrift: Masthead Bermudan Sloop. Sail No: 76. Colour: aquamarine. Length OA: 8·5 m. Beam: 2·2 m. Draft: 1·4 m. Auxiliary engine: diesel 10 hp. Launched: May 1979.

A major portion of the preparation towards my Mediterranean dream had been completed and the realisation of my ingrained dream now seemed to be that bit closer.

There is absolutely no substitute for experience and naturally, the older one gets, the more experience is gained. However, I have noted that whilst my experience appears to enable me to give clear-cut advice to others, I often fall well short of such clarity when making personal decisions.

I say this because I've noticed that it isn't my experience that changes my likes and dislikes; such things seem to happen unconsciously as the years roll on. Hindsight may confirm what I should have done, but I tend to ignore my experience to suit my desires at the time. So my choice of boat owed little to experience: I just liked the shape of it.

I can now confirm with hindsight that my choice of vessel was a good one, but *Spindrift* did look alarmingly small when she was launched and whilst my dream was as strong as ever, my inner confidence wasn't flying as high as I would have wished. What was required now was a passage or two made in inclement weather conditions to fortify my confidence in her; my experience of sailing off the north-eastern coast told me that I wouldn't want for such conditions. Passages to Holland, France and cruising the east coast of England and Scotland gave me confidence in *Spindrift's* ability to cope with the sort of weather conditions that by and large scare me witless.

Following an uncomfortable crossing from Ijmuiden we dropped anchor in Whitby Harbour a little after 2.00 a.m.: it was cold, damp and June. Happy to be safely in port we were all out to the world in minutes.

Customs generally adopt a friendly approach, but I could never shake off the feeling that just beneath the surface, they harboured a suspicion that you may well be the Mr Big of an international smuggling ring. When viewed on an approaching high-powered boat – loudspeaker-voiced and uniformed – they have a presence. Even though my duty-free drink store is well below the permitted level I have to fight the urge to dump it all overboard.

Lynne shook me awake.

'There's someone knocking outside, Dad.'

I scrambled into my crumpled, damp jeans; presence and pyjamas don't go together. I noticed the bulkhead clock was showing after 9.00 a.m. as I poked my head up through the hatch. Customs had arrived in the form of one officer in a crumpled uniform.

The Whitby customs service didn't have a high-powered boat; in fact, they didn't have a boat of any description. The bright yellow Woolworth's inflatable must have been borrowed or commandeered in true *Dad's Army* fashion from some young holidaymaker: it certainly lacked presence.

It seems he spotted our Q flag – the yellow pennant you're obliged to display when entering one country from another by sea – at 8.00 a.m. and it had taken him an hour to get to us. He handed me the form that skippers of vessels from foreign ports are required to complete and deposit in the post box provided. After a few weather-related pleasantries he paddled his way back to the quay. It was good to know that the shores of Great Britain were safe from the illegal entry of goods and people.

I relaxed in the cockpit with a mug of coffee and contemplated the situation. Jean, Lynne and Stuart had joined the shoppers and holidaymakers ashore and as it was June, they were clad in heavy sweaters like everyone else. At such times my dream of sailing off to the Mediterranean was intense. I recognised that our trip to Holland was most likely the last holiday cruise that we would have with our family in UK waters. We had been fortunate in that our children were still prepared to come on holiday with us, let alone be subjected to the discomforts of life at sea in a small boat.

Only four of us had cruised to Holland in the summer of 1981. Ian at the age of twenty had decided to forgo the joys of this year's North Sea sailing holiday, and had convinced the ICI management that they could not face the future with confidence if he were to take a two-week break. He was a luxury holiday man and whilst I was disappointed to see the first break up of full family holidays, I could see his point; for North Sea cruising was hard work and whilst enjoyable, it often fell short of being truly relaxing. I realised that in my all-consuming dream to sail away to the Mediterranean, I had failed to consider sailing in other UK areas more suited to cruising than the North Sea. Whitby was quick and easy to access, but after years of sailing from there the advantage of speedy access was rapidly falling down the plus list. Once I begin to go off something, there is little or no time span between going and gone. The following sailing season *Spindrift* was in Scotland based in Troon Marina.

After exploring the Isles of Arran, the Kyles of Bute and Loch Fyne on weekend trips, we went by way of the Crinan Canal for an extended cruise of the Western Isles: surely the best cruising area in the whole of the UK. I won't dwell on the intense pleasure and satisfaction we experienced when sailing this area, for this isn't a sailing story, albeit boats do figure strongly.

My dream of getting away from the proprieties of life in the middle lane probably started in my schooldays, a period not much to my liking. The sailing bit came later, offering, as it does, the opportunity to be in an environment that demands that you make all the decisions related to your own welfare, without assistance or hindrance from any other source. Getting away from it all can be achieved in many ways, but if you've got a boat, then sailing away seems to be a logical step.

North Sea sailing fired my yearning to sail in warmer and more exotic locations and I did wonder whether, had I always sailed amongst the Western Isles, my resolve to sail off to the Mediterranean would have been as strong. Well, yes, it would actually, for whilst the Western Isles were beautiful, sailing amongst them was often uncomfortably cold and wet.

Many people have said to me that they didn't possess the courage to give up everything and sail away to an unknown future. To those people I would say that in my case, naivety figured more strongly than courage, for I never really doubted that we would enjoy ourselves and that everything would work out well. If anyone was courageous it was Jean, who would have been much happier staying at home; Jean was genuinely apprehensive with regard to our future well-being. I have to say that even with my tunnel vision, there were times when my resolve weakened and staying at home did seem to have a lot going for it.

It was during such a period that some of our very close friends went for a short holiday. We spent an evening with Roy and Jean Poulter having a few drinks prior to them taking off to welcome in the New Year on the French Riviera. We never saw Roy again. He was admitted to a French hospital complaining of stomach pains and died a week later from pancreatic failure at the age of forty-eight.

The usual comments were paraded. "This life isn't a practice run"; "You never know when it's your turn"; "You should live every day as if it were your last". We all decide to alter our ways, yet the best most of us achieve is leaving work a little earlier for about a week and then returning to our old ways. Responsibilities, as we perceive them, take over. But in this instance, Roy's death had a profound effect on me. If I had previously entertained any lurking doubts as to the expediency of going for my dream, they were now well and truly expunged.

My resolve to stick to the plan was further strengthened by the fact that I was unhappy at work. As production director of a manufacturing company, it was my lot to reduce the labour force over a period of time. The head office in London had issued instructions that all employees being made redundant – even those who had worked most of their lives for the company – should receive the absolute minimum redundancy payment that would legally stand. All this was happening at a time when the state-owned coal industry was reducing its labour force by offering huge redundancy and early retirement packages; it was a demoralising period.

You will have surmised that the arguments for putting off my dream to sail away were becoming thin on the ground. The die was cast when a communication from head office confirmed that they were negotiating the sale of our company to a competitor: after years of rivalry we were now to be friends.

I didn't like the new owner and did little to disguise the fact and after several months of constant disagreements – and I must confess some considerable hostility on my part – we agreed that our chances of achieving a successful relationship were less than nil. Preparations for our lifestyle change had been activated; our adventure had its feet in the starting blocks.

A few weeks after leaving my new employer I was offered a job with one of the companies in the group that had previously employed me. I was to be self-employed and would project-manage, for the first few months, a contract to build two Mormon churches. It was agreed that I would leave once I had the two projects up and running. I programmed six months for the task, for I felt that to remain involved beyond that time would weaken my resolve to continue chasing my dream.

It isn't easy to take that final step; giving up everything in pursuit of a lifestyle that is outside society's social safety net. Going abroad to start a new career is difficult enough, even when the move is under the umbrella of the company that employs you, complete with the social aids and benefits that are transferable between EC countries. Relocation in a floating home is altogether more risky. If it's your intention to sail between different countries then you can forget state assistance in any form.

I never could quite understand how some non-British visitors could enter Britain and receive medical treatment from the National Health Service with apparent ease. Don't even try to get medical assistance for your backache whilst on a Greek island, unless you have the appropriate cash in hand.

I had reached the stage where thinking too deeply about our move was too scary; it was far better to concentrate on the jobs to be done. The two main tasks were preparing The Cottage for sale and finding a suitable property that would provide a comfortable home for our children and peace of mind for their parents.

We had considered leaving our children in the family home, but realised that the upkeep of a property built in the 1800s would be asking a bit much of three young people. The ideal property for them would be an apartment with no maintenance or gardening responsibilities. It would be even better if the apartment were newly built, offering several years without the need to paint and decorate. Fortunately, there were several new projects to view at the time and we selected one in the small village of Scarcroft, midway between Boston Spa and Leeds.

The builders must have been heartily sick of the sight of me, for I gave them no respite from my constant pestering, to ensure that the apartment was completed on the agreed date. Our beloved cottage was sold, but I dare not ask Jean if she thought that we were doing the right thing.

Can you believe that after years of planning we were running out of time? Ian and Stuart had booked their holidays and were to join us in Cannes in August. It was late April and we needed to be leaving Troon no later than the beginning of June, to ensure that they wouldn't be sleeping on the beach in our absence.

We all moved into the flat in May and as there were only two bedrooms, Jean and I were invited as our children's first guests to sleep on the floor. We were to be fed and cared for by our family until the weekend when one of them would drive us up to Troon.

Our last meal on the Friday night seemed unreal; the memory of it still makes my eyes prickle. We all tried to be upbeat, and indeed there was an element of excitement for everyone. For Jean and me it was our pending adventure and for our children it was the fact that day-to-day parental support – sometimes viewed as interference – would be a thing of the past. On reflection, that element of excitement we all felt was heightened by a very strong dose of apprehension.

Our children were now full-grown adults and we enjoyed their company; we were going to miss them so very, very much. I would even miss those nights when I was aroused from a television-induced sleep by a room full of giants, all eating fish and chips and smelling of beer; our children's gang of friends tended to be physically large, with matching appetites. After their weekly Friday night out, they invariably all returned to The Cottage to clear us out of bread, butter and pickles.

I reflected on this memory when at our last family dinner prior to our leaving, we'd had a super meal and all sat chatting around the cheese board. The general conversation stopped dead when Lynne blurted out the words, 'Mum, do you really need all that cheese; have you any idea just how much it costs?'

No doubt Lynne's first cheese-buying experience – now about to become a regular weekly feature – had been an unwelcome shock, but it just about summed up how uptight we all were; the next day we left for Troon.

With Stuart driving the car we set off on a journey of silences stitched together by small talk. We all had our own thoughts; Jean's centred on leaving her home and family for a future that offered only uncertainties. I naturally had niggling worries, but there was the added pressure of knowing that I was the one responsible for the unsolicited change in my family's life. I was also emotionally charged by the realisation that Stuart, the most self-sufficient of our offspring, was actually going to miss his mum and dad. The emptiness that we were left with when Stuart drove away from Troon Marina was one that gives Jean and me the shivers to this day.

Now that our journey was actually under way and my dream about to be realised, it was strange that our visit to Troon seemed little different to a normal sailing weekend; provided, that is, that I ignored the feeling of apprehension in the pit of my stomach. It didn't take long for a sense of surrealism to impress itself upon me; I felt as if I was viewing everything from a distance. This strange, ethereal feeling that I had was most probably down to the fact that I wasn't sleeping very well. I lay at night making lists of things to do before sailing; lists that grew ever longer at the rate of two additions for each task completed.

The feet that I was going to push into my new sailing-wellies were definitely several degrees below the accepted norm; not only that, but I didn't feel too well, either. The gum above a top back tooth was swelling nicely and as it was the shape and size of a large pea it had altered the contour of my cheek.

The dentist's receptionist was clearly in love with the dentist as well as herself. She was a well turned out 40-year-old who was full of her own importance, devoid of charm and totally disinterested in my plight.

'I think I may be able to fit you in if there's a cancellation over the next week or two.' She was clearly unaware that her winning smile came over as a smirk. 'Perhaps you could call back in a few days; I might have some news for you.' Her eyes softened. 'The dentist,' she informed me, 'is always extremely busy.'

I'm sure that in a perkier mood and without the speech-slurring gumboil, I could have delivered a withering response, but as "Gep shtupped" lacked both style and witticism, I settled for scornful body language and made a lofty exit.

The doctor's receptionist, however, looked and sounded like Dr Finlay's housekeeper, Janet. She was sympathetic and allowed me to see the doctor at once. He inspected my gum and pronounced that I had an abscess and should go and see a dentist!

Troon had lost its appeal and I wanted to be away. Stuff the dentist and double stuff his receptionist and whilst I was at it, stuff the abscess. I purchased an extra box of painkillers and settled our marina bill.

Back on board *Spindrift* I importantly announced to Jean that we were setting off the next day.

'Yes, I thought we would be, everything's ready,' she smiled. 'Would you like a cup of tea?'

How do women know what you're going to do before you've even decided? Jean was busy stowing loose items likely to fly around in a rough sea; her demeanour suggested that leaving wasn't such a big deal. I sat at the chart table to plan our first passage; I'm not sure why, for I knew it off by heart. I'd already done it about twenty times before.

So, this was it. All that time dreaming and planning and now we were ready for the off, ready for the start of our big adventure. The thought crossed my mind that sometimes I can be a real plonker.

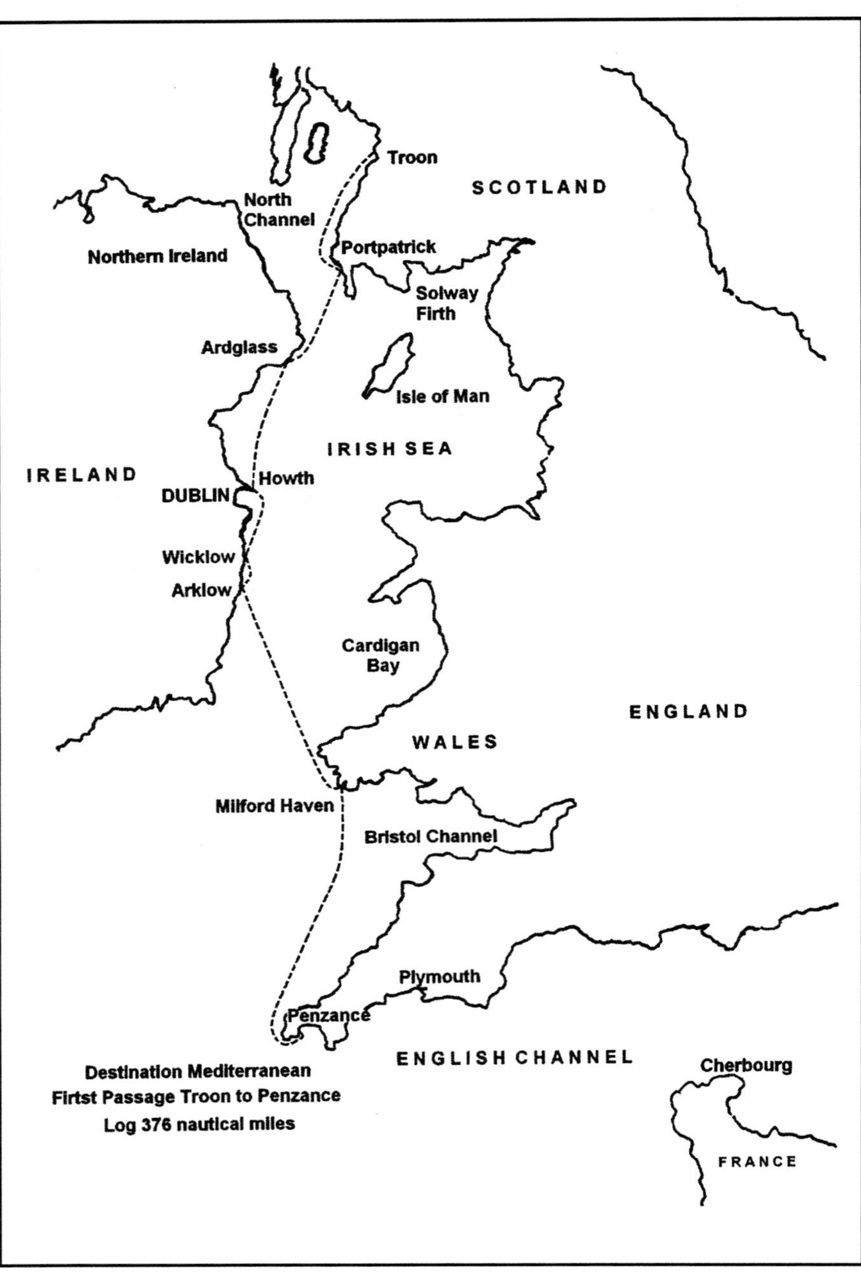
Troon
SCOTLAND
North Channel
Northern Ireland
Portpatrick
Solway Firth
Ardglass
Isle of Man
IRISH SEA
IRELAND
Howth
DUBLIN
Wicklow
Arklow
Cardigan Bay
ENGLAND
WALES
Milford Haven
Bristol Channel
Plymouth
Penzance
ENGLISH CHANNEL
Cherbourg
FRANCE
Destination Mediterranean
Firtst Passage Troon to Penzance
Log 376 nautical miles

Chapter Two

Port captain likes whisky and the shipping forecast is rubbish.

I've often heard the words "I'd like to go sailing like you, but I suffer from seasickness." Well, I can confirm that many sailors suffer from seasickness and I'm one of them. I'm most vulnerable just after the winter lay-up. Eat the wrong things and over-imbibe just prior to casting off is a good way of ensuring an uncomfortable sail. However, the two main causes of seasickness are disorientation and apprehension.

As a child, I suffered from carsickness; any journey over 5 or 6 miles had me wishing for an early death. As for large boats such as cross-channel ferries, they have me feeling green during harbour manoeuvres. I'm told that it's something to do with the inner ear not giving the brain the appropriate information: hence, you think that you're standing upright, when in fact you're already at 80 degrees from the horizontal. However, in a small boat with a bit of a sea running, the movement tends to be so violent that you don't require the inner ear to tell the brain that if you don't grab hold of something quickly, you'll fall flat on your back.

On small boats I'm not as prone to seasickness as a result of disorientation. I can only conclude, therefore, that when I feel nauseous the cause is apprehension; in other words, I'm scared. Being scared is perhaps no bad thing, for it makes you err on the side of caution, which is an admirable trait when in charge of a small vessel, or a large one for that matter.

Bad weather, poor navigation, out-of-date charts and over-reliance on seagoing safety regulations; all can be dangerous. Regulations designed to increase the margin of safety for mariners are much the same as the regulations for drivers of motor vehicles: they only offer protection if everyone observes the rules.

For instance, the International Collision Regulations clearly state that when two vessels are on a collision course, the vessel with the right of way – I'll not bore you with all the detail – should maintain course and speed. It also states that: power-driven vessels shall keep clear of sailing vessels when under sail and not using engines. These regulations, which are agreed internationally, do not, of course, apply to Spanish fishing boats or Greek vessels of any description.

It's definitely advisable for all skippers of vessels, be they large or small, to exercise extreme care and err on the side of caution at all times, but most specifically when navigating in Greek or Spanish waters. They should never insist on their right of way over another vessel, unless they happen to be on a collision course with a pedalo.

So, as the first passage of our adventure was also the first passage of the year, I decided that the 50 miles or so trip from Troon to Portpatrick would do for starters.

We slipped out of Troon Marina just after 7.00 a.m. on 29 May 1984. Jean was still in bed and there was nobody around to wave us off; I felt very lonely and absolutely great. I was experiencing a whole range of emotions, but the overriding one by far was excitement.

At seven thirty Lady Isle was abeam and I set a course for Ailsa Craig, the enormous island rock lying about 10 miles west of Girvan and a navigator's dream, for there's no way that you can mistake it for any other landmark.

On an average road, the drivers of two approaching vehicles can pass within feet of each other without any qualms at a combined speed in excess of 100 miles per hour; yet here I was approaching Ailsa Craig at about 5 knots and the rock loomed so large that I felt the need to give it about a quarter-mile clearance. Not that I was overawed, you understand; just practising prudent seamanship.

We left Ailsa Craig astern at about 11.15 a.m. with Jean still in bed. She had poked her nose out of the hatch a couple of hours earlier, but decided that the excitement of it all was too much and so she retired back to her bunk. The fact that *Spindrift* was rolling around in a rather sloppy sea and a light following wind may have also been a factor for her state of slumber, or idleness.

The wind increased to about 13 knots and I was able to get the sails up and kill the engine. With the *Spindrift* now acting like a proper sailing boat with no engine noise Jean resurfaced and provided lunch: this was what it was all about.

It lasted for about half an hour before the wind dropped and we were back under engine again. Still, we'd at least had a brief glimpse of how good sailing can be and we entered Portpatrick Harbour at

4.30 p.m. Not a memorable journey in seagoing terms, but it was the first leg of our adventure and in that sense I shall never forget it.

We were snugly tied up to the quayside and I wasn't best pleased when I spotted another yacht preparing to come alongside. It's not that I'm antisocial, but a boat tied alongside with a thoughtless crew aboard does tend to get to me, particularly if on their return from the local bar they clump noisily over the deck in the early hours of the morning. But this was the start of a new life and aggravation was to be a thing of the past, so I took the newcomer's warps and helped him moor up. Back in the cockpit he held out his right hand for shaking and with his left he passed me a gin and tonic. The first day had really gone quite well.

Our next passage was a 40-mile hop across to Ardglass, Northern Ireland, and a little lie-in was in order, particularly as a 9.00 a.m. start would give us the best tidal assistance. By the time Jean and I had surfaced, our neighbours had already left without making a sound and I started off the day with that niggling guilty feeling. Early risers have a knack for making me feel contrite at such times. I really hate it when those who are unable to lie in bed beyond 6.00 a.m. tell me how wonderful it was first thing and how I've missed the best part of the day.

As we motored beyond the harbour entrance we met a southerly breeze, that coupled with the sea squeezing between the north-east coast of Ireland and the Mull of Kintyre, created an uncomfortable sea swell in the North Channel. Motoring once again we rolled our way to Ardglass Harbour, where we tied up alongside the fishing boat with the smartest-looking paint job; much in the manner that new car owners park next to clean cars in the hope that doing so will lessen the chance of their new pride and joy being scratched.

Our arrival had been watched by a uniformed official standing on the quayside high above us and once we had secured our lines he climbed down the iron rungs to the deck of the fishing boat. I couldn't think what it was that I had done wrong, for we were still in the UK and were not required to display the Q flag.

'Will ye been coming far?' he asked conversationally.

'No, we've just come fr –' I started.

'There's a swell out there today so ther'is. Watched ye rolling out there, an a'm thinking ye'll be pleased it's over, so ye will. Ye'll be safe enough for the night a'm thinking. Will ye be staying long?' He raised his eyebrows as if an answer would now be in order.

'Well, we were plann –' I began.

'If ye's staying long, ye'd be better over there so ye will.' He pointed further along the quay.

'I think that this will be fi –' I tried to assure.

'Ye see the swell comes across fro –'

'Drink? Would you like a drink?' My first completed sentence stopped his verbal flow as he moved from the fishing boat deck into *Spindrift's* saloon with the speed and grace of an Olympic athlete.

The whisky bottle – only half full – was soon emptied and I opened a new one; he had now taken to pouring his own. About an hour later, having poured the last dregs of the second bottle into his glass, he remembered that his wife was sitting in the car waiting for him on the quay.

'Why didn't you say she was up there?' I spoke without thinking and wondered if my concern may be taken as an invitation for his wife to join us. I quickly added.

'You'd best be off, then; I don't want your wife blaming me for keeping you.'

'Ah ye'v nerry worries bout that sir; she's a wonderful woman so she is.' He shook his head as if amazed at just how wonderful his wife really was. He placed his hand on my shoulder and fixed me with a watery stare. 'A wonderful woman so she is.' He stumbled into the cockpit. 'Ye'v a wonderful boat, so ye have sir.' Everything now was wonderful.

His movements on leaving *Spindrift* lacked the feline grace that he'd displayed when coming aboard. As he negotiated his way across the deck of the fishing boat with its hydraulic winches, coils of rope and stacked fish boxes, there was not so much as a stumble; he paused before each obstacle and with studied deliberation he skirted it with feet to spare. Clearly, it wasn't the first time he had negotiated the congested deck of a fishing boat after partaking of the odd whisky. I watched him climb up to the quayside scaling what was now, owing to the falling tide, a very high ladder indeed.

I presumed that his welcome drinks with visitors were one of the perks of his job. The thought did cross my mind that I hadn't asked for any proof of identification. Nah, it couldn't be: he was wearing a uniform.

The next day was to be a 70-mile passage to Howth Marina, Dublin, and I was pleased to note that the forecast was for the wind to strengthen from a southerly to a westerly force four. It would give us a good broad reach under sail and as we would be in the lee of the land mass the sea would have no swell.

Next morning I checked out the sea conditions by looking over the harbour wall. From my position it was difficult to assess the wind strength, although the white caps on the waves suggested it was brisk; it was clear however that the predicted change in direction from southerly to westerly hadn't yet taken place. I radioed the coast guard and he confirmed the same forecast as the one issued some twelve hours earlier. The westerly shouldn't be long in coming, but for a while we would be tacking hard on the wind, so I hoisted the mainsail and number two Genoa whilst we were in the harbour and motored out.

Spindrift took off on a fast broad reach across the north-driven white horses and I switched off the engine as we creamed along at 6 knots, I knew that this would change as soon as we had enough sea room to alter course to a near to southerly one as the wind would allow. It did occur to me that the wind was in excess of the force four that had been forecast. We altered course and immediately we were covered in spray whilst our speed dropped to 4 knots; where the hell was the westerly? I called the coast guard on the radio and was given the same weather forecast.

The problem with sailing generally, and in UK waters in particular, is that the weather, tide and sea conditions rarely combine to be in your best interests. When cruising, your destination can be variable and you have plenty of options, but when passage-making there are only two: you go or stay where you are. Or if, as in our case, you have already set off then you carry on or go back whence you came. I decided that as the wind was eventually going to be westerly, we would carry on under mainsail and power, which would allow a course set closer to the present southerly wind.

By 1.00 p.m. the wind was measuring 20 knots and gusting higher; a full force five no less and still southerly. As I spoke to the coast guard my voice had an edge. I was aware that the forecast they give out on request is from a meteorological office, so I didn't actually tell them that their forecast was rubbish; however, I pointedly suggested that they took a look out of their window.

Spindrift log 16.00: course 130 degrees; wind: south force six; remarks: steep breaking waves, foam and spray all over. Tacking out to sea to clear Cloger Head. It should have read Clogher Head, but I wasn't too interested in spelling at the time. We were now talking major discomfort. I had managed to stay reasonably dry by leaving Spindrift to make her way under auto helm whilst I kept watch behind the spray-hood. Now, however, I couldn't see well enough through the windscreen, so I was hit full in the face every time I looked over it. Jean, sensible girl, was in her bunk resting her eyes; well, to be fair, all of this was my idea.

Spindrift log 17.00: course: 210 degrees; wind: force six–seven; remarks: put third reef in main, waves keep stopping boat. I'm very wet and cold. *Spindrift* log 18.00: skipper has been seasick, sailing and navigating very hard. I felt better having been sick, but I wasn't a happy bunny.

It was now blowing a full force seven and had I consulted the Beaufort scale of wind force, it would have confirmed the blindingly obvious that we were in a near gale. It would also – in its bland, unemotional language – describe how the sea would heap up and how white foam from breaking waves would be blown in streaks along the direction of the wind.

No mention of the noise, that awful bang as a wave crashes against the hull and that fearful shudder that shakes through the mast and rigging right down into the heart of the boat. No mention that you will now be hanging on to whatever fixed item you can find, whilst dreading the possibility that something out on deck may need attention.

Now, I'm aware that many yachtsmen reading such words will raise their eyebrows at such piteous talk. 'What sort of sailor is he, for heaven's sake?' they would declare. Well, for starters I was a scared one; being to windward of rocks in the Irish Sea with 30-knots of wind against the tide is fine for the likes of Sir Chay Blyth, but frankly I didn't think much of it.

It's my opinion that the Beaufort scale of wind force is OK for large racing yachts crewed by hairy-armed gorillas, but for normal people in little 8.5m sailing boats it seems to be a little understated. The scale tells us that a force seven is a near gale and the section for those people on land states: whole trees in motion, inconvenience felt when walking against wind. Now I don't know anything about Mr Beaufort, but I suspect that he didn't take his holidays in a small boat.

Well, for the benefit of those of you who are planning to do so, I can confirm that if you are in a small boat heading into a 30 knot wind and big waves, you're in a full-blown gale. Ignore all bar talk to the contrary and never feel inadequate in the company of those who claim to enjoy such conditions. Above all, never heed advice given by such so-called sailors – their aim is to impress rather than inform and their hot air could prove as dangerous as any other strong wind.

At 8.00 p.m. the tide had turned to match the wind that had dropped slightly to a force six; still a strong blow, but the tide change had altered the state of the sea to something more manageable. Better still, I could now see Lambay Island; just another three hours or so would see us in Howth Marina. Jean had a wan smile on her face when she looked up through the hatch, things were definitely improving and she passed me a mug of coffee, the first since breakfast: wonderful.

By 9.00 p.m. the wind had dropped to 20 knots and we were flying; the lights of Howth were now in view, a welcome sight indeed. At 10.00 p.m. the wind was cranking up again but we were only about an hour from the marina, so as far as I was concerned it could do what it wanted.

It was pitch-black when we felt our way into Howth Marina, where a waving torch guided us to a pontoon. With a sigh of relief we tied up at 11.00 p.m. I was totally knackered and Jean was very tired.

I couldn't believe that the marina attendant wanted me to fill in a form and pay cash for a one-night stay; apparently, yachtsmen had a tendency to leave the marina at dawn to avoid paying. I refused to even look at his form, let alone fill it in, pointing out that they wouldn't get me out to sea – even at gunpoint – at any time during the following day, so he agreed to postpone business transactions until later. The rate was £7 per night, the costliest marina we had ever stayed in and to my mind it was worth every penny. We stayed an extra night enjoying the delights of hot showers and dining out.

Our next ports of call were Wicklow and Arklow, both of which were depressing, particularly Arklow on the sixth of June; Lynne and Stuart's twenty-first birthday. Of all the decisions Jean and I have ever made, being away from our children on that day was the worst. We rang home to wish the twins a happy birthday from a vandalised and smelly phone box. We felt very low and far from cheering Lynne up, we only managed to make her feel worse. Now in tears, she handed the phone to Stuart, who protectively scolded us for making Lynne cry. Docks are rarely uplifting places to be: Arklow on 6 June 1984 sucked.

We clearly hadn't seen the best of Ireland and so were not too unhappy to leave at 7.00 a.m. 7 June 1984. Jean had now found her sea legs and we had meals and things. We picked up a mooring in Dale Flats, Milford Haven, fourteen hours later, where we suppressed a very strong desire to nip up to Yorkshire to see the kids. Next day, we prepared for the passage to Penzance, from where we would leave UK waters.

When planning a passage, the weather, tide and preferred time of arrival at the next port are all-important factors. For this passage, my main aim was to sail round Land's End in daylight; one reason being because I'd never seen Land's End from the sea and it would be a new experience. The other was because I felt that daylight was preferable when navigating this area, for the chart gloomily warned with its wiggly line symbols that in strong winds the seas would be heavy and confused. The chart maker's sadistic nature was allowed free rein, for the chart faithfully recorded the location of the area's many wrecks with little drawings of sunken vessels. Such detailed information can be a little disconcerting. Imagine planning your holiday by car with a road map that recorded the location of every road death accident since records began.

What makes the Land's End wrecks more alarming is the fact that the majority of them are in deep water with no adjacent rocks; it would seem that huge seas powering in from the Atlantic simply overwhelmed the unfortunate vessels. If you consider the likely chaotic conditions when a wind-driven flood-tide sea arrives at Land's End and thrashes around whilst it makes up its mind whether to flow into the English Channel or the Irish Sea, then it's best that you keep your imagination on a tight leash.

The forecast was good and the predicted west by northerly force three to four settled to an even westerly force three. With *Spindrift* creaming along under sail at nearly 6 knots Jean took over the helm, so that I could get some sleep before the night watch.

The night watch was superb, with a moonlit clear sky and a flat sea. Jean offered to take over at 5.00 a.m., but didn't exactly argue when I suggested she had another hour in her bunk. The sun was a big red ball and I was just beginning to feel the warmth from it. We were in for a good day, but would have to motor, for there wasn't a breath of wind. Jean arrived in the cockpit at 6.00 a.m. with mugs of coffee as our engine pushed us briskly along on a flat, glassy sea.

I was totally relaxed and looking forward to a few hours' sleep, so I updated the log and then sat on the edge of my bunk to undress. Now all of you readers who have lived with your partner for many years will understand the power of one-word communication. Just the one word said in a certain way requires no further embellishment. I was half undressed when Jean said, 'Alwyne!'

It was an "I don't know what I'm looking at, but I'm sure you're not going to like it" type of Alwyne. I have rarely moved faster. I stood in the cockpit with one trouser leg around my ankle and stared at a solid white wall about 10 yards high with no apparent ends. The sky was blue above it and the sea a shiny mirror before it. I cut the engine speed and then stopped the boat with a blast astern and still we approached the solid white wall.

There was about a half-knot tidal current pushing us towards the fog and perhaps the fog was rolling towards us, it was difficult to be certain. There was no scale to anything; it was surreal and I wasn't sure if the gap between the fog and us was 50 yards or 500 yards: it was the former.

We slid sideways into the fog wall that was so thick that I unconsciously braced myself for the collision. The hairs on our heads, clothes and my arms and legs were immediately covered in thousands of fine white water particles as the fog folded around us like a predatory ghost.

Brilliant! I had planned this passage to sail around Land's End so that we could see it and we couldn't even see the end of the boat. Our VHF radio then informed all ships in our area that there was fog about; it was good to have it confirmed. There was also a precautionary message, warning us to keep a keen lookout for a fishing boat in our area with a malfunctioning radar scanner; the message offered no suggestions as to how we might achieve such a safety precaution. I engaged forward gear, pointed the *Spindrift* back onto the correct compass setting and went below to get dressed; sleep was out of the question.

Sailing in fog is simply horrible; there isn't anything that can be trusted. Visuals are out, for even in thin fog your imagination provides more input than your eyes, and in thick fog, if your eyes can confirm it, you will probably hit it. If you don't have radar, sound warnings are the thing to go by and they will assist provided, of course, that you have the hearing technology of a bat. After many hours of scientific on-site testing, I'm able to assist all future fogbound navigators with Alwyne's Law: in conditions of dense fog, the direction from the ear to any sound source can be determined when the sound source can be seen.

Sailing in fog has always been hazardous, but the dangers are massively reduced if you have radar. If you don't have radar equipment there's an assortment of position-finding gadgetry that may assist. The most common one for small boats was the Radio Direction Finder (RDF) that could be of assistance or considerable hindrance, dependent on prevailing conditions. Advertisements for such equipment suggested pinpoint accuracy: in reality, their accuracy is akin to that offered by seaweed for weather forecasting.

The theory behind an RDF is that you listen for a Morse code call signal transmitted from a fixed position identified on your chart, a lighthouse or lightship, for instance. Then you search for the signal by wafting around a receiver with a compass mounted on top; when you have identified the signal you locate its direction by pointing the compass at the null: the direction from which the signal is at its weakest.

Now I want you to imagine this. You're being bounced around in a rough sea and it's very noisy; wind and waves tend to enjoy making a noise because it helps to make things scarier. So you're wet, cold and stumbling around in the cockpit and if you've been lucky enough to hear a signal, all you have to do is carefully rotate the receiver. When the signal is really difficult to hear, then all you need to do is record the compass bearing. Simple; what do you think so far?

You need three compass bearing lines for a position fix and I have to be fair and point out that the RDF operating instruction manuals never claim that the bearing lines that you've drawn on your chart will cross at an identical point. The crossing lines will describe a triangle known as a cocked hat and the smaller the cocked hat the more accurate your position fix will be. It follows, therefore, that if your cocked hat covers an area of the Bristol Channel and the M6 motorway, you should proceed with some caution.

Throughout the ages, mariners have crossed the oceans without the aid of electronic equipment and all those years of experience have been utilised by the British Admiralty and the authorities of other seagoing nations to formulate the International Regulations for all mariners.

The regulations have a large section devoted to safety at sea in dangerous fogbound conditions; so as I slowed *Spindrift's* engine so that I had a better chance of hearing something before I hit it, I was pleased that in my pilot books I had the relevant regulations listing the designated sound signals for vessels sailing in conditions of poor visibility; it was comforting to know that they were there at the flick of a page.

- A vessel making way should sound a long signal on its foghorn every two minutes.

- A vessel not making way should sound two long signals on its foghorn every two minutes.
- Vessels not under command or sailing/fishing/towing/ pushing or generally not easily manoeuvred should sound one long, followed by two short blasts every two minutes.
- Vessels that are towed and manned should sound one long and three short blasts every two minutes.
- Pilot vessel on duty should sound one long, followed by three short blasts every two minutes, plus a further four short blasts in between.

I hope you are still with me because there's more:

- Vessels at anchor under 100m in length should ring a bell for five seconds every minute.
- Vessels at anchor over 100m in length should ring a bell for five seconds every minute at the forward end and bang a gong for five seconds every minute at the aft end. All vessels at anchor may also give warning of possible collision to approaching vessels with one short, one long and one short blast.
- If your vessel is unfortunate enough to have run aground, you will be required to sound all the at-anchor signals, preceded and followed by three separate and distinct bell strokes.

In addition to those listed here, there are a variety of foghorn, whistle and bell signals from lighthouses, lightships and buoys all itemised on your chart of the area you are unfortunate enough to be fogbound in.

Regrettably, the entire list here is rendered virtually useless because refraction – the change in direction of sound waves – ensures that in fog you don't have any idea which direction the sound is coming from. Should you be fogbound in an area in which several vessels are confirming their status, panic is as good an option as any.

We could certainly hear signals from time to time and there were occasions when we could actually identify what the sound signals were, but never were we able to pinpoint the actual direction of the sound source until we were hit by the ear-numbing blast of the Longships Lighthouse foghorn. We had groped our way through the fog for nearly six hours hearing real and no doubt some imaginary horn signals and then suddenly we knew exactly where we were.

The Longships Lighthouse is situated on a group of rocks a mile to the west of Land's End and we, with our wide eyes, white knuckles and sticky-uppy hair, were 50 yards away. We saw part of the structure and the menacing adjacent rocks through the swirling fog seconds after we received the cacophonous confirmation that we were immediately adjacent to Longships. How we got so close to such a loud foghorn without recognising the danger I will never know, but it did confirm the accuracy of Alwyne's Law.

Our position fix was now about as accurate as they come and I set a course to find the bell buoy marking Runnel Stone rocks some 4 miles to the south-east. From there we would alter course, to take us into Mounts Bay and then to Penzance.

Some time after rounding the bell buoy we heard voices and I swung *Spindrift* hard over to starboard – how the hell could I be so close to shore? The fog became brighter and suddenly, as if pushing our way through a thick curtain, we burst out into brilliant sunshine: the sky was clear blue and the sea was sparkling.

The coast was a good mile off to port and the voices that we had heard were from the anglers fishing from a flotilla of assorted craft. I can't say that they looked particularly happy as we threaded our way between them, but then anglers rarely appear to be happy. Perhaps they have an inner happiness that doesn't show on the surface, or perhaps we were too close to their lines, or maybe they just thought we were very odd. Well, we were wearing waterproofs and ridiculous grins, whilst they sat straight-faced in T-shirts. Whatever their thoughts were, we were just delighted to be out of the fog and close to harbour.

Penzance has a rectangular harbour basin with lock gates that open for a period either side of high water. We arrived at 2.30 p.m. just on the high tide and the lock gates were open; we were welcomed by a friendly harbour master, who took our warps and helped us to tie up. He chatted away in that friendly, distinctive Cornish accent and without demanding deposits or asking for forms to be filled in he gave us that most treasured item revered by all small-boat-owners: the key to the toilet and shower room. Over the years we have entered many harbours, docks and marinas, but without doubt the welcome we received at Penzance still remains to this day the best ever.

All Yorkshire folk know that only in our county can one really trust the natives. There are even dubious areas just within our own borders; I refer to that western border, where you can never be certain whether or not some cross-border marriages have diluted the Yorkshire strain.

I have to say, however, that whilst I cannot vouch for the whole of Cornwall I can confirm that Penzance is a town where I felt instinctively comfortable. Harbour master, customs officials, shopkeepers, all were friendly – even the dentist.

Since leaving Troon my gum abscess had continued to give trouble. Following the lack of concern experienced with the Scottish dentist – whom I never met and therefore have to agree that he could well have emigrated from England – I entered the nearest surgery with hope rather than conviction that my problem would be solved. How could I have ever doubted? A stunning young female receptionist made me feel like the most important patient she'd seen that day.

The dentist was young in the way policemen appear to be when you're past a certain age and strangely, for someone so young, he treated me as though he was actually interested in my plight. He could save the tooth if treated over a four-week period or he could drain and extract in ten days. I chose the extraction, for we didn't have the time to spare.

A sailing friend of mine had offered to crew for us on one of the early passages and I invited him along for the Irish Sea passage. Call me a cynic, but I wasn't surprised when he found that his diary only allowed him to help on the cross-channel bit: dinner in France has the edge on Dale Flats, Milford Haven. Paul duly arrived in Penzance, but we had to wait for my tooth extraction before we could leave.

Our arrival in Penzance coincided with the miners' strike and although Mr Arthur Scargill had announced that he and his picket lines were ensuring that imported coal wasn't a possibility, *Spindrift* was covered every day with a thick coating of black grit not unlike coal dust. I also had a very strong suspicion that the black stuff the grab cranes were loading into wagons from the holds of a large ship was in fact coal.

However, King Arthur – as the media had dubbed him – confirmed that coal couldn't be imported into the UK and that the vast majority of the country's populace was fully in favour of his total blockage of all coal imports. Seems that spin was alive and healthy in the 1980s.

Coal shortages were no longer a worry for us; coal wasn't a commodity that figured high in our future plans. We looked to the Mediterranean sunshine to make heating bills a thing of the past and tomorrow, we would take the next step on our adventure and go foreign.

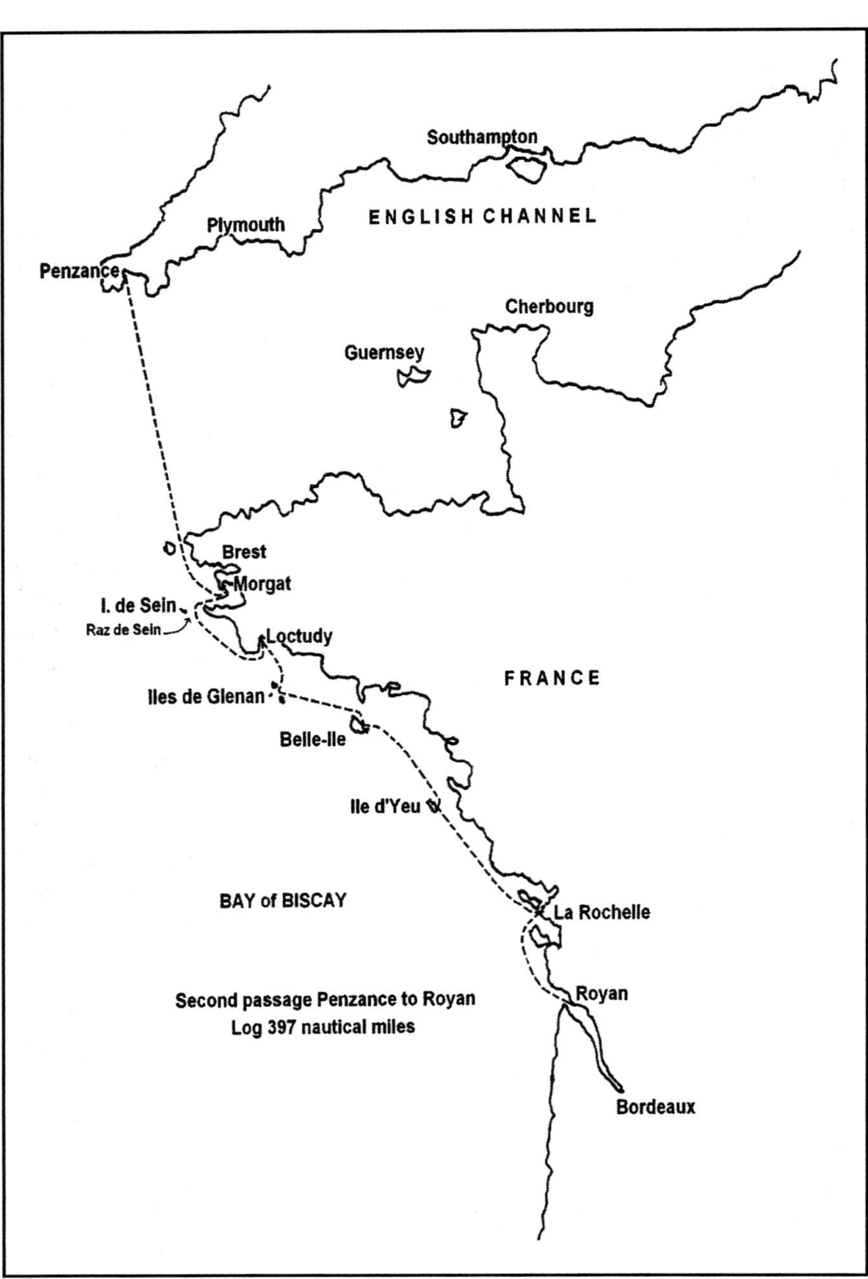

Second passage Penzance to Royan
Log 397 nautical miles

Chapter Three

Goodbye UK. The French are OK, they understand if you shout.

This was the day we were leaving the UK with no return projection: 16 June 1984. Planning over the years had always been concentrated on the period up to leaving the UK and now we were about to enter the "it will be all right on the night" zone. Our only diary date was to be in Cannes for Ian and Stuart's summer holiday; other than that, we had no idea where we would be or what we would be doing one year hence.

I recognised that our venture had no specific goal: something Spock would have deemed illogical. Climbers who scale mountains because they're there seem to have a more valid reason for doing what they do and more to the point, they always know when they have achieved their objective. We on the other hand weren't quite sure what the overall objective was and would therefore experience some difficulty in monitoring the relative success or failure of our venture.

Is it being responsible to knowingly plan a future on the basis that you just want to do your own thing? Are those well-worn phrases "life is not a practice run" and "you never know when it's your turn" really strong enough motives to prompt one to embark on a life-changing venture?

Well, like most of us, I have used those phrases, along with the other well worn "if you don't do it now, you may never get another chance" clincher. So why was the only phrase commanding centre stage in my mind on this day the plaintive and at this moment totally pointless question: "I wonder if we are doing the right thing?"

We left Penzance harbour at 10.25 a.m. in bright sunshine and Paul – excited to be sailing across the English Channel – was doing most of the talking. I don't think he noticed that Jean and I didn't contribute wholeheartedly to the conversation; our original excitement now rather subdued as England's shoreline sank below the horizon.

Our destination was Morgat, just south of Brest, where Paul would leave us. The trip was uneventful other than an exhilarating 12-knot swoop through the Chenal du Four; 6 knots of boat speed and 6 knots of tidal current shot us out from between the Île de Béniguet and Le Conquet, like a cork from a bottle.

We tied up in Morgat at 2.00 p.m. the next day, approximately twenty-seven hours after leaving Penzance. Morgat was, as they say, "a nice place, but I wouldn't want to live there". Paul organised himself a lift to Cherbourg for the next day and Jean and I were able to settle back into a more relaxed and comfortable lifestyle. Those of you who have lived on a small sailing boat will know exactly what I'm saying here, although I'm sure that for most of you further clarification is unnecessary.

I was feeling good, for the sun was shining as I sat in the cockpit planning our next passage, when happy Harry on the next boat – actually it was happy Pierre – disturbed my contented mood with his alarming description of the Raz de Sein.

Pierre was doing much arm waving, sucking in of lips and Gaelic shrugs and grunts. The Raz – which you all know or will have guessed is French for race – was the stretch of water between the Isle of Sein and the mainland. This hazard was apparently, for the small-boat weekend sailor, fraught with more danger than a world circumnavigator could expect when rounding Cape Horn. Naturally, the French could sail this area because they were French and therefore possessed the necessary skills required to navigate such dangerous waters.

'But you, ahaaa,' he used his Maurice Chevalier accent, 'you are Eeengleesh, you have nothing like thees in Eeengland.' Pierre gave a sympathetic shrug. He explained that it would definitely be better in my case, to go the extra few miles out to sea and around the outside of the Île de Sein and the shoal area to the west. True, it would add about 15 miles to the journey; however, 'In the eenterest of safetee,' more shrugs, 'well worth eet, *oui*?'

I was warned also to keep well to the north, lest we be sucked through the channel sideways. He underlined the danger by calling his friends from adjoining boats who, on hearing of my proposed passage, did a formation routine of pursed lips, big shrugs and arm waving. Passers-by, who had hitherto walked on our side of the pontoon, now put distance between us, lest some of our madness be catching.

I spent a sleepless night worrying about the coming ordeal and delayed our start so that we would have the tide in our favour. We left Morgat at 4.30 p.m. and smiling bravely we waved sticky, wet-palmed goodbyes to our French doomsayers.

We approached the Raz de Sein with considerable trepidation, but decided that we should just have a look before committing ourselves to the extra three-hour detour around the outside of the island and the shoal area. We circled just north of the gap between the Pointe du Raz and Île de Sein. I didn't expect a waterfall, but presumed that there would at least be some white water in evidence.

There was nothing, just clear, smooth water with not so much as a ripple and with the combination of tide and boat speed it took us all of four minutes to pass through the hazardous area without incident. Without the pre-match hype, we would have passed through it without noticing. I've no doubt that with wind against tide the area would have to be treated with respect, but no more so than countless danger areas common in UK waters.

No matter, we were on our way again and unless we ran out of time, we were now cruising rather than passage-making: to the purist, it's the same thing, but I think cruising sounds more relaxing. We anchored for the night in Loctudy, a nice quiet backwater, and many boats were laying-to floating moorings with plenty of swinging room. The area pilot stated that visitors could pick up a vacant floating mooring, but must be prepared to move if the owner returned.

Picking up a floating mooring is less hassle than anchoring, but anchoring is far less hassle than having to move if the owner of the mooring returns. If the owner returns from a day trip, the most likely upheaval time would be during dinner but could also occur an hour after you've gone to bed. We decided to anchor beyond the last mooring buoy out of everyone's way and enjoy the solitude of this delightful anchorage.

Jean was preparing dinner and I was checking the chart for the next day's passage, when we heard the shout; I've noticed that shouts in all foreign languages tend to sound aggressive. I'm sure that most of you who have taken a holiday on the continent have at times been surprised to see smiles on the faces of the two people that you had presumed were having a violent argument. Well, the shout sounded aggressive to me, so I put down my glass of wine and climbed into the cockpit oozing ambivalence. A couple of men were sat in a rowing boat about 3 Yards away.

'Yes?' I snapped in Basil Fawlty style.

The unshaven leader, who was manning the oars, pointed towards my anchor chain and delivered a speech at breakneck speed without pausing for breath. In such situations most Englishmen make themselves understood to a non-English linguist simply by speaking slowly and increasing the volume. We do this because we're aware that all foreigners are of limited intelligence and have hearing defects.

'The ... pilot ... book ... states ... that ... I ... can ... anchor ... here,' I shouted in a slow Yorkshire accent.

The unshaven one delivered another torrent of incomprehensible verbiage. My schoolboy French was under pressure now, so I did what I always do in such circumstances: I called for Jean.

'Tell him we've every right to be here and we're not moving,' I instructed.

Jean smiled at them and wished them good day. Then she explained that her French was limited and requested that they speak slowly. The unshaven one beamed through his whiskers and started laying on the charm, as Frenchmen are apt to do when talking to females.

'Tell him to bog off,' I urged.

Jean was still smiling and appeared to be generally passing the time of day with him.

'What do they want?' I guardedly enquired.

'They're here to lay a new mooring and are worried that they may snag our anchor. I think they're saying it will only take five minutes and then we can use it for a week if we want to. And stop looking angry. Smile at them; they're being very friendly and helpful.'

I cast a weak smile in their direction, inwardly annoyed with myself for allowing the French to demonstrate such superior civility. I thanked them in my version of French, but I have to say that they didn't look too impressed and I was pointedly ignored during the remainder of the conversation: Jean was clearly *numéro un*.

We tied up to the new swinging mooring and settled back with a glass of wine, knowing that when we left we wouldn't have the hassle of cleaning mud off the anchor and chain before stowing it prior to getting under way.

There was another shout and this one sounded no friendlier to me than the first one. This time, there was just one man in a rubber dinghy, who was saying exactly the same words at exactly the same speed as our previous visitors. The only difference was that he kept gesturing towards our boat and then pointing back towards the other moored boats.

With commendable calm I explained slowly and loudly that we had been given permission to use the mooring for several days and that we weren't about to move today or the next day for that matter.

He moved the dinghy closer and tapped the side of *Spindrift* and pointed again towards the other moored boats, all the time prattling on excitedly without pause for breath. Right, that's it, I'd had enough; I wasn't going to be pushed around any more! I drew in breath to deliver a full Yorkshire broadside and he smiled: Jean had joined us.

'*Bonsoir, Madame.*' He launched into another non-stop garble. However, by now, I was picking up the odd word: it seemed that he wanted to borrow some food and drink from us.

'This is François and he's invited us to join him and his wife for drinks and nibbles. I think he's saying that he owns a Mirage 28 just like ours. It's moored over there,' Jean pointed to a group of boats about 80 yards away and then hissed under her breath, 'and stop scowling.'

I put on my best friendly grin and leaned over to shake hands. François rowed over at 6.00 p.m. to collect us, which saved us the hassle of having to inflate our own dinghy. I really cannot understand why the English should have such a downer on the French.

The evening was a big success and by the time we were nearing the end of the third bottle of wine, I was expansively explaining why the French and the English have such an affinity. Unfortunately, Jean never has more than one alcoholic drink in a day, let alone an evening; the downside for me being that she can always recount my previous evening's dialogue in accurate detail and it never sounds as good in reprise.

François had purchased his Mirage 28 fully fitted out from the builder Thames Marine and was very keen to see the difference we had made by doing everything ourselves; so we invited them to join us the following evening on *Spindrift* for drinks and nibbles. The evening was again a huge success.

Over the years that we have spent in various countries, it has never ceased to amaze me just how much information can be exchanged between those of differing nationalities, having at best an elementary knowledge of each other's tongue, but a shared similarity in the art of sign language.

The next day, several sailing boats from Loctudy were heading for the Île de Glénan and as the islands were on our route we accepted an invitation to sail in convoy with them. *Margidic*, as Yvonne and François' boat was named, was clearly slower than *Spindrift* and in the interest of Anglo–French relationships, and because Jean insisted, I spilled wind from our sails for the whole journey; François was delighted that our two boats performed in such a similar manner.

The Îles de Glénan are a group of low-lying islands that are teeming with wildlife but are exposed to whatever the Atlantic chooses to throw into the Bay of Biscay; it was definitely a summertime only haven.

We had another good night crowded into a small boat with our very amiable new French friends. I had to wonder if we were all getting on so well together because we were sailing addicts or were the French much nicer people than the English generally give them credit for? Future contact with French authorities, and in particular the customs service, along with all of Cannes shopkeepers, did nothing to persuade me that such fanciful thoughts should be encouraged.

After due consideration, I decided that the English are more in tune with our French neighbours who abide west of a line drawn from the Cherbourg Peninsula down to Toulouse. There was much waving and "bon voyaging" as we left the anchorage in the Îles de Glénan and set sail for Belle Isle about 40 nautical miles to the south-east.

We met Sue and Peter in Belle Isle, who were on a five-week cruising holiday, and enjoyed sailing in company with them for the next six days, calling in at various harbours and marinas on the way to La Rochelle.

We tied up alongside the reception pontoon in La Rochelle Marina and as there was going to be a delay in the allocation of a berth we decided to pass the waiting time in the town and were joined by Sue and Peter.

The picturesque harbour and its surrounding bars and restaurants had a captivating atmosphere and within minutes we were racing back to the marina in a taxi. We had seen three vacant berths in the harbour and we wanted two of them; we attracted a few strange looks as we gunned our way out of the marina.

Some way up the channel from the marina we approached the superbly imposing gateway into La Rochelle. We felt a touch insignificant as we passed between the soaring, circular stone-built towers guarding the entrance to the town's inner harbour. With great relief, we tied up to what had become the last two empty berths. I passed four gin and tonics up to Jean just as Sue and Peter arrived with four more.

That night we dined at one of the many fish restaurants that surrounded the harbour, where we ate oysters, lobsters, cheeses and incredible pastries from a calorie-laden sweets trolley. We drank wine recommended by the waiter, who saw it as his job to ensure that we left his restaurant happy and well satisfied. We had chosen the restaurant at random, but I'm sure that we would have enjoyed similar food, drink and atmosphere at any one of a dozen choices available.

We awoke on Sunday morning to sounds of much activity; it was a festival day and the place was buzzing. Along the quayside and surrounding streets were stalls temptingly offering an incredible range of food and drink. We wandered around the town until lunchtime, when we purchased piping-hot moules marinière, gambas, some fresh baguettes and a bottle of chilled wine. Back on board *Spindrift* we sat in the cockpit eating our lunch and watching the town's water-sports competitions taking place in the harbour. Tomorrow, we would be making the short passage to Royan, where we would begin our river and canal journey; the short cut to the Mediterranean.

La Rochelle had given us our first taste of the continental lifestyle we had envisaged and we remember it fondly as the place where it all came good. We have since travelled there by car, to see if it was merely some magic of the moment that had made things right for us. It was all that we remembered; so much so that driving back there to spend a holiday is high on our list of future things we plan to do. The next day we said goodbye to Sue and Peter; we were sorry to leave them as we had enjoyed their company and judging by their downcast faces as they waved us off, they were also sad that we were leaving. For them it would be worse: they were going back to the UK and work, whilst we were now really getting into this doing our own thingy bit.

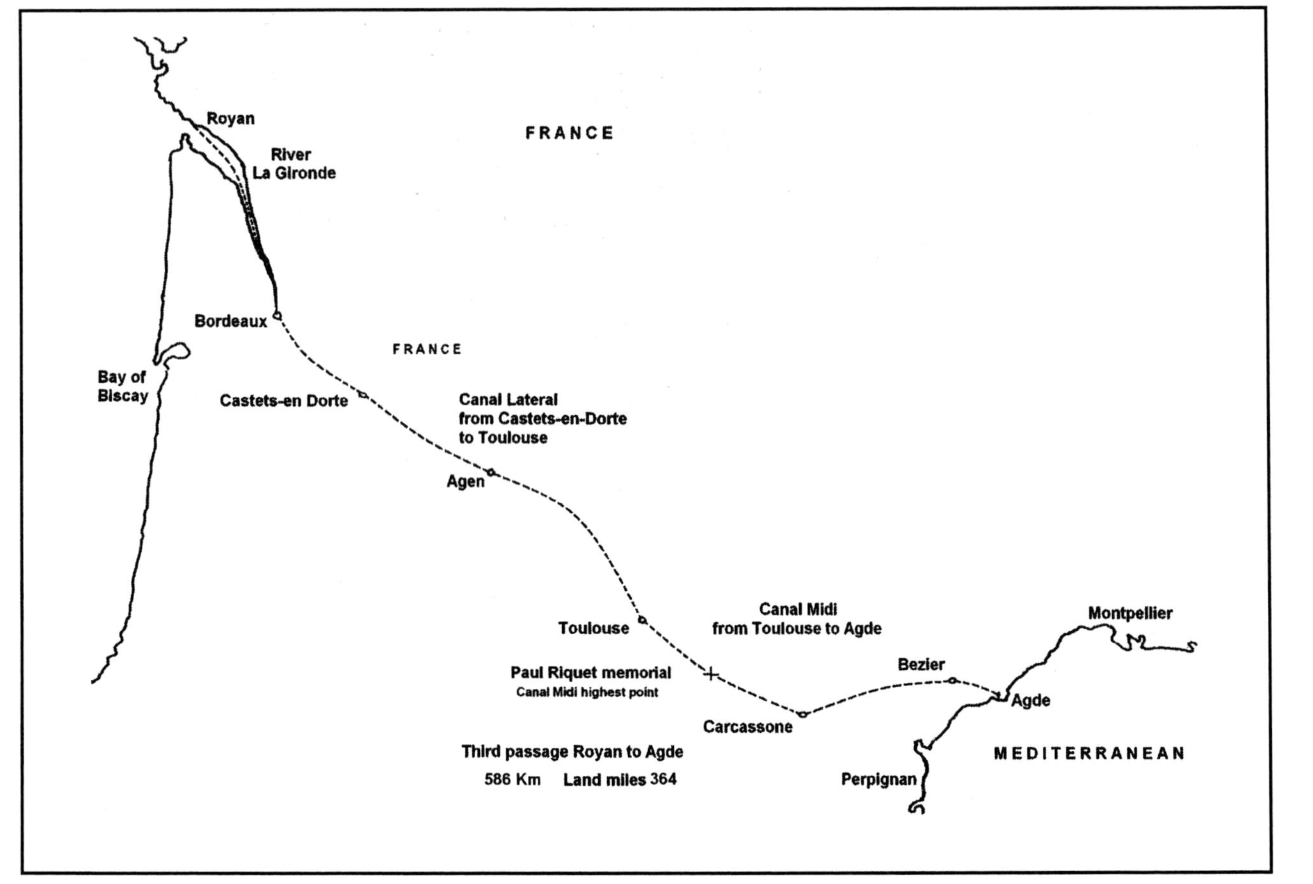
Royan
FRANCE
River
La Gironde
Bordeaux
FRANCE
Bay of
Biscay
Castets-en Dorte
Canal Lateral
from Castets-en-Dorte
to Toulouse
Agen
Toulouse
Canal Midi
from Toulouse to Agde
Montpellier
Paul Riquet memorial
Canal Midi highest point
Bezier
Agde
Carcassone
Third passage Royan to Agde
586 Km
Land miles 364
MEDITERRANEAN
Perpignan

Chapter Four

Canal Midi: it's a water journey, but you need good tyres and a bucket for cherries.

Situated at the mouth of the River Gironde was the harbour of Royan, from where we would sail upriver to join the French waterway canal system, which allows boats with a draught of up to 1.6m, to make the 586km journey from the Atlantic to the Mediterranean: thus cutting out the 1,800 nautical mile (3,334km) trip around the Iberian Peninsula. The marina at Royan had all the services plus a fifty-franc-per-night fee. A book by Adlard Cole told us that we could stay in Royan free of charge; he is twice the sailor I am, but his financial advice is suspect.

We were able to give *Spindrift* a good wash down, likewise our clothes at the launderette and ourselves in the showers: clean place, Royan.

Here, I fitted the timber cradles that I had made in England ready to house the mast, which we would have to take down at Bordeaux. After Bordeaux, the river and canal bridges were too low for Spindrift's fully rigged mast to pass beneath.

We zoomed up to Port de Pauillac on the tide and the next day we turned from the river Gironde into the river La Garonne that would take us to Bordeaux and the last marina – Le Point du Jour – that could offer the crane service we required for the task of unstepping *Spindrift's* mast; a task made more difficult by the 5-knot current swirling around *Spindrift's* hull. There was an added difficulty in that the crane operator was proving to be heavy on advice and light on finesse.

After two years of building *Spindrift* I knew her every nut, bolt and screw and I wasn't about to have her damaged by acquiescing to the demands of an untidy and unshaven crane driver, whose main aim was clearly an early finish to his working day.

I managed to convey by sign language only – for this was not a time for Jean to control negotiations – that he should henceforth keep his advice to himself and do only as instructed. Things went swimmingly after that and whilst we parted the best of friends, I suspect that I had ruined his normal day of assisting yachtsmen to damage their boats.

This marina had the tyre market sewn up, which isn't a service you would normally expect to be provided by a marina. The problem with navigating on a canal is that it offers so many opportunities to people and things to damage your pride and joy. The normal inflatable fenders utilised to protect your boat's topsides – that bit between the waterline and the deck – are totally inadequate in a canal environment. Canal barges, lock walls and holiday-hire craft will always find a gap between fenders to gouge your gel coat or paintwork. The odds of gaining many such gouges are considerably increased on a 430km canal journey.

Damage limitation could be gained simply by surrounding your craft with the continuous rubber tyre protection similar to that utilised on fairground bumper cars. You can discard your tyres at the other end of the canal, where they are sold to boat owners making the reverse trip. We're talking high mileage tyres here.

Our next job was to fit *Spindrift's* rubber protective barrier and for some obscure reason I selected, from the pile of tyres available, only those with a good tread. Freud would no doubt be able to explain that one.

To stop the old tyres from marking *Spindrift's* shiny topsides, we wrapped them all in cast-off clothing that we had decided would be surplus to the requirements of our approaching Mediterranean lifestyle; it did the trick, but I felt like the skipper of a floating Chinese laundry.

It was midnight when we completed all the preparations for the canal journey and we were tired but happy to be ready for the part of the journey that promised to be more leisurely than most seagoing passages.

70km from Royan the river Gironde splits into two rivers; La Dordogne to the south-east and La Garonne to the south-west. A passage of 20km along La Garonne would take us to Bordeaux and after a further 56km we would lock into the start of the Canal Lateral.

From Royan to the start of the Canal Lateral at Castets-en-Dorthe is approximately 160km but the navigation guide for the last 76km of the journey is written in a way that ensures maximum apprehension for any newcomer considering such a journey. The guide is doom-laden with dire warnings of hazardous shoals, strong currents and hidden dangers waiting at every bend of the winding Garonne. If road maps offered information in a similar vein, none but the foolhardy would venture out. I admit that water has a habit of hiding things from view, but warnings don't have to paint such a detailed picture. A sign warning that you should "beware of the dog" is adequate; further information describing the size of its teeth is totally unnecessary.

The guidebook had clearly unnerved the little French skipper of a small motor craft; he and his wife had watched us throughout the previous day as we prepared Spindrift for the journey. They had been in the marina for three days and their reaction to the information in the guidebook had been similar to that of rabbits caught in headlights. They seemed to think that we knew the way and asked if they could accompany us on the journey to Castets: clearly, our floating laundry was a comfort to them.

We cast off in perfect weather; the sky was blue, the sun was hot and the journey unremarkable. Even the huge canal lock at Castets wasn't as alarming as the navigation guide would have us believe.

There is no doubt that chugging along a canal is about as restful as boating can get. A large 100-ton working barge gunning its engine to negotiate a tight bend is best given a wide berth, but such encounters are infrequent. By far the greater danger was a head-on encounter with one of the dozens of hire crafts that throng the Lateral and Midi canals; approximately 12m long by 2.7mwide wide, the rectangular river boats were piloted too often by the totally unaware or those who couldn't care less.

Unlike traditional canal craft, these boats were steered from the forward end and judging by the alarmed expressions on the faces of many helmsmen/women, they weren't particularly easy to manoeuvre. In addition, most helmsmen/women didn't seem to understand that whilst their crafts were long and wide, they only had a draft of 0.6m and could comfortably float in the shallower water at each side of the canal. They didn't appreciate that whilst *Spindrift* looked smaller, she required a minimum water depth of 1.5m to ensure that her keel stayed clear of the bottom and as the maximum draft of vessels allowed to use the canals was 1.6m we were reluctant to navigate too close to the canal banks.

Some of the more irritable holidaymakers who demanded far more canal width than they required, mistook our refusal to stick ourselves in the mud on their behalf as unreasonable aggression and thus we witnessed the forbear of road rage. Canal rage differs in that it's not very easy to step off one boat to bang on the windscreen of another.

I hasten to add that anyone reading this book shouldn't be put off such a holiday; the odd awkward group isn't as intrusive as those rowdy groups that sometimes commandeer the hotel swimming pool; on a canal, they are much easier to avoid.

We were enjoying the canal journey, which was both leisurely and relaxing. Long stretches of the canal were tree lined, with the overhang of branches meeting in the centre, allowing only dappled patterns of light through the leafy roof and thus foiling the July sun in its effort to force its heat into the cool green corridor. Lunch was always taken before exiting such leafy protection, regardless of the hour, should the next tree-lined corridor not be in view.

The huge vineyards were a surprise to me; in my mind, the word vineyard conjures a mental picture of hillside terracing or even a field with rows of vines, but always with boundaries that could prompt the remark, 'Oh look, there's a vineyard,' and 'Oh look, there's another one.'

We travelled for days, albeit slowly, through mile after mile of regimented grapevines as far as the eye could see. Travelling by road through France's vine-growing regions may give an inkling that the wine producers have a fair-sized operation going for them, but you need to travel through their waterways to comprehend the vastness of the industry.

When we are told of surplus wine lakes, I suspect that the information is being somewhat understated: the term wine seas may be more appropriate. There was the odd 100 acres of sunflower crops dotted about – all their blooms facing the same direction– suggesting a craving by farmers for a change in scenery, but without doubt the grape is king.

Many of the locks were unmanned and automated, but the manned ones often had lock-keepers who, once you were locked in, so to speak, exerted a degree of pressure on travellers to purchase presentation packs of the local wine; their mark-up wasn't inconsiderable when compared to the general retail price. However, an unhappy lock-keeper can contribute in no small measure to the degree of difficulty you may experience in clearing these water barriers. Displaying your previously purchased presentation pack doesn't promote the same response as the one adopted by a poppy seller on seeing your flower-adorned lapel. Consequently, you find yourself well stocked for a journey's-end celebration; courtesy of your newly acquired extensive and unselected wine stock.

We could speed our clearance of the manned locks by assisting the lock-keeper to open or close the lock gates, but the automatic locks could be negotiated much quicker. On the upward journey, whether the lock was manned or automatic, Jean had to transfer from our moving boat and climb the iron ladder fixed at the entrance. She would then collect the warps I threw up to her whilst I manoeuvred *Spindrift* into position.

Going downstream was a bit easier for Jean, because we were entering a water-filled lock, which cut out the iron ladder climb, but sometimes the distance from deck to quayside forced her into a knee scuffing scramble to get ashore. From time to time there was a display-of crew dissatisfaction and on such occasions I was able to point out how her efforts were clearly a beneficial contribution to figure and fitness; a bonus that clearing 118 locks would provide.

There is no doubt that Jean is a better person than I in every aspect of human behaviour. I tend to be selfish, sceptical and intolerant; I also swear a lot. My brother-in-law was convinced that without Jean's influence, I would be an all-round bad egg; fortunately, no one ever took any notice of anything he had to say.

Jean has a driving licence but never drives; principally because she has never found a way of making the car reduce in size to leave the way clear for all other road users. Being nice and considerate to other people is all well and good, but an hour in a supermarket usually strips me clean of any of the good intentions I may have set out with.

Following a hire craft carrying four German couples on holiday had a similar effect on me. The men were large, overweight and glistening with suntan oil; presumably applied too late, for they were also pillar-box red. They all wore those skimpy swimming trunks favoured, for some unaccountable reason, by men with large, protruding stomachs. I know what you are thinking and I agree; being fat, red and slippery shouldn't promote a feeling of aversion towards them. Actually, I didn't mind their appearance at all, for it gave me quite a lift to note that they all looked in pretty poor physical condition for men some fifteen years my junior. No, it was three totally separate issues that stirred my dislike of them.

The first being that by following them, *Spindrift* had to nose through a constant stream of floating melon and other assorted fruit skins, along with discarded salad stuff, empty beer bottles and cans. The second was that when we entered a lock with them, they all slobbered around on deck, whilst Jean cranked sluice-gate handles and helped push open or close huge lock gates. But all this was as nothing when compared to the cherry incident.

We were moving along the canal at a comfortably measured pace, when we approached an automatic lock. The lights were showing red and green, signifying that we should give a quarter turn to the pole suspended from the centre of a wire stretched across the waterway, which in turn would start the automatic sequence of closing the upstream gate and emptying the lock prior to opening the downstream gate. Once we were inside, the gate would automatically close and water from the higher level then poured in through the sluice gates and up the boat rises.

Each automatic lock is similar in that there is an unoccupied lock-keeper's house, an untended garden and a control box with a lever to be thrown when you're ready to exit. Once the lever is thrown, you have three minutes to untie your warps, get back on board and clear the locks before the gates close.

This particular lock differed only in that just in front of the empty house stood a magnificent cherry tree laden with large, ripe and sweet yellow-red cherries. Jean refused to pass me a bowl to fill with – what she termed as – stolen cherries.

'How can they be stolen if no one lives here any more?' I argued.

'If you take something that doesn't belong to you, it's stolen,' countered Jean.

'What about when you pick wild flowers from a field, they don't belong to you,' I clinched.

'That's different,' she insisted.

I always find that statement to be a poor argument, but it seems to work for Jean. I was eventually given a bowl along with permission to collect windfalls. So I collected some windfalls for Jean and then climbed the tree to harvest my share.

My peripheral vision picked up the movement and I realised that Jean had thrown the lever. I almost fell from the tree and raced to the quayside clutching my bowl of cherries; I half jumped, half fell into the cockpit and gunned *Spindrift* out of the lock as the gates began to close. I fumed as Jean read her book and *Spindrift* forged her way along the canal at the maximum permitted speed; I wasn't in a meandering mood.

We came across the Germans at the next lock and as we approached their boat, my eyes were drawn to its coach roof deck, where stood a large plastic bucket piled high with yellow-red cherries; all was downhill from there.

Jean and I have a rule that we never carry an argument into the next day and whilst I was livid at the time, I never refer to the incident more than two or three times a year.

We joined the Canal du Midi at Toulouse and carried on climbing for another 50km to the highest point of the canal system at Col de Naurouze. Historians will tell you that here, you should visit the beautiful park and the Obélisque de Riquet, erected as a memorial to the builder of the Canal du Midi, Pierre Paul Riquet, Baron de Bonrepos.

We passed through the area without realising its significance: it could have been marketed better. I suppose you could argue that it was in line with the baron's persona, for he died penniless in 1680, just a few months before the triumphant inauguration of the canal that had taken him fourteen years to build. We will never know how he felt in the afterlife; not so good I would imagine, considering how profitable the enterprise became after his death. His family and heirs benefited financially for the next 112 years, until the French Revolution.

Travelling downhill now, the locks were more numerous; some were strung together in ladders of three and four. A large sailing yacht handled by an all-female crew of two mothers and four early to mid teenage daughters was pressing us. I slowed to one side and waved them through, but caught up with them tied up to the towpath just before the next lock. We decided to have lunch and moored upstream of them. Considering the hurry they appeared to be in when they had passed us earlier, it seemed strange that they had tied up rather than pass through the lock.

The skipper walked up the towpath and although she was French, she addressed us in perfect English, as so often is the case. It transpired that the two families owned the yacht and they were taking it through the canal to Cap d'Agde, where their husbands were due to meet them. Things hadn't gone too well for them at Bordeaux, where the heavy-handed crane operator had not only delayed them, but had also damaged their mast in the process.

The chances of them arriving at Cap d'Agde on time were looking slim and the waiting husbands would apparently not be best pleased. Just to make things worse for them, the female lock-keeper having seen them approaching, had decided to close the gates and take an early lunch break. The official guide states that lock-keepers stop for lunch between 12.30 and 13.00; apparently, the delightful lady in charge had closed the gates ten minutes early.

Whatever the French is for infuriated, our lady skipper was it in spades. Had the lock keeper been a man, I doubt that he would have had the nerve to close the gates in her face. She was certainly fired up, but we were blissfully unaware of the root cause of her anguish. Tomorrow, 14 July, was Bastille Day and by 8.00 p.m. today, all locks would be locked locks, so to speak. If we didn't make it to Carcassonne before 8.00 p.m., we would be stuck out in no-man's-land and apart from the obvious delay, we would be a bit short on the provisions front. I love fresh crusty French bread, but the crusty freshness has a very short shelf life; like one day.

We agreed to travel together, to speed up the time travelling through the locks. Keepers allow twenty minutes for a boat to pass through a lock; however, with efficient help the time can be reduced to around eight or nine minutes. It was 34km to Carcassonne through fourteen locks and we'd have to average 4 knots between them to beat the deadline. Not a problem on a straight waterway with no other traffic, but given the large number of tight, blind bends and the ever-unpredictable Blue Line hire cruisers it would be a very tight schedule to meet.

At 12.53 p.m. the lock keeper and her dog ambled along the towpath. Our new-found sailing partner's temper erupted and she leapt from her boat to confront her tormentor; the mental picture you may have formed of this less than helpful lock-keeper will, I'm sure, prove to be accurate in most aspects.

She was large, scruffy and had an attitude: definitely not service-industry material. Her Alsatian matched her in relative size and attention to neatness, but it did appear to be more approachable than its owner, in that it was wagging its tail. Our sailing partner was petite, and totally irrelevant to this story, she had those looks that men tend to stare at whilst holding in their stomachs. The argument that followed was the most vicious encounter between two women that I have ever witnessed; even the dog retreated some distance and cowered with its tail between its legs.

I suspect that the infuriating woman, whose slow saunter up the towpath seemed designed to antagonise, was beginning to regret her ill-thought-out strategy. Realisation that she was in an argument with a tigress possessing a mind and vocabulary way beyond her ken had been slow but nonetheless sure. The appearance of two more approaching boats had her scurrying back to the lock to carry out the duties that figured most prominently in her job description. I awaited my instructions from the undisputed Admiral of the fleet and seven hours later we tied up in Carcassonne canal basin, time 7.56 p.m.; we had made it, but only just in time.

Jean was preparing coffee and I was rummaging around for some tonic to put in my gin, when we were hailed from the quayside.

'Hello there, *Spindrift* ...' there was a short pause. 'Anyone aboard?'

I poked my head through the hatch.

'Ah, there you are, saw the Red Duster when you locked in, good to see another British ship. Mine's the Nich 32 just up the quay, hmm.' He beamed a large smile at me.

I noted his boat with the Blue Ensign proudly flying from the aft flagstaff; it was twice the size of my red one. You have to have a warrant to fly a Blue Ensign and be a member of a Royal Yacht Club, or a serving or ex-serving member of the armed forces, that sort of thing. I stood up straighter as he thrust his hand towards me.

'Pompy Sharp's the name,' he crisply intoned.

I shook his hand and introduced Jean and myself.

'So, what sort of a trip has it been? You only just made it in time, hmm?'

He stuck his chin forwards as he said hmm, which appeared to make his last statement into a question that didn't demand an answer. I answered anyway.

'Well, apart from a fat lock-keeper and a boatload of fat Germans, it's been perfect.'

Pompy raised his left wrist, holding it with his right hand about 18 inches away from his chin, and stared at his watch for a few seconds.

'I make it twenty fifteen hours. Drinks and a bite on board the Nich with us? Number two is preparing everything now. Twenty thirty hours, hmm?' he jutted out his chin once more.

Jean and I exchanged glances – socialising was the last thing we felt like doing right now, but it would seem churlish to refuse and anyhow, I doubt that declining the invitation would have achieved any success.

We joined them on board at eight thirty and were introduced to his number two, his wife Ingrid's designated title; a charming German lady of very ample proportions. Oh dear, I wondered, did Pompy pick up on my earlier description of the lock-keeper and the Germans. He was nicknamed Pompy when he joined the army from Portsmouth and on his tour of duty in Germany he had met and married Ingrid, who was both a generous and an entertaining hostess. We had a really super evening with them and I think I got away with it.

Our planned lie-in ended abruptly at 9.00 a.m. A mass rally of the region's Boys Brigade had stealthily congregated on the quayside within a few metres of Spindrift and on a prearranged signal, they all hammered their drums enthusiastically. From a prone sleeping position I was 2 feet in the air within a nanosecond. Well, now I was awake I may as well make the coffee.

Bastille Day had dawned sunny and cloudless, not at all like public holidays in the UK. The Bastille Day committee had planned a full itinerary, with lots of fancy-dress processions, bugles and drums. The important factor was noise – it seemed you must have noise – although it needn't necessarily be tuneful. Similar to continental trumpet-blowing, drum-thumping football supporters.

The big event was the water sports held in the large canal basin. There was a long, greasy pole – which no one mastered – and a floating version of a jousting contest: all competitions were designed to dump the loser into the water and to promote loud applause and more trumpet-blowing.

It was pleasant sitting on deck in the sunshine with a glass of wine, but two hours of watching people fall into the water was akin to hearing the same joke constantly repeated. Yet, all that was a belly laugh compared to the finale, in which two men in a rubber dinghy with an outboard motor entered the arena; one man manoeuvred the craft in a circle, whilst the other opened two large baskets and threw out about twenty wild ducks. A whistle blew and hordes of youths plunged into the water in pursuit of the ducks; if they caught one they could keep it. Ridiculous, I thought; obviously the ducks would fly away and, indeed, they would have done had their tail feathers not been removed.

In England, even the fox isn't denied its natural assets prior to the hunt, though fair play wasn't a feature of this competition; the release of the tailless ducks brought the roar of the day.

That evening, we dined out with Ingrid and Lionel. I have nothing against nicknames, but I felt that Lionel was an improvement on Pompy. We ate Cassoulet, the speciality of the district that rather like so many district specialities turned out to be the local version of stew. After dinner, we joined the crowds jostling towards the ramparts and fortifications of the old town, which provided a dramatic setting for the fireworks display. All in all an enjoyable day, but it would have been better had the ducks escaped.

We decided to stay on for the Sunday and leave on Monday, after we'd stocked up on food supplies. We waved off the intrepid French female crew as they headed for the first lock-opening of the day and inspected the food parcel they had left us: a chicken, tins of caviar and various pâtés.

'My mother said would you accept this and thank you for your assistance.' The youngest member of the crew, about 12 or 13 years of age, handed over the gift as she spoke to us in English, with only the slightest hint of a French accent.

Some academics pontificate ad infinitum in praise of the English teaching techniques, whilst underlining the difficulties that they have to contend with. Problems such as the low levels of funding resulting in inadequate facilities, too many students per teacher and a shortage of text books and chalk. What it seems they will not contemplate, even to a very small degree, is the slight possibility that their method of teaching foreign languages may leave a little room for improvement.

Wherever you travel on the Continent, you can communicate in English with children whose only contact with our language is during school English lessons. Apparently, they talk far more than they write and in doing so, they amass a considerable vocabulary. Time enough for those with an aptitude for foreign languages and the desire to study the subject at a higher level, to forge ahead on a more academic tack.

The continental teaching system seems to acknowledge that young children learn their own language long before teachers complicate the issue with their superior knowledge of adjectives, verbs, tenses and a sprinkling of past participles. The phrase 'When is a food shop?', whilst incorrect, would get foreign visitors to the UK much further than rolling their eyes and rubbing their stomachs.

We parted company with Ingrid and Lionel when they branched off onto the Canal de la Robine bound for Port-la-Nouvelle and then Spain. Sailing is a life where you're constantly making new acquaintances and sadly, constantly waving goodbye.

Having been on rivers and a canal for fourteen days the urge to get to the sea was, as they say, upon us; there wasn't far to go now for *Spindrift* to have the feel of saltwater around her hull once again. We stopped for the night at Béziers and the following day we would negotiate its giant's staircase of seven locks.

One has to marvel at the skills of the seventeenth-century engineers; Pierre Riquet must have gulped or at least swallowed hard as he stood at the top of the steep hill contemplating the construction of those seven adjoining locks. All he had to do then was to build a viaduct over a valley to enable his beloved canal to continue its incredible journey.

At the beginning of our Canal Midi passage, I did think that taking fourteen years to complete its construction was maybe a bit over the top; but by the time we reached the end I could only wonder at the fact that it had ever been built at all.

Just another lock to go after the unique experience of sailing over the viaduct and we would be at Agde, where a final lock would set us down onto the waters of the River L'Hérault, just 3 miles from the Mediterranean Sea.

We didn't have a good night moored alongside a small quay on the busy, noisy river and we found ourselves unable to sleep as Spindrift was bounced and tossed by the wash from the endless traffic of working boats not subject to the speed restrictions that apply on the Canal Midi. We had become accustomed to the tranquillity of canal life; welcome to the real world. It was Friday and if I failed to get our mast stepped today we would be stuck here for the weekend, a prospect that rudely jerked me out of my canal-induced lethargy.

I walked about 2 miles downriver and eventually found a boatyard with a suitable crane. It was just high enough to handle our mast, but it wasn't motorised. A series of large wheels with protruding handles had to be turned to make it work, but the yard had no one available or willing to operate the relic from bygone days. I presumed that the man who accepted my fifty-franc note in exchange for his permission to use the ancient crane did actually work in the boatyard.

Having studied the ancient crane for a while and turned a few wheels I was encouraged to note that its jib and cables moved quite freely. The task, however, was no easy one, for the river traffic had Spindrift pitching around and forming a very unstable platform on which to work. Jean had the unenviable job of guiding the mast foot into its mounting whilst trying to keep her balance on Spindrift's lurching deck. Her crane operator, who was experiencing a rather severe learning curve, didn't help Jean's plight. When the mast was at last in position and fully rigged, I went in search of the yardman, to thank him for the use of the crane. I couldn't find him anywhere and as no one seemed to know what I was talking about I beat a hasty retreat, before someone asked some awkward questions.

Spindrift once again felt like a seagoing yacht; it now had a mast and boom and no longer sported an outer layer of pyjama-clad tyres. Although it was only a three-nautical-mile coastal sea trip to Cap d'Agde Marina, that three-mile stretch of sea was Mediterranean Sea, the very one that I had dreamt of sailing on for so many years.

It sparkled, it was blue and the spray that kept bursting from our bow was warm. Nearly 6 knots under sail, yet in shorts and T-shirts there wasn't a goose pimple in sight. Jean and I hugged each other.

'Do you know what, Jean?' I shouted over the noise of slapping waves and spray.

'I think we've done the right thing.'

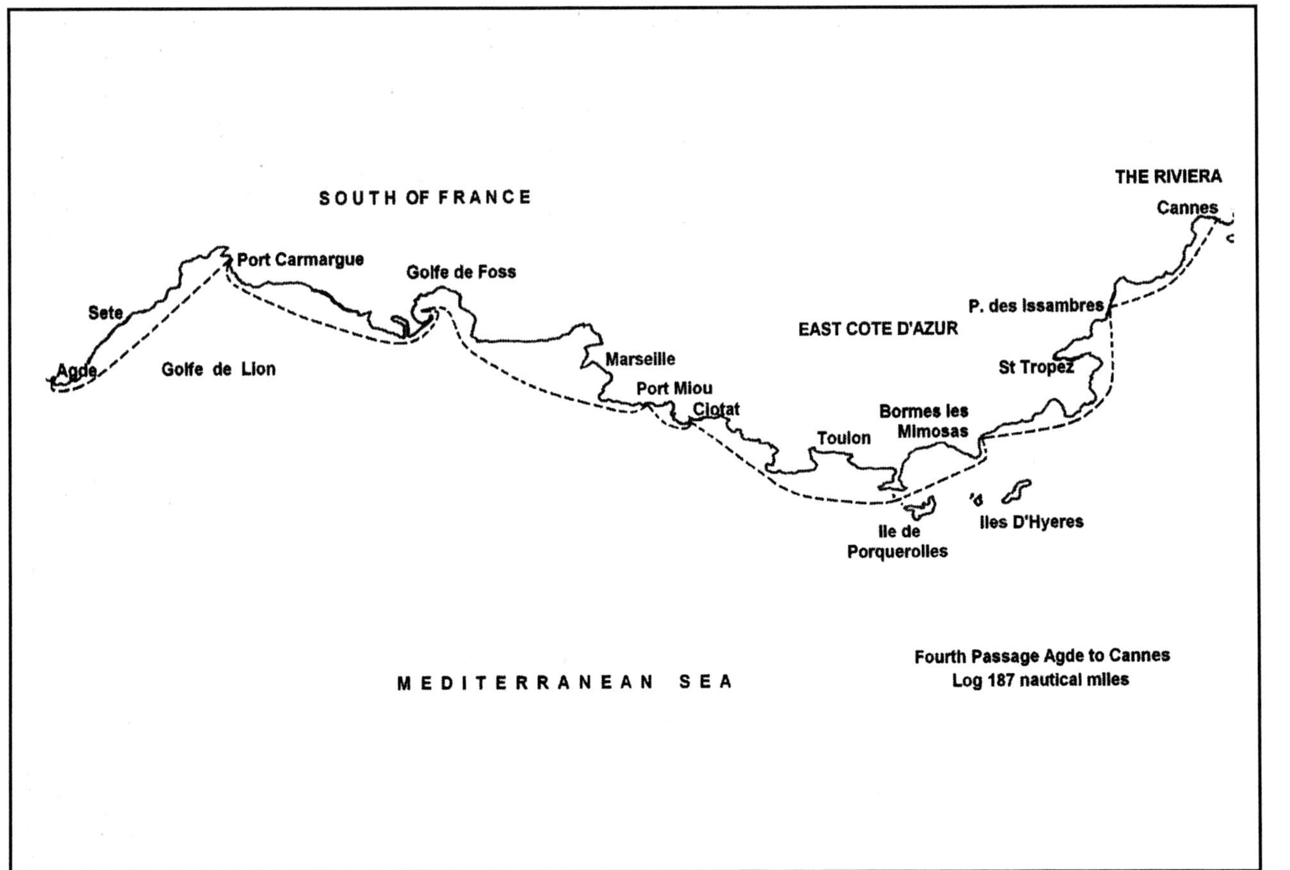
THE RIVIERA
Cannes
SOUTH OF FRANCE
Port Carmargue
Golfe de Foss
Sete
Agde
Golfe de Lion
P. des Issambres
EAST COTE D'AZUR
St Tropez
Marseille
Port Miou
Ciotat
Bormes les
Mimosas
Toulon
Ile de
Porquerolles
Iles D'Hyeres
MEDITERRANEAN SEA
Fourth Passage Agde to Cannes
Log 187 nautical miles

Chapter Five

The Riviera is brilliant, but don't try to keep up with the Joneses.

We were feeling good – our welcome to the Mediterranean was all we could have wished for and the weather was fantastic. I mention the weather, because as an Englishman I know the importance of the subject.

I've never quite worked out why so many English conversations are weather related. I suspect that it may well be that it's about the only subject in England which is totally classless and can be agreed upon regardless of political or religious belief. Weather-wise, we English seem quite happy to highlight our country's perceived downside, while the Irish, Scots and the Welsh, who generally experience far worse weather conditions, seem able to convert cloud-enshrouded mountains, misty, rainswept valleys and saturated heather into a source of tremendous national pride.

They accept 60cm of snow as something that happens in winter, whilst 50mm of the same stuff in England has schools closing and the traffic authorities telling us all to stay at home. Sadly, such advice is being acted upon with increasing gusto. There is a distinct lack of the bulldog spirit in England when it snows these days.

Well, I may scoff at my compatriots for their obsession with the weather, but the subject played no small part in our final decision to sail away from it all. To those of you contemplating a similar move, I can confirm that whatever it is that you want to do, doing it is much better when it's warm.

Snow was the last thing on our minds as we sailed under a cloudless sky into the huge Cap D'Agde Marina. We are talking big marinas here, so large in fact that two of our friends who had a holiday home in the area searched for half a day trying to find us. I accept that my directions could have been partly to blame.

We had an enjoyable two days with them, which included a picnic at anchor out in the bay, where we were accosted by French customs. I can only think that our friends Janet and Brian Small had aroused the suspicions of the customs officers, for we had been sailing in French waters for over a month without so much as an enquiring glance. The officials may well have been particularly bored that day, because I doubt that we looked like international smugglers; they asked questions that I didn't understand and I gave answers that they didn't understand. Finally, they lost interest and left us in peace.

The next day, after sad farewells, we sailed out of Cap d'Agde Marina on the final leg of our planned journey to Cannes; that was as far as our plan went. We would then be in that mode generally referred to as going with the flow; or, hoping for the best, was another way of putting it.

The "flow" in Mediterranean terms is slower in lifestyle pace and virtually nil in terms of tidal currents. Navigators – struggling to make sense of the ever-changing tidal conditions in north-western European waters – should go to the Mediterranean, for there it is unbelievably easy.

If you point your boat in the right direction in the Mediterranean, you will get to your destination without having to make any allowances for the unseen influence of tidal current. Ignore such influences in tidal waters outside of the Mediterranean and you'll most likely be toast.

We stopped for a night in Port Camargue, a concrete jungle of flats and jetties, so we left as quickly as possible the next day. The following night we anchored in the Golfe de Fos, which was surrounded by industrial complexes. Come on, Med, this isn't in the dream; the weather clouded over to emphasise the point.

Port Miou on 25 July was straight from a picture book: a narrow opening between rocky cliffs that led into a totally sheltered marina, a very safe haven for just thirty-four francs. Unfortunately, the little marina was so sheltered that when we slipped our mooring the next day, we were totally unprepared for the Mistral. I should have twigged when *Spindrift's* speed picked up to 5 knots with just the main sail hoisted, but having cleared the marina's narrow entrance the bay still offered sheltered waters and in bright sunshine with a following wind everything looked rosy.

Well, it did until we cleared the headland, where on this beautiful crystal-clear sunny day, we strayed like dummies into the path of a full-blown Mistral. I use the term "we" only because Jean and I were together: the actual decision to leave or not to leave port is always mine. Jean always defers to my decision in seagoing matters and I suspect that at times such as this she questions the wisdom of such deference.

There was no excuse, for it is widely known that the Mistral is a wind with a penchant for arriving out of a clear blue sky and boosting to full gale force within minutes. I had stupidly failed to notice the warning signs that usually foretell its imminent arrival.

We were surfing down waves well beyond *Spindrift's* top displacement speed and because Jean refuses to take the helm in rough seas, she was now struggling on a lurching deck to put a second reef in the main sail; turning back was out of the question. I aborted plan AP, anchoring in the Porquerolles some 40 miles on, to plan CC; chickening out in Ciotat just 5 miles on.

Jean was now back in the cockpit having successfully shortened the main sail, which made Spindrift a lot easier to handle, but we still covered the next 5 nautical miles in a little over half an hour. Whilst it was exhilarating, it was also a touch unnerving to note that although we were sailing just off the south coast of France in July, there wasn't another boat in sight.

Ciotat sits in a small bay with a small island just off the seaward western arm of the bay. Wearing full waterproofs we approached the island in good spirits and as we were clearly the only mariners braving such conditions, there was an element of superiority in my demeanour. There was no doubt that our appearance in the marina entrance would create a stir. Those who had cancelled their sea journeys on account of the Mistral would definitely feel inferior; the French would now see what we British sailors were made of. Nonetheless, I determined to conduct myself with modesty and would wear an expression suggesting that such sailing conditions were the norm for us Brits.

'Bonjour,' a windsurfer happily hailed midst a cloud of spray as he powered across our bows and out to sea; he headed at speed away from the shelter that we were seeking. Deflated ... yes, I think deflated is as good a word as any to describe my demeanour as we entered Ciotat.

We left Ciotat in sailing conditions that you dream about, on an easterly course, with a fresh north-westerly offshore wind; just perfect. As we passed the Porquerolles the wind changed to a fresh south-westerly: equally as good as a north-westerly, but warmer. The only downside of travelling east was that the marina charges were increasing with every mile. My charts weren't the only indication that we were approaching the Cote d'Azur; the decks of passing boats were littered with topless sunbathers, which can be a distraction to navigators.

We motored out of Port des Issambres mid morning 28 July some 20 miles from Cannes and were hoping that our friends Brian and Maureen would be in port and not out on charter. Brian was the man who had taught me to sail many years earlier.

I had reached a point in my life when even I realised that playing cricket at weekends was somewhat selfish. Watching Dad dress up in white to run up and down a field with a piece of wood in his hand didn't figure high on my young children's list of favourite pastimes. Furthermore, Jean was asking very serious questions with regard to cricket teas; I couldn't for the life of me find a good answer as to why my cricketing activities should involve her in sandwich and tea-making on summer weekends. Sailing, a full family participation sport would fit the bill, I decided.

All my summer holidays as a boy were spent at Morecambe. There was a man-made boating pool between the piers, which held seawater when the tide went out; I seemed to spend all my time there fishing for crabs with a mussel on the end of a piece of string. However, if I persisted long enough, I could persuade my mum to take me out on the sailing trips that operated when the incoming tide reached the end of a long wooden jetty built across the flat, sandy beach.

Dad and my sister always declined such outings, but I knew that Mum enjoyed them as much as I did, so I always managed to get about four trips in: they were the highlight of my holiday. Sadly, my mum died when I was 12 years old; she would really have enjoyed sailing on *Spindrift*.

I cannot determine if those early sailing excursions were in some way responsible for my desire to own a boat of my own one day; a desire that visited my dreams for as long as I can remember. Some entrepreneurs have made their first million by the time they reach their late teens, but for most of us the general rule seems to be that money is never available at the time that it would be of most use.

Children with the ability to eat enormous amounts of cheap confectionery without being sick, rarely have the cash to indulge this unique attribute. Most young men cannot afford the sports car of their dreams and once married, the first house purchased is usually a compromise. By late middle age you can now afford that two-seater, but even if you could manage to climb in and out with some degree of dignity, the ridicule factor becomes the new barrier. No matter how much you love that little sports number, to the outside world you're just an old swinger trying to recapture your youth.

Many of the things that you really wanted to do but didn't, owing to lack of funds or because the money you had was needed for more important things, such as repainting the house, will all be there for you in later years when you can afford them. Surprise, surprise, you don't want to do them any more: hang-gliding, bungee jumping and living on a small boat no longer appeals. But you shouldn't bin those dreams too quickly; the chances are that with a little extra effort you will find a way to achieve them.

So, I decided to purchase a boat; fortunately, I received some invaluable advice from a friend of long standing who told me not to buy a boat, but first to join a yacht club and learn to sail. Simple advice and obvious really; nonetheless, more people do it the other way around and I would have been one of them had it not been for the good advice I received from Brian Bottomley.

Brian was the Commodore of Whitby Yacht Club and he invited Jean and me to meet him there on the following Saturday night where he introduced us to Brian Wormald; he was the skipper of a new Nicholson 30 and was looking for one more crew member to join his racing team.

I was lucky, for Brian was a very experienced and skilful sailor; even better, he was one of the rare breed of sailor who could skipper a boat without ranting and raving at his crew. For every skipper with this talent there are many who make Captain Bligh look like a Sunday school teacher, shouting at their crew members for failing to carry out some incoherent order, which as often as not was a cover-up for a mistake of their own making.

That year, Brian took on two complete novices in John Thompson and myself, yet he was rarely outside the first three finishers. I never missed a race throughout the season, which enabled me to soak up more sailing skills in one year than I could have learnt in five years of trial and error on my own. The experience also cemented in my mind that if you wanted to get the best out of sailing, then whilst good boat-handling skills were important, good navigational skills were essential.

Regrettably, Brian became one of the casualties of the newly introduced VAT. He had expanded his business just prior to the market difficulties that followed the implementation of the new tax and subsequently lost his business and home. A group of moist-eyed friends gathered at the end of Whitby pier seven months later to watch *Steelaway* set sail for the Mediterranean. Aboard the steel ketch with a friend to assist on the journey were Brian, Maureen, their 11-year-old son and a cat of indeterminate age. We are talking big gambles here; he had a 15m ketch-rigged sailing boat with a question mark against its suitability for charter work and a very thin wallet. However, successful ventures are often spawned from such seemingly unpromising beginnings.

Success didn't come easily and it took much hard work in the early days, earning money repairing marine engines and doing a bit of charter work. Then they sold off one yacht to buy a bigger one, until eventually they acquired *Jolly Joker*, a 27m motor yacht based in Cannes. There followed years of successful charter work and a unique lifestyle that very few businesses could offer; not many can thank a government tax for their financial success.

As we approached Cap Roux we heard a radio transmission between *Jolly Joker* and another motor yacht; Brian was confirming that their charter had just finished and that they would be in port for several days. I think he was more than a little surprised when he heard my radio identification call.

'Did you say *Spindrift*?' he replied.

'Yes, Brian, it's me and I would really like a gin and tonic with ice and lemon.'

'Can't be done,' he shouted. 'It's Champagne or nothing.'

We received a welcome to remember and if you think that such a welcome would make packing everything up and sailing away from home a touch easier, you'd be absolutely right.

I don't know who first coined the phrase "It's not what you know, it's who you know", but probably the understanding of the old adage was common long before money was invented and access to the grapevine was all-important. Computerisation has altered the dynamics of information exchange. One shudders to think what impact it would have on everyone's lives if the world's computer system crashed beyond repair. However if it ever did happen, access to the grapevine would most likely regain its original status. You may ask, what's all that got to do with sailing into Cannes? Well, try getting a permanent mooring there without connections to those in the know and all will become clear.

Port De Cannes attracts the wealthy and the famous, but surprisingly, by virtue of its public port status, it offers the cheapest mooring rates along that very expensive stretch of coast known as the Riviera. There are moorings on the west quayside and central pontoons, but the place to be is the Jetée Albert Edouard. "That" as they say "is where it's at".

The Jetée Albert Edouard is situated directly adjacent to the new festival building and gardens; it's the Film Festival's focal point. Companies pay big money to charter the huge gin palaces moored along the prestigious quay, where guests are wined and dined and contracts exchanged amidst relaxed opulence.

This impressive quay with its row of large motor yachts is a tourist attraction throughout the year and at festival time it becomes a grockle's paradise. The Jetée has a dogleg bend and the motor yachts to each side of the angle have their sterns well apart and their bows closer together; the triangular strip of water between them is just big enough to moor an 8.5m sailing yacht should the harbour master allow. The mooring will never be obtained courtesy of the Internet; no, as I said earlier, it's not what you know but who you know, and I knew Brian and he knew the harbour master.

The grockles would stare open-mouthed as they looked up at the multiple-decked and gleaming motor yachts displaying their illustrious owners and celebrity guests. When they reached the dog-leg they looked down at *Spindrift*, no bigger than some of her neighbours' tenders; it offered light relief for the grockles and possibly the comforting thought that they too could one day afford to get in amongst the high rollers.

For those of you who are unfamiliar with the term grockle, it's a Devonshire dialect word for a tourist, especially those from the Midlands and the north of England; probably not originally intended to compliment.

We lay on thick soft mattresses and drank champagne on *Jolly Joker's* top sun deck and whilst we were aware that this wasn't going to be our general future lifestyle, it was nonetheless heady stuff for the newly arrived dream seekers. We enjoyed hot showers and then, after more drinks, we dined out at one of Cannes, innumerable restaurants, many of them offering an incredible variety of three and four-course meals at English pub-food prices.

Time had raced by on our journey, accelerated by our fear of being late for Ian and Stuart's arrival for their holiday with us in Cannes. We had, of course, spoken to them many times on the telephone since leaving England, but the need to hug them was much like that of a desert traveller desperate for water.

We arrived at Nice Airport in plenty of time; approximately ten minutes before their flight was due to leave Manchester Airport. We figured that we'd be less agitated there than sitting on board *Spindrift.*

In spite of their holiday haircuts we spotted them immediately as they waited in the crowd to clear passport control, yet their eyes seemed to flit past us without recognition. On reflection, it was probably not surprising, for we left England with sad pale countenances, displaying a measure of anxiety, and no doubt the lead-up to our departure had taken its toll on our disposition. Now, we not only had a healthy tan and an apparently fitter and leaner appearance, but we also had the ear-to-ear grins that never featured in the lead-up to our goodbyes.

Their holiday didn't last long enough for us and we were pleased to note that they would have happily stayed longer. Strange, because their holiday wasn't a whirlwind of sightseeing tours of the area, for they spent every day on the packed beach on the other side of our quay. Somewhat dissimilar, I hasten to add, to the packed seaside beaches of England; for instance, there were no deck chairs, sand castles or buckets and spades: just row after row of topless, suntanned nymphs and goddesses. It clearly put them off their food, for it was never easy to get them back on board for lunch.

Yet again, saying goodbye was difficult and over the years it never got any easier. Our sadness after Ian and Stuart left was tempered with the knowledge that Lynne and her friend Jane were due to arrive soon for their summer holiday.

They had only been on board for a day when that little strip of the quay to which *Spindrift* was tied became excessively populated with aimless young men studying their feet and casting furtive glances towards *Spindrift's* deck or cabin or anywhere else on board that Lynne or Jane happened to be.

Contrary to what Jean would have everyone believe, I wasn't horrid to the young, hopeful feet-shufflers, for it's not always easy to keep control of a hosepipe when washing a dingy, but with regard to those arrogant creeps with long, greasy hair and designer stubble, who to my mind loitered with intent, then yes, I'll go along with horrid.

During Lynne and Jane's stay, *Spindrift* became very high profile. When my bikini-clad daughter and her friend sunbathed on Spindrift's cabin top, it seemed that they'd become the must-see attraction for grockles and neighbouring crew alike; skippers with whom I hadn't previously conversed were now stopping for a chat.

A couple of berths away from *Spindrift*, the motor yacht *Brielle* was preparing for a promotional photo-shoot session. The main theme was to be *Brielle's* gourmet cuisine and the centre page of the glossy charter brochure would feature a lobster-laden table. The owner skipper Alan Mortleman suddenly altered his sales pitch by inviting Lynne and Jane to nibble lobster and sip champagne on the foredeck, aft deck and in the main saloon; seemingly, *Brielle's* guests always dined in bikinis.

I have to say that throughout Lynne and Jane's stay with us, I was a little miffed to note that whilst they went to almost excessive lengths to deny any passer-by a chance glimpse of them topless, they totally discounted my presence; it's not exactly morale boosting to realise that you've become totally inconsequential.

All too quickly Lynne and Jane's visit came to an end and in the airport departure lounge we sadly waved our goodbyes; we really hated that bit.

Having settled into our new lifestyle, that which at first had appeared unreal, was now just the norm. By and large, the norm back home is a neighbourhood made up of people with differing jobs and a wide variety of interests and aspirations, yet the diverse nature of such a community somehow adds strength and balance.

The community on the Albert Edouard Quay was different to the norm in that they all had virtually identical jobs, pastimes and aspirations. The majority of the charter-boat skippers and owner skippers moored to the main quay were English and through Brian and Maureen we soon got to know them all. There were many invitations to parties and dinners, which we enjoyed, and many offers of hot baths and showers, which we wondered about. We even had dinner invitations that included pre-dinner showers, which we accepted as genuinely kind gestures from friends who understood that life on a small boat had its inconveniences; nonetheless, our deodorant expenditure increased.

Every community has a character that drives a project forward, be it a street party, bonfire or leading the campaign against a developer's plan to build a new supermarket on the village green. On Cannes Harbour's main quay, every skipper was a character and there wasn't a herding instinct in sight.

Nevertheless there was a subtle hierarchy which no one openly acknowledged, similar to that hierarchy prevalent in clubs throughout the world. I use the simile because it seemed to me that the residents of the Albert Edouard Quay shared more in common with a members' club than that of community membership and, as with all club memberships, there were cliques.

There were boat-owner skippers and skippers who worked for boat owners; where one stood in the club membership hierarchy was generally based on the size of the boat you commanded. The success level of an individual's charter season or how high up the rich list the skipper's boat owner was could have an effect on one's status within the club membership.

As a result of our friendship with Brian and Maureen, Jean and I had been introduced directly into the clique at club committee level and as we presented not the slightest threat to anyone's status at any level, all happily accepted us as ex-officio committee members.

The most successful boats were run by husband and wife teams. There were single skippers who ran boats with a senior stewardess acting as the hostess, but these skippers seemed to lack basic interviewing skills, for on so many occasions they would finish up with a stunning-looking stewardess who had absolutely no previous experience in such a role.

During the charter season the motor yachts literally become ships that pass in the night. Once back in harbour there is a frenzied cleaning, polishing and maintenance period, followed by the replenishment of the ship's provisions, an operation that seems to demand that huge quantities of food and drink be taken on board. Just who eats and drinks it all is a mystery to me, because the majority of the female guests looked as if anything more than a lettuce leaf would outface them.

The ships would then leave port to do the milk run that is Monaco, Nice, St Tropez and back to Cannes. I personally prefer Cannes to all the other ports along the Riviera. I also include St Tropez, which isn't on the Riviera – as some travel writers who should know better would have you believe – for it's situated on the east Cote d'Azur.

Chartering, although lucrative, is by no means an easy job; the crews' involvement with their clientele is far more concentrated than that between hotel staff and their guests. The ship charter business is at the top end of the leisure industry and must provide premier service and cuisine, but perhaps most important of all is the creation of an ambience in which guests feel happy and comfortable. The boat style plays a major role in the creating a favourable atmosphere, but the skipper and his wife or partner add the touch that counts.

Charter boats are hotels with a difference: there is no star-rating system, although the price will always offer a clue. Obviously, the size of boat, number of crew and level of opulence is taken into consideration when costs are negotiated. A weekly rate of £10,000 to £150,000 will usually secure you a vessel to suit your needs, but you must take note that those weekly rates don't include the add-on costs for food, drink, fuel, and port charges. Of course, there are bigger ships available should you have a desire to spend seriously big money.

There was a competitive element along the quay and charter success was measured by the day; a subject always introduced at a party by the current league leader. Some well-established owner-skipper boats have regular customers, but the rich and famous are seldom creatures of habit and they rarely plan their leisure time in detail.

There isn't much worse for the skipper of a charter boat than to be tied to the quay during the holiday season and they will usually negotiate a deal if they experience a quiet period. However, the wealthy rarely become so by throwing money away and they are fully aware that last-minute bookings can gain substantial reductions. The result is a cat-and-mouse situation between skipper, agent and their prospective client. When skippers of moored boats are seen polishing the aft deck handrails, then it's odds on that there's a charter agent in the vicinity.

One of the most surprising discoveries we made in Cannes – which clearly highlighted the level of our naivety at the time – was the incredible gap between the relative wealth of those people we had hitherto considered to be rich and those who really were. The really high rollers in Cannes would view the assets of those named in the UK list of its richest people as loose change. A millionaire possessing an ego prone to fragility should steer well clear of Cannes.

There is much to be said for the adage that money cannot buy you happiness and an argument to prove that saying can be easily formulated. Nonetheless, whilst there is no doubt that a rich man learning of his wife's infidelity will experience much unhappiness, the same discovery would hardly be a bundle of laughs for the poor sod with a mortgage and an overdraft. The millions spent each week on the purchase of lottery tickets suggests that being unhappy and rich is a risk that most of us are prepared to take. Young people are urged to study hard so that one day they may earn a living in a chosen trade or profession. No one advises their children to set out with the prime aim of becoming a millionaire: except perhaps millionaires.

Not surprisingly, men of Arabian extraction figured largely on the list of the Cannes mega rich. Generally, immensely wealthy Arabs didn't fall into the self-made man category and their spending habits suggested that their wealth hadn't been gained by burning the midnight oil.

The *Empress of Cannes*, a beautiful, traditional ship of classic design, was moored four berths along the quay from *Spindrift*; the staterooms and salons were a mixture of French-polished mahogany, luxurious carpets and expensive yet tasteful decor. Jack Chester, a retired businessman and restaurateur, had sold his businesses and bought the *Empress of Cannes* to enjoy a different lifestyle, but once a businessman always a businessman and his boat was available for charter to anyone who could afford the not inconsiderable fees. He and his attractive partner, Barbara, ran the ship like an exclusive hotel; the crew were never noticeable but always on hand. He loved giving dinner parties and I doubt that anyone invited ever found that they had a prior engagement.

I had noticed that a large black stretched limousine, marginally smaller than a tour bus, delivered three or four Middle Eastern gentlemen to the *Empress of Cannes* about once a week. A few minutes after their arrival, eight or nine female family members clad in jellabas and yashmaks arrived courtesy of a small minibus; the differing mode of transport was clearly not a reflection of a need to economise. The gentleman that was picking up the charter tab had also taken for the summer a large, mansion-sized villa in the hills above Cannes and the entire top floor of a large hotel overlooking the promenade and beach.

Jack explained that they had chartered his boat for three months at full rates and thus far hadn't slept aboard or even had a day out at sea. They dined on board once a week at the most and always ordered a banquet-style dinner for twenty guests; never did they serve more than fourteen. After dinner, the men were whisked away in their limousine, whilst the ladies left in their minibus; it was unlikely that both vehicles shared the same destination.

A British registered vessel occupying a prime outer mooring on the Albert Edouard Quay, was bought for many millions and extensively refurbished for millions more. The aft deck had been converted into something resembling that of an aircraft carrier, a rectangular structure jutting out atop and beyond the vessel's rounded stern: it looked hideously ridiculous.

The deck's main purpose was apparently to stage a Chelsea Flower Show-type garden display. The ever more prosperous-looking florist – who must have thought that his birthday had arrived when he landed the contract – changed the theme daily. You would be right to wonder if such a display was compatible with a boat's supposed basic function, that of going to sea; clearly, its seagoing performance was of secondary consideration at the refurbishment-planning stage.

Marble bathrooms are plentiful in luxury motor yachts, but such finishes are usually taken into account in the ship's initial design. Ripping out polished wood and replacing with marble slab walls and floors could very easily, and in this case did, give the craft a considerable list. The counterbalance ballast failed to fully eradicate the ship's list, but it did contribute to a need to paint a new waterline several inches above its designed displacement marks. As the alterations had increased the yacht's propensity to wallow alarmingly in all but the very calmest of seas, the owner never actually instructed the skipper to take it out of the harbour. It should be noted that the refitting of this once proud ship owed more to the skills of a house interior designer than to those of a marine engineer, but then a marine engineer wouldn't have had the flair to contemplate wall and ceiling coverings of genuine suede and snakeskin.

Ridiculously, all this extravagance was merely a stopgap, a distraction until the owner's new ship being built at ludicrous cost was completed. I don't suppose that the owner of the vandalised vessel would be worried that when he had no further use for it, prospective buyers would be thin on the ground. The ship would never again be a seagoing vessel; its only hope would be to bolt it to the harbour floor and clad it in brickwork.

It was enjoyable living in such an environment, but we decided against trying to keep up with our neighbours.

Chapter Six

The French revert to type. Goodbye Spindrift and hello to our new boss.

Plans to celebrate my fiftieth birthday aboard *Spindrift* were undone by the French customs authority. When they informed us that we wouldn't be allowed to live on our boat for the next six months, my distrust of the French was replaced by a healthy dislike.

I was well aware of the EU ruling that enabled citizens of member states to buy a new boat in their home country and base it in another, thus avoiding payment of VAT on the purchase price. The regulations allowed the boat owner to live aboard for a maximum of six months per year. However, when building *Spindrift,* I had paid VAT on every nut, bolt and screw. Also, before leaving Penzance, I received from the customs office the appropriate documentation for submission to any interested European customs officials, confirming that *Spindrift's* VAT had been paid in full and that *Spindrift's* tax status was compliant with all the regulations and directives pertaining to the European Union member countries. No surprise, then, to learn that all the EU countries recognised the common sense and fairness of the directive; with, as you might expect, the exception of France.

My letter to the Royal Yachting Association – I had kept up my membership subscription for just such an eventuality – was answered promptly and at length. I'll not bore you with detail, but the gist of it was that the Treaty of Rome had decreed that VAT paid in the country of origin would be recognised by all member countries. This rule didn't become mandatory immediately, but whilst member countries were expected to operate within the spirit of the legislation, it was left to each individual country to implement the new law to suit their own timetable.

True to form, the UK administration implemented the rule to the letter with little delay. Spain, Italy and Greece didn't immediately change their law; they just didn't bother to enforce the old one. France, as ever, ploughed its own furrow and as an immediate change offered no self-gain, they continued enforcing their existing laws with above-average enthusiasm. Discussion was out of the question; we could live on a boat in France twelve months out of twelve, when they received payment of a sum equal to 17 per cent of *Spindrift's* total value. Our payment of VAT in the UK was simply not recognised.

Meanwhile it was, of course, perfectly acceptable for French nationals to benefit from the UK's desire to curry favour with EU bureaucracy. UK politicians invariably adopt a somewhat smug and superior attitude when citing the swift and efficient manner in which British bureaucrats implement all European directives. In the meantime, their European counterparts display that arrogant superiority derived from their ability to implement all advantageous directives before they have the actual legislation in place, whilst those not to their liking are introduced with maximum delay; to be last is to win. I leave you to decide which creed you would prefer your own representatives to adopt, bearing in mind that you do pay their wages.

My meeting with the French customs official was unsatisfactory and extremely frustrating, for they displayed unbelievable intransigency. Of course, much of my frustration was down to my inability to speak French. Being able to order a meal in a restaurant or to enquire in which direction the railway station lies is not enough; neither is that admirable ability that some posses to communicate at a level that I would mistakenly perceive as fluency. No, what is required when dealing with officialdom in any language is absolute fluency; a fluency not just in the spoken word, but an understanding of those unspoken words, those between-the-line nuances.

Many interpreters deemed to be fluent in a foreign language might well be hard pressed to conclude negotiations to match their client's expectations. Even barristers presenting an argument in their own tongue can fail to serve their client's best interests if they are not skilful in the use of verbal nuances and adept at vocal inflection.

My interpreter in this instance – Jack Chester's partner Barbara from the *Empress of Cannes* – was incensed by the intransigent stand taken by the customs official and she let it show. I'm fairly sure that the fact that she was a petite and an extremely attractive lady influenced my decision to curb a desire to throw something, preferably the customs official, out of the window. Our meeting was, of course, all to no purpose, for nothing changed, the options remained as stated at the outset: pay

French VAT, sell Spindrift and buy a French vessel, vacate *Spindrift* for six months or sail out of French waters.

Winding up the meeting, the customs official ignored Barbara and addressed me in the manner of a generous benefactor. He confirmed that I could enter the boat for maintenance purposes. Also, I could, should I so wish, live aboard the boat next door, but I must not seek to inhabit *Spindrift*; all this delivered in as near fluent English as makes no difference.

Historically, the British have always prevailed in battle with the French, but there is no denying that politically they have us beaten. Over the years I have given the subject some considerable thought and have concluded that we, the English – I'm not sure that the Scots, Welsh or the Irish can be included in this claim – will never better our European counterparts in tactical diplomatic warfare, simply because we are so predictable. Our partners, some would say the opposition, plan their strategy with the almost certain knowledge of what our response would be to any combination of scenarios. Only when we are at war do we discard the restraints of the rulebook. Actually, whilst that used to be the case, I suspect that our political masters no longer have the bottle that their predecessors could be relied upon to display.

The French propensity for partiality was highlighted when they decided that all charter boat owners sailing French waters, under the Panamanian flag of convenience should pay a special extra tax, unless they could prove that their vessel complied in every detail with the French safety regulations. This decision was prompted by French charter boat owners, who complained that the large numbers of Panamaian registered charter and pleasure vessels utilising French Mediterranean ports, were not subject to the same stringent regulatory confines as themselves. They had a point, and as the French are masters of instant off-the-cuff arbitrary decisions, port authorities told owners of Panamanian registered charter vessels to pay the tax or leave French ports. Whilst the new rule didn't appear to be recognised by statute, targeted boat owners that didn't want the hassle left the cote D'Azur and the Riviera in droves. Meanwile the Spanish, Italians and the Greeks were happy with the sudden influx of foreign boats and the subsequent upturn in the fortunes of their own boating industries.

Apparently, the French strategy backfired because the Panamanians – unlike the English – weren't predictiable and they responded in a classic Gallic style by threatening an increased tariff for all French-registered vessels that passed through the Panama Canal – the shortcut between the Atlantic and the Pacific Ocean.

The French immediately discarded their tax initative but the damage had been done and the banished Panamanian registered vessels did not return. Such was the stuff of dreams for us – the banished Brits. Predictably there was no sign of home country assistance in the form of like-for-like treatment for French citizens living on board French boats in the UK.

Our dream to sail away, or at least my version of our dream, usually fuzzed over the detail of how we would provide the necessities of life; I confess that at such times I've been known to adopt an approach to these matters such as that favoured by the wonderful Charles Dickens character, Mr Micawber: something will come up.

Boat insurance, medical insurance, mooring fees and a general propensity to live beyond our means had prompted me to take on a few carpentry jobs on boats along the quay. In addition, Jean and I did some stand-in crew work for some of the charter boats when they were short-handed. This subsequently turned out to be advantageous, for when the time came to leave *Spindrift*, we had several offers of work that included living accommodation; at least we would have a roof over our heads.

Decisions, decisions: we had supposedly put all that behind us; we mulled over the idea of sailing to Greece with its cheaper cost of living, but we wanted to do it when we wanted to do it, not to suit the French and certainly not in November.

I rather fancied being a skipper; this, I concluded, was the answer. I had observed the lifestyle of all these guys along the quay being paid to sail a boat; that, I thought, is the life for me. Jean, on the other hand, wasn't entirely convinced; she rightly concluded that cooking in a compact galley – boat terminology for very a tiny kitchen – and serving meals to as yet unknowns, lacked some of the glamour that I was trying to project in my sales pitch.

In fact, Jean was back-pedalling rapidly on my "it would be boring to spend every day sunbathing and doing nothing" theory. Jean had another point: she didn't want to live on board a boat with crew, indeed she went even further and refused point-blank to do so. I recognised that concessions would have to be made.

What was required here was a considerable amount of good fortune. There were always more skippers available than there were jobs and most new positions were filled before the majority of the out-of-work skippers became aware that there had been a vacancy.

There is a considerable risk element involved for boat owners when offering – and for skippers when accepting – the responsibilities of running their yachts. Yet, the negotiation stage, if one could call it that, generally bore no resemblance to that which would apply, if one of the yacht owner's companies were seeking to take on a new employee. I've known situations when owners of boats costing millions of pounds have handed the responsibility for its welfare to someone who provided less detailed information on their suitability for the job than one of their own companies would demand from a prospective lavatory cleaner.

The ideal skipper, if there is such a one, should first and foremost be a capable seaman/woman. After that, the list varies to suit personal requirements. For instance, navigational skills are for the most part essential, but if a boat is based in and only cruises around Mallorca, then almost anyone could find the bay or harbour they were looking for with the aid of a tourist's road map and reasonable eyesight. The days of the salty old sea dog skippers of timber sailing boats, whose duties started and ended with the coaxing of the owner's vessel from port to port with the aid of a brass compass and lead weights on a piece of string, are over.

Today's motor yachts are floating holiday homes packed with sophisticated equipment, machinery and water-sports toys. Electronic state-of-the-art navigational equipment provides the skipper with the vessel's geographical position with pinpoint accuracy: sometimes. All well and good, but if that position happens to be in some remote Greek or Turkish anchorage and the ice-maker packs in, then Captain Cook himself would find it difficult to escape the owner's displeasure; the skipper would do well to have an idea as to how to renew the sound of ice chinking in the glasses with minimum delay. He should also possess the ability to ensure that the water maker produces a sufficient volume for each guest to partake of multiple showers.

Skippers must also ensure that showers never run short of hot water and that the air-conditioning system never runs out of cold air; the electricity supply required to power such necessities is also needed for other essential equipment, such as hairdryers and curling tongs. The aforementioned indispensable equipment will only work if the provider of power, namely the generator, never, ever stops. The downside of achieving such efficiency is having to smile at the latest guest who draws you discreetly to one side to whisper quietly:

'By the way, captain, do you think you could make that generator thingy a bit quieter at night?'

In addition to this, we mustn't forget the large bank of service batteries required to power the electric motors driving bilge pumps, shower pumps, toilet pumps and fridge-freezers. These batteries must never lose power, particularly if you want the radio transmitter, navigation lights, automatic pilot, anchor winch and the engine starter motor to work.

Whilst most skippers would deem the main engines to be of paramount importance, most owners would rather limp along on one main engine than be without the Jet Ski, the jet-bike or the outboard motor. This last piece of equipment drives the craft that pulls the water skiers and it also takes the guests ashore for shopping sprees, or to dine at that beach restaurant famed for its seafood cuisine. All of this machinery and equipment has to function without fault during the course of the cruising season and to that end, the winter period is devoted to maintenance by those skippers who take pride in their vessel and wish to keep their jobs.

You could be forgiven, therefore, for assuming that were an owner to find a skipper with the nautical skills of Captain Cook, coupled with the engineering know-how of George Stevenson, then God would be in his heaven.

Not so, there is a much bigger issue at stake here – in a word, personality, for unless the personalities of skipper and owner are compatible then the union is a non-starter. This is the reason that many owners choose their skipper without any apparent detailed investigation into the practical abilities of the chosen one; this also accounts for the high incidence of successful applicants who could more accurately be described as con men. Fortunately for the con men, very rich men rarely, if ever, admit to making mistakes, so the con men are able to move from job to job without the burden of their shortcomings being publicised.

I suspect that had I been aware of the preferred level of aptitude for matters psychological and mechanical required to become a successful skipper, I wouldn't have felt so confident when Jean and I walked up the gangplank of the motor yacht *Blue Skye C* for our interview.

The interview came about because those previously mentioned all-important factors, luck and knowing the right person, happened to be in place. *Blue Skye C* was a beautiful motor yacht built in Holland in the 1960s. She had a 24m steel hull, teak deck and a low-profile timber superstructure. The centrally positioned wheelhouse had all-round vision above deck level, leading to a dining area and a very large aft deck.

Access to the guests' accommodation was down a staircase from the wheelhouse aft and another forward to the main saloon, galley and crews' quarters. Below the wheelhouse and main saloon was the engine room packed with machinery, all of it dwarfed by two 475hp turbocharged Caterpillar engines; it really was some piece of kit.

Following the death of the owner of *Blue Skye C* – a member of a family who owned a grocer's shop; well, a few actually, known as Sainsbury's supermarket chain – the skipper Johnny Johnson learned that he was a beneficiary in the late owner's will which bequeathed to him a large percentage of the boat's value when sold plus a cash sum. The executors left it to him to arrange and negotiate the sale of the vessel. I don't believe that this situation is the norm when a boat owner dies, but in this instance the skipper, who had been with the boat for many years, had become as much a trusted friend as an employee.

It didn't take very long to find a prospective purchaser, for *Blue Skye C* was a displacement motor yacht admired by everyone who saw her; even the owners of the new breed of speedy semi-displacement yachts, all shiny plastic and stainless steel, viewed her with admiration. The prospective purchaser immediately fell in love with her and agreed to pay the asking price on the condition that Johnny Johnson found a skipper and wife team to run the yacht for him. As I've said before, you need to know someone in the know and luck is important, too; well, I knew Johnny Johnson, so how lucky can you get.

Mr Geoffrey Ambrose Hubbard, and the financial director of his group of companies, greeted us on the aft deck of *Blue Skye C.* In his late sixties, Geoffrey Hubbard, or GA as I came to know him, had the strong physical build and the pugnacious looks and demeanour of the 1930–1940s Winston Churchill: he was a self-made man without the usual hang-ups. I learned that he had an ability to second-guess his contemporaries and was never easy to predict; in fact, he turned doing the opposite to that which was expected into an art form. I took an instant liking to him and his sense of humour; I could tell that Jean felt the same way, as indeed did most women, for they recognised an element of the rascal in him.

The interview took the form of a conversation – in which GA did most of the talking – based on all things nautical, relating tales of his sailing experiences and details of the previous boats he had owned. From time to time, his financial director, Walter Hicks, made the effort to introduce an element of professionalism to the interview by asking what he deemed to be pertinent questions. His approach no doubt born from many joint business meetings that left him holding the baby if things subsequently failed to work out as expected.

One question, however, which on my own I would have fielded without qualm, was made difficult because Jean, who doesn't tell lies, was sitting beside me.

'Have you had experience of handling a motor yacht of this size?' Walter enquired.

Had I answered an unequivocal affirmative, Jean's facial expression and body language would undoubtedly have blown the gaff. I confirmed that I had taken the helm of the 27m motor yacht *Jolly Joker*, but I didn't expand on the time spent doing so. Neither did I offer the information that I had never actually manoeuvred it into, or out of, its mooring. GA jumped in, disdainfully informing Walter that a man of the sea wouldn't pose such a question.

'Of course he can handle a boat this size,' scoffed GA, 'handle one you can handle them all.' It was at that point that I realised we had got the job.

Earlier, I derided the method adopted by wealthy boat owners when choosing a skipper, but I'm now a convert to the system. There's a risk element for both skipper and owner alike, but it's the owner who risks most; the skipper may find himself out of a job at the drop of a hat, but the chances are that the only damage would be his injured ego.

However, if the owner makes a bad choice when choosing a skipper, in addition to a ruined summer season for himself, family and friends, the incompetence of his chosen skipper could cost him a six-figure repair bill; or, even worse, place all his guests in jeopardy.

Yet even the most professional and exhaustive selection methods could fail to correctly predict an applicant's ability to make the right decisions and take the appropriate actions in difficult or dangerous sea conditions. Neither would such selection methods necessarily highlight an applicant's propensity for making basic but costly errors. The scope for such errors in the boating industry is infinite and being a good sailor is similar to being a good sportsman or politician, academic or plumber; it doesn't guarantee common sense.

So all things being equal, choosing a skipper on the basis that you like him may not be as stupid as it first appears. It's rather like that dent in your car – the damage would have been easier to take had your daughter been the driver, rather than that arrogant, spotty new boyfriend who raises your blood pressure on sight.

We were offered and accepted the job of skipper and wife team running *Blue Skye C.* The crew complement for a 24m motor yacht is usually four, made up of skipper, cook, stewardess steward/deckhand; in some cases read deckhand as engineer. However, we had recognised whilst in Cannes that most problems on board charter boats tended to be created by the crew.

I suggested to GA that if his guests would like to be involved with warps and fenders when manoeuvring into or out of a mooring and were prepared to keep their own cabins tidy, Jean and I would be able to run the boat without extra crew. Like any businessman, he was attracted to the idea of reducing the crew costs, but I'm certain that the thought of all his guests having to do a bit of work was the clincher, for it would have appealed to his sense of humour.

There were many occasions when we desperately wished that we had extra crew, but mostly we were happy to be on our own and not to have to suffer those irritating crew personality clashes that can make life on board a ship quite miserable.

A two-week handover period was arranged, during which time Johnny Johnson would teach me as much as he could about the workings of *Blue Skye C,* after which I was on my own.

Living on a large motor yacht in Cannes didn't strike me as too bad a deal, even though there was much work to be done. Several cabins had to be refurbished and the wheelhouse rearranged to make way for a new radio transmitter and navigational equipment. I also had to find space in the engine room for an extra generator and a washing machine.

There was a huge list of other jobs to be done and each one completed generated another two. *Blue Skye C* was booked into the boatyard on the island of St Marguerite to have the underwater hull area cleaned and treated with antifouling paint.

The short passage to the island was an opportunity for me to get some boat-handling practice without the pressure of spectators. I admit to an increased level of apprehension when manoeuvring *Blue Skye C* into the boatyard cradle; I could have done without the crosswind.

We were looking forward to completing all the preparation work. Then we would be out there, cruising the Cote d'Azur and the Riviera. We would be calling into St Tropez and Monaco and sampling the delights of French cuisine in the millionaires' playground.

The letter from GA confirmed that I had six weeks to get *Blue Skye C* prepared for our summer cruise to Greece.

Moving *Spindrift* to Port De La Rague approximately 4 miles east of Cannes left us feeling sad and somehow guilty. *Spindrift* had been central to our adventure and now we were leaving her to fend for herself. Not only that, but we were leaving her for a motor yacht of all things; a boat without sails had never been part of our dream.

But *Blue Skye C* was a classic vessel, to which I had already become quite attached. So leaving *Spindrift* was easier than it would have been had our new home been one of the new plastic gin palaces that now outnumber proper boats in the Mediterranean by a considerable margin.

We sailed out of Cannes Harbour at 8.30 a.m. on 4 May 1985; it should have been 7.00 a.m., but when I pressed the starter buttons there was a healthy whine of starter motors and nothing more. Imagine if you will the opening night of the play you have rehearsed for weeks and as the curtains open to a full house, you can't remember the words.

My mind went blank, everything had been working perfectly before GA arrived the previous day; he was looking forward to his first passage on his new boat and his happy countenance had now assumed a baleful glare. We were both thinking on similar lines: how long would I keep the job. I felt that going down to the engine room would be the correct action at this time and I refused GA's offer of help, so that I could twiddle things with my fingers crossed.

Down in the engine room I sped along the chequered-plate walkway between the two huge but silent Caterpillar engines. Beyond the engines was a raised workshop area that also housed a dual-engine control panel; I couldn't start the engines from there, either.

I can hear you all shouting, it's the fuel, it's the fuel, in true pantomime fashion and I can confirm that I was being as thick as Buttons for a while there. After lifting half of the engine-room deck plates, I eventually found the valve that had been closed by the engineer who had been working on the generator the previous day. I had paid him and wouldn't be seeing him again; what a lucky man.

The engines roared into life and I made my way back up to the wheelhouse in my sweat-soaked, oil-stained white uniform. I never did ask GA what he thought of his skipper on that first morning; some things are best left unsaid.

We were bound for Livorno, with a short stop at San Remo to take on duty-free fuel. The Cannes port captain wished us bon voyage on the radio as we cleared the harbour entrance; I kept my answer short and professional, '*Merci,* out,' I answered. I'm not sure he understood, for I hadn't lost my Yorkshire accent whilst living in Cannes.

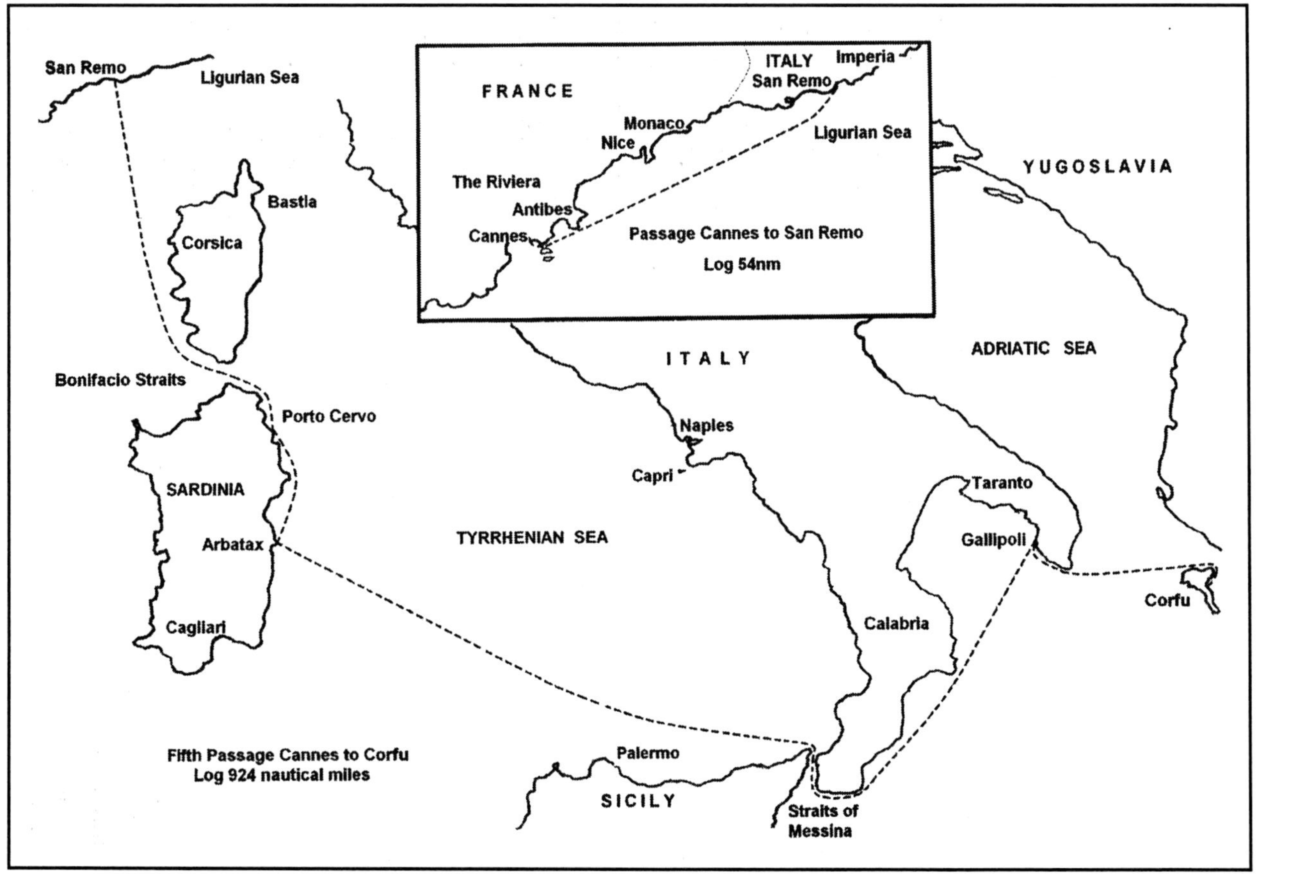
San Remo
Ligurian Sea
Bastia
Corsica
Bonifacio Straits
Porto Cervo
SARDINIA
Arbatax
Cagliari
Fifth Passage Cannes to Corfu
Log 924 nautical miles
FRANCE
ITALY
Imperia
San Remo
Monaco
Nice
Ligurian Sea
The Riviera
Antibes
Cannes
Passage Cannes to San Remo
Log 54nm
YUGOSLAVIA
ITALY
ADRIATIC SEA
Naples
Capri
TYRRHENIAN SEA
Taranto
Gallipoli
Corfu
Calabria
Palermo
SICILY
Straits of
Messina

Chapter Seven

Corfu-bound in Blue Skye C, despite an owner and skipper contretemps. The first hearing of, 'Drink, dear boy?'

I noticed that the wind was increasing as we topped up our tanks with 5 tons of fuel; it underlined its intention as we left San Remo and set a course for Livorno at 2.00 p.m. It wasn't long before a south-easterly force six was backing and making it impossible to maintain our course. New courses set for La Spezia and then Rapallo met with the same fate and by 6.00 p.m., a north-easterly seven had forced us onto a course of 180 degrees; my first day as captain with the owner on board wasn't going well.

Having failed to start the engines first time, I now couldn't get him to the port of his choice. Worse than that, I wasn't even taking him to Italy. Our cruise plan was to sail to the Isle of Corfu, calling into various ports along the Italian coast. The admiralty charts that I had purchased for that area had cost over £100 and we were heading for Corsica.

Things didn't get better and by midnight, the seas were big and the autopilot had packed in; the euphoria of my first skipper's job was dissipating rapidly. Twelve hours later we were approaching the Bonifacio Straits that separated Corsica and Sardinia. I'm told it's a most beautiful cruising area, but without proper charts on this grey and blustery day in May, the rock-strewn South Channel seemed pretty hostile to me.

All those pristine charts of the west coast of Italy and I was stumbling into Porto Cervo with the aid of a small drawing in the pilot book; asking a fisherman the way is practical, but hardly professional. My entry into Porto Cervo was hardly professional either; I was aiming for one mooring just as GA said I should make for a different one and consequently I fluffed both; the wind made the final choice.

Owner–skipper relationships were on a downward trend. Most skippers try to get the feel of a new boat by going out on manoeuvres in open water before the owner arrives on board. The tight work schedule had precluded this option, other than our quick visit to the St

Marguerite Island boatyard. Now that the owner was on board, learning curves were a luxury I couldn't bank on.

Things came to a head in Arbatax, a commercial port some 70 miles south of Porto Cervo. I wasn't in a good frame of mind, for whilst I hadn't had the best of luck to date, I knew that I'd made some elementary errors by my efforts to impress the owner with my cost-effective management. I had never skimped on charts when passage-making on *Spindrift* and the costs were down to me, so what the hell was I doing trying to save a multimillionaire the cost of a couple of charts. GA hadn't even noticed that I was navigating along the Sardinian coast with just the area pilot, but I knew and I wasn't best pleased with myself.

There was a strong wind blowing from the west as we entered the Port of Arbatax, so I asked Jean to set up the mooring warps for us to lie starboard on to the quay and bow to windward. GA didn't agree, for he wanted to lay stern-to the wind with the bow facing the harbour entrance, so I asked Jean to move the warps over to the port side.

When we turned, aiming to lie portside on to the quay, the strong wind would be pushing our stern, so I told Jean to ensure that our stern warp was secured first. There was no need for engine power, as the wind was moving us smartly towards the port attendant waiting on the quay to take the stern line from Jean. As soon as he had the line, I would give the engines a squirt astern. *Blue Skye C* would then lie quietly tethered by the stern line, whilst we secured spring and bow line at our leisure.

As Jean hurled the line ashore, the attendant turned his attention to GA, who was standing on the foredeck, shouting at him to collect his line. I couldn't believe my eyes as I watched everything now in slow motion; our stern line, now lying unattended on the quay, slowly slipped back into the water.

Jean was now struggling to haul in the thick, heavy warp, hanging from our stern with most of its length submerged. I couldn't hold the stern up to the wind using the engines, for the submerged warp would surely foul the propellers, so I rushed out onto the aft deck to help get it back on board. Gradually gathering speed *Blue Skye C*, now tethered by the nose, swung away from the quay, akin to an 80-ton wind-powered pendulum. As *Blue Skye C* swung bow into wind she slowed and came gently to rest in the position I had originally planned, albeit via a somewhat circuitous route.

I fastened some spring lines ashore, yanking the warps aggressively, but it did nothing to release my pent-up anger. I knew that my skipper's performance thus far had been woeful and I recognised that it was all of my own doing. In my efforts to gain the approval of my employer, I had forsaken prudent seamanship and common sense; clearly, things had to change. Jean was talking to GA when I entered the wheelhouse and I asked her to leave as I turned to face GA.

'We had better talk, Mr Hubbard. Things are going from bad to worse.'

Whilst he surely recognised his own contribution to our mooring cock-up, he wasn't about to admit it.

'You should always moor a ship of this size facing the entrance; it makes it easier to leave,' he attacked.

'No, Mr Hubbard, you handle boats big or small to suit the prevailing elements. All boats react in the same way, only the speed with which it happens differs,' I countered.

GA sucked in his cheeks and I recognised that we were at a crossroads, things had to be sorted.

'Our problem, Mr Hubbard, is nothing to do with which way the boat is facing; it's to do with who makes the decisions. All my actions to date have stemmed from a childlike desire to please my employer, resulting in rank bad captaincy and for that I apologise. So, if you feel it best for us to end our association now, Jean and I will go back to France on the first available flight. However, if you wish me to remain as your captain, then you must accept that all future seagoing and boat-handling decisions will be mine and mine alone.' Behind my back, my fingers were crossed.

There was a harrumphing sound and a pursing of lips. 'Right,' he said and went down to his cabin.

'Are we still employed or am I packing?' Jean enquired as I entered the galley.

'I think we're on probation, but I fancy your job's safer than mine.'

I slumped into a chair and poured myself a glass of wine. I wondered how things would go from now on. We still had 750 miles to sail to Corfu and GA's first guests were due in two weeks' time. If he wanted rid of me, it made sense to wait until we arrived in Corfu. What the hell, I told myself, we would be better off on *Spindrift* and I'd had enough of employers anyway, that's one of the reasons we left the UK in the first place.

I emptied the wine glass in one gulp and contemplated my next move. I wouldn't be happy walking off the boat here in Sardinia, but it was GA's call now; for better or worse, I'd said my piece. I looked up as GA poked his head through the opening to the galley steps and beamed down at me.

'Drink, dear boy?'

I felt that my chin was bumping my chest with each affirmative nod; I closed my mouth with a relieved sigh and joined him for a pre-dinner drink.

As I said earlier, GA was a difficult man to second-guess, but the incident gave me an insight into his nature. He was rich and owned a group of private companies and with no shareholders to consider he was the boss supreme, but he didn't like yes-men. Certainly, he liked to get his own way, but he also expected the people he paid, to do the job he paid them to do, and that in his book was the most important factor.

There was to be just one more uncomfortable period before we completed our passage to Corfu; I cannot remember another one throughout the next six years that we worked for him.

We left Arbatax at 9.00 a.m. the following day and I was keen to sail into an area in which I could navigate with the aid of proper charts. I was able to record our position on a proper chart sixteen hours later; the log reading was just over 82 miles at an average speed of only 5.12 knots. Even those of you with no interest in such statistics will recognise that we were experiencing more problems.

The first delay occurred when I noticed that the automatic steering mechanism appeared to be struggling to maintain a steady course; *Blue Skye C* was trying to drag herself to starboard. After an hour's inspection of the steering system – no easy task at sea, as most of the cable and chain mechanism is routed through the bilge area of the ship – I could find no apparent malfunction.

Naturally, the problem proved to be where I least wanted it to be; it was in the hot, noisy engine room, where the boat's wave-induced lurches were the hardest to predict. I discovered that the forward starboard stabiliser fin was locked into a downward position and acting as a break to that side of the hull.

Drenched in sweat, I attempted to digest the Vosper stabiliser manual; even if I couldn't solve the problem, I needed to centralise the fin, to stop the drag effect. It took half an hour to diagnose that the cause of our problem was an airlock in the hydraulic system. I solved the problem in seconds by over-loosening a valve and as it came off in my hand, a jet of hydraulic oil hit me between the eyes. My God, my eyesight was all blurred; well, it would be, wouldn't it, as my spectacles had been squirted to some distant place. My efforts to stem the jet were, of course, futile and I was now soaked from head to foot in both sweat and hydraulic oil.

The stabiliser control system was situated in the wheelhouse, so the only way I could stop the oil jet was to slither my way to the engine room control board and shut down the boat's engines.

Jean and GA peered apprehensively through the engine room door, but their initial concern for my safety dissolved into unsympathetic hilarity; I personally had difficulty in appreciating the humour of the situation.

The luck factor was in there somewhere when I realised that I was still clutching the small bleeder valve; the chances of finding it had I dropped it would have been slim indeed. After half an hour's search, I found my spectacles slopping around in hydraulic oil beneath the starboard engine and it took another half-hour to clean up the oil from the chequered plate walkway; the full clean up would have to wait.

After reinstating the valve and topping up the hydraulic system's reservoir tanks, I apprehensively pressed the engine starter buttons.

'Yes!' I shouted as the hydraulic ram centralised the stabiliser. Proper engineers will no doubt sneer at my amateurism, but to my wife and GA I was a star.

After my shower and a change of clothes I was virtually piped onto the bridge. I suspect that it wasn't so much admiration of my engineering skills, as relief that the next 700 miles would continue to be stabiliser assisted.

The second problem came to light as GA and Jean went off watch. Whilst checking the engine monitor gauges, I noticed that the starboard engine's water temperature was higher than normal, so I closed the engine down.

You cannot stop one engine on a two-engine ship without catching the attention of those on board. Indeed, two-thirds of the ship's complement had questions; so did the other third, but I didn't let on. I explained that we would run on the port engine until the starboard engine had cooled sufficiently to enable a check of the cooling system to be carried out.

I started the engine again after checking that the cooling water level was as it should be. After stopping the engine for a third time, I had run out of things to check. GA was of the opinion that the sender unit – a little gizmo that transmits temperature information to the gauge in the wheelhouse – was faulty and should therefore be ignored.

'You could well be right, Mr Hubbard, but if the warning gauge is warning that there's a problem, I think it best we take notice. If we keep running and seize the engine, we're looking at six-figure costs.'

He considered the point for all of two seconds.

'It's only money.'

I had no come back to that.

'One of my companies has some of these Caterpillar engines in stock; if this one packs in we'll fit a new one.'

It was as if we were discussing the fitting of a new torch battery. I'm not certain how you see it, but it certainly impressed me.

I'd never heard an engine of any size seize up, but I presumed that a 475hp engine seizure would be quite a dramatic moment and wouldn't go unnoticed. We covered another 200 miles before my toes began to uncurl. GA was right, the sender unit ultimately proved to be faulty, but I wouldn't advocate GA's diagnosis technique unless you have very deep pockets.

We approached the Strait of Messina in the evening of the second day. The admiralty pilot describes the area as follows: *The currents and whirlpools, famous from antiquity, are such as to necessitate some caution in the navigation of the Strait. Moreover, in the vicinity of the high land on either side, vessels are exposed to violent squalls, which descend through the valleys with such strength as, at times, to inconvenience vessels.*

As I have previously mentioned, information for navigators isn't always comforting; however, we passed through the Strait in a flat calm and saw no sign of whirlpools; but the sight of the 233m high steel pylon supporting the Sicily end of the overhead electricity cables draped between Sicily and Italy was impressive. The cables strung across the one-and-a-half-mile channel drooped at their lowest point to 70m above the water and then rose high into the Italian mountains that border the Strait. Presumably, the line inspectors are out-of-work aerial circus performers.

We had rounded the toe of Italy by 22.00 hrs, approximately 150 miles from Gallipoli, which was to be our next port of call.

Our "Loran C" position finder was more accurate well away from land. Close to land and in certain weather conditions it left much to be desired and when in the vicinity of a "Loran C" transmitter base line extension, all you received was gobbledegook. No, I'm not sure what a base line extension is, either, but it's drawn on the LC plotting chart and when you're near one, gobbledegook is what you get. The LC master station at Catanzaro had three of these base line extensions and the chart showed that we would cross two of them, so we would get no viable position information for the last 120 miles of this passage.

This was no real problem, as I always plotted a dead-reckoning position and if that position varied substantially from that indicated by the electronic gizmo, I would discount the gizmo's information.

However, GA had recently shelled out close on £2,000 for the new and much vaunted position finder and in his book it shouldn't, ergo couldn't be wrong. When I switched the equipment off – no point wasting battery power – GA suggested that it be left on as a cover, in case I got my dead-reckoning calculations wrong.

'Might as well leave it on, Alwyne; it could be useful for you to check your figures against,' he suggested.

'There's no point, Mr Hubbard. Checking my estimated position against one that's incorrect would be of no help to me,' I explained.

'Yes, but it might not be wrong,' he countered.

'Well the chart specifically highlights the fact that in this area it's going to be wrong and my calculations confirm that it is wrong, so there's little point in leaving it switched on,' I added politically. 'It's not the equipment that's faulty, it's the scrambled information it will receive from the transmitter.'

I showed him the LC plotting chart with its boxed caution note printed in a bright shade of magenta: *CAUTION. The area inside the hyperbolic line adjacent to the Base Line Extension is unreliable.*

'Ah, well, they will have printed that just to cover themselves.' He beamed, having confirmed that the system really had no shortcomings.

'Well, if that's the case, I'd best not use it, just to cover myself.' I replied tartly.

I wasn't about to enter into any further dialogue on the subject, for I was finding his apparent doubt in my navigational proficiency extremely irksome. He harrumphed and pursed his lips; I recognised this as his way of biting his tongue and there was little chitchat for the next few hours.

Throughout the next day the heat haze kept visibility down to about a quarter of a mile. GA had taken up a position above the saloon staircase and was staring through the wheelhouse windscreen with a grim Churchillian countenance; conversation was still a tad stilted.

The heel of Italy stretched for approximately 20miles to the south-east of Gallipoli and it was some part of this coastline that GA spotted through a brief gap in the heat haze.

'Alter course, Alwyne, the land is over there.' He pointed over to starboard.

'No point in going in that direction, Mr Hubbard, if we're heading for Gallipoli.'

'When you're lost and you see land, the best thing to do is to get nearer to the coast and follow it. That way you can't miss your port.' He seemed to be getting agitated.

'I'm not lost, Mr Hubbard, we will be in Gallipoli in two hours.' I was already agitated.

GA went down to his cabin, presumably to stave off an argument, and I fumed silently, for I was becoming extremely pissed off with GA's consistent lack of faith in my navigational abilities. Navigation was my thing. It's what I did best.

Jean gave me a look, which translated into, 'I know you're a good navigator, but you're sure you're right, aren't you?' I returned her look with a withering stare.

'I'm sorry, pet,' she soothed. 'I'm not doubting you; I just want things to go right for you.'

With an estimated 10 miles to go GA returned to the wheelhouse.

'How long do you think it'll be, Alwyne?' He really was making an effort and I felt I should meet him half way.

'Oh hello, Mr Hubbard. About an hour I should think. The haze is beginning to thin, so if you keep a lookout straight ahead over the bow, we should see the St Andrea lighthouse fairly soon now.'

He stared ahead with the odd glance to starboard; he knew for certain that there was land to the east. Suddenly, he let out a triumphant shout.

'It's there, look, dead ahead.' He was happy, all grumpiness gone.

St Andrea Island on which the lighthouse is constructed is low-lying and the 141-foot-high white octagonal tower appeared to rise straight out of the sea, exactly on our compass course. With visibility rapidly improving and the late afternoon sun reflecting from its stark whiteness, I couldn't help viewing it as a one-fingered salute – Gallipoli was just to the side of it.

'I think that calls for a drink, dear boy.'

'Seems I'm in favour again,' I murmured as GA went off to prepare the drinks.

'That was a bit risky, telling him the lighthouse was dead ahead before we could see it,' Jean whispered.

'Not really, I spotted it through the binoculars about ten minutes ago.'

Jean strangled her laugh in a coughing bout as GA handed her a gin and tonic.

'Drink that Jean, that should do it.'

I have to say that GA was a big man in such situations; whilst he never ever said you were right and I was wrong, he did acknowledge by his demeanour that that was the case. He never made excuses, simply forgot the incident and never referred to it again.

In retrospect, the trip from France had been good for both of us, for we now knew each other better. He was a good sailor in that he could be relied upon in any weather conditions, I never saw him remotely seasick or queasy and whilst he had the odd bad mood, they rarely lasted for long; he was mostly very good company.

The navigational incident must have made its mark, for several weeks later we had Mike Goodyear, chief executive of GA's group of companies, as a guest on board for a week's cruise. We were on a passage from Corfu to the Lefkas Islands and were heading for the Lefkas Canal, situated a midst a low and featureless coastline. Mike pointed to the only visible buildings on the coastline about 10 degrees to port of our course and hesitantly asked if we should be altering our course towards them.

'If Alwyne says it's straight ahead, it's straight ahead,' snapped GA.

Mike took the rebuke with good grace; I winked at him to let him know I understood.

We were pleased to tie up alongside in Gallipoli harbour after fifty-six hours at sea. We didn't expect any specific welcome from the local fishermen, but would have preferred that they'd waited until we had completed our mooring procedure before stealing one of our new fenders. The taunting, sneaky smirks displayed on the faces of all the fishermen who had witnessed the unwelcoming act of pilfering did them no credit.

Small wonder that entry to the port office was gained via a heavy iron gate unlocked by a mean-looking policeman toting an automatic weapon. The offices were cell-like and but for the weaponry, the staff were prisoner-like, but without the jollity. We agreed that we would depart the next day as soon as we had taken fuel on board. We also decided to eat on board that night, rather than leave *Blue Skye* C to the mercy of some of the unsavoury-looking characters that had gathered on the quayside within – and the term is relevant in both its forms – spitting distance.

Our departure was delayed by the fuel tanker's late arrival, so GA went off touring the town whilst we took 6 tons of fuel on board. He arrived back smiling broadly just as the tanker departed. Following him was a scruffy individual pushing a rickety barrow, who I think was also smiling; he didn't have many teeth and the few that had survived were mainly black, so his smile, if that's what it was, fell well short of being a thing of beauty.

'Wine dear boy.' GA shouted to me from the quay. 'I found this place in one of the backstreets and tried these two.' He pointed at the two carboys perched precariously in the wheelbarrow.

I cast a dubious glance at the two 25ltr carboys. 'Did he tread the grapes?' I enquired with a nod towards Gummy.

'If you think he's bad, you should have seen Slack Alice who sold it to me,' he beamed.

Gummy held on to his barrow with one hand whilst struggling to push his tip into a pocket with the other; he was clearly familiar with the unsavoury practices that seemed to be a feature of this fishing port.

'We'll serve this from cut-glass decanters; everyone will think it's wonderful' GA enthused as we manhandled the containers into the wheelhouse.

'Are you sure it'll last? I mean, fifty litres will take some time to drink.' I was visualising the next four months in the galley working around the two large glass containers.

'Oh yes, no problem, it has a high alcohol content; we could preserve things in it. Get a glass and try it! Get three, we'll all have some.'

There was a white and a red. I'm really a red wine person, but I thought that white would be more appropriate for mid morning drinking. The first decanting glug missed the water jug and I was reassured to note that there was no discernible chemical reaction as it soaked into the carpet. GA smacked his lips with relish.

'There, what did I tell you, real wine of the area, no chemicals added, what do you think?'

I managed to control my countenance.

'It's different. It certainly has a distinctive aftertaste, I think it needs chilling.'

Jean nodded in agreement and GA concluded enthusiastically.

'You're right, dear boy, put some in the fridge, we'll drink some at lunch time.'

I moved the carboys down into the galley. I don't know what the Italian name is for their large wine containers, but as they were similar to the English carboy usually clad in a protective basket and used for containing corrosive liquids, I felt that few would argue with my choice of noun.

Having delayed our start until the following day we made an early start and edged out of Gallipoli Harbour at 5.15 a.m. There was no wind and the glassy water surface was unbroken by the slight swell. With about 115 miles to go, we would be in Corfu by mid afternoon.

We dropped anchor and came in astern to the customs' quay in Corfu Harbour. To enter Greece by boat you have to use a designated port of entry, where the Greek Transit Log is issued; the transit log is the most important ship's document whilst in Greek waters and without one, you are going nowhere. Even the smallest island will have a man in uniform who will, if it's not too hot, demand to see the transit log, especially if he deems you are good for a packet of cigarettes, but more of that later.

After we'd dropped anchor and tied up to the quay, a port policeman asked us to move further along, to make room for a naval vessel which was due to arrive later. Our anchor winch, which was hydraulically driven via the port engine, was very powerful, provided that the centrifugal clutch did whatever centrifugal clutches are meant to do. Should the clutch fail in its effort to centrifuge and in this instance it did, there was a special attachment designed to take an extension lever that would enable the anchor to be cranked up manually; we discovered that the Italian fishermen had taken a shine to more than just one of our fenders. We finally retrieved the anchor after two hours of struggling with a very large Stillson wrench.

The following day I let it slip that I was going into town to locate a length of stainless steel pipe to replace the missing anchor winch extension lever.

'Leave it to me, dear boy. I'm going into town; I'll get it for you.' GA strode off purposefully.

The exit from the quay was through the customs buildings about 70 metres to our right and directly opposite us was a row of iron railings, separating the 40-metre-wide quay from the road and footpath leading into the town.

I was in the engine room stripping down the non-centrifugaling centrifugal clutch, when GA hailed Jean. He shouted from the other side of the railings, asking her to take the pipe from him, so he didn't have to carry it all the way around and through the main entrance.

Jean poked her head through the engine room doorway.

'You'd better come and look at this; I don't think it's quite what you had in mind.'

I stared in disbelief at the twisted length of rusty gas pipe that Jean had placed at the bottom of the gangplank. I groaned inwardly; I had a good idea what was coming. I walked down the gangplank as GA arrived.

'Stroke of luck, dear boy, found it on a rubbish tip just up the road. All we have to do is straighten out the length we require and cut it off. You can keep the rest in the engine room; it will come in handy for all sorts of things.'

I cast around for a way out without hurting his feelings. I thought that we'd had enough confrontation on our trip to date. Besides, I now understood GA's mode of address. I had learned that "dear boy" signified that everything was going well and I was almost part of the family; it was Alwyne if he was out of sorts and if he referred to me as Captain I wasn't flavour of the month. I was "dear boy" at the moment and was loath to provoke a status change.

'The problem is, Mr Hubbard, that this pipe isn't big enough in diameter to fit over the lever stub on the winch.' I tried to sound disappointed that it wouldn't do the job.

'That's no problem, dear boy; all we have to do is find a short piece of bigger pipe and fit it onto the end,' he beamed; he loved to be involved with problems.

'We don't have the means of welding it on.' I sounded disappointed.

'We'll use one of those new metal fillers to glue it together; they're stronger than metal, y'know.' He was really warming to the subject.

'It's very bent.' I was losing confidence.

'We can straighten it in your vice in the engine room. We'll heat it first with a blow torch, it'll be easy.' He was on a roll.

'It's awfully rusty.' I already knew the answer.

'We'll treat it first with rust inhibitor and then paint it.' He sensed victory.

I decided to change tack.

'I had in mind a nice piece of stainless steel of the correct diameter, just cut to length.'

He sucked his cheeks in and rolled his eyes.

'Have you seen the cost of stainless steel these days, particularly when they know it's for a boat, they just double a figure.'

What does it matter, I thought, it's his boat and if he wants it done that way, why should I object to it. I picked up the rusty, tangled pipe and then thought sod it, and put it down again.

'Mr Hubbard, a few days ago you were all set to shell out many thousands of pounds if we'd damaged an engine by letting it overheat. Now, you want this mangy piece of metal fixed on the foredeck of your classic ship in order to save a tenner. I'm having real difficulty with the concept here, Mr Hubbard.' Shit, I thought, why don't I keep my big mouth shut.

GA looked at me quizzically and then grinned.

'Yes, you're right, throw it away and we'll get one in stainless steel.'

He turned on his way up the gangplank and looked at his watch and then at me.

'Drink, dear boy?'

Chapter Eight

The Greek Navy on parade. GA thinks his guests will like rough seas.

Our plan was to make Gouvia Marina our Corfu base, approximately 5 miles north-west of Corfu Harbour. However, as the port authorities showed no immediate sign of moving us on, we decided to find an engineer to sort out our hydraulic winch problem, whilst we were conveniently close to the town of Corfu. Thus, we had a front row, dress-circle view of the Greek Navy strutting its stuff.

Menacing is the first word that springs to my mind when encountering a naval vessel at sea. Dark grey and bristling with guns, they appear to slide effortlessly through the water, their decks clear of crew except for the bridge deck, where the watch officer scrutinises you through super-efficient binoculars.

Stupidly, you seek to assure him that you intend him no harm, by letting him see your hands empty of firearms; you relax a little as you note that the ship's 150mm gun barrels don't appear to be swivelling in your direction.

Your friendly wave, however, isn't immediately returned and the binoculars seem to delve into your innermost thoughts. At last, he raises a farewell hand and leaves the bridge deck. For the next few miles you show no sloppiness, proper hand signals, everything.

The Greek minesweeper, its deck heaving with national service conscripts, was preparing to moor alongside the part of the quay that we had just vacated. It was a naval vessel and it was dark grey, but the menace element came from the manner in which it manoeuvred, rather than any warlike potential.

The skipper had made his presence felt, I trust unintentionally, by scraping his hull across our anchor chain. As the minesweeper was considerably larger than *Blue Skye C*, we were shaken like a puppy on the end of a leash; he had our full attention.

There was much running, pushing and shoving by the boisterous ratings; they were anything but clear as to their specific function relating to the mooring-up process. Their progress was further hampered by numerous small groups of off-duty ratings, some clearly disinterested in the proceedings, others shouting out in a mixture of jocular encouragement and derision.

Senior officers were loudly berating junior officers, who were shouting orders at their charges. Clouds of black smoke emitted from the exhausts, as first the port and then the starboard engine roared in objection as they received a series of conflicting instructions: full ahead to full astern, with a mixture of indecision between. Noisy would describe it, so much so, that passers-by on the other side of the railings had ceased passing by and were forming themselves into a respectable-sized supporters' club.

The comedy of errors had no doubt commenced, as always, by an initial breakdown in communications. I presumed that the captain wouldn't take kindly to being questioned on the subject by the English skipper of a private motor yacht, so I can only surmise with regard to the minutiae.

However, it matters not if it was noticed before or after they hit my anchor chain that their fenders were on the wrong side of the boat, but it would have been better had they managed to transfer them without dropping one into the water. Perhaps the petty officer would have made allowances for this error had the remaining fenders been retied at the correct height; for had the fenders been 1m lower, they would have intervened betwixt hull and quay, thus preventing much damage.

There was a toe-curling crunching sound as the minesweeper's wooden hull came into direct contact with the stone quayside situated below the well-intentioned yet underemployed swinging fenders.

I think that the helmsman was acting with good intentions when, with engines protesting, he struggled to put space between hull and quay. Regrettably, the helmsman's success was a contributing factor in the failure of the well-built rating responsible for throwing the bowline ashore, to succeed in his task. All on board, along with some shore-based spectators, derisively cheered the unfortunate lad – whom I thought had made a creditable effort with his throw – when the warp fell into the widening gap between boat and quay.

All attention was now focused on the well-built and very red-faced rating in charge of the bowline. Having retrieved the wayward warp, he began preparations for another throw, whilst being encouraged by the chanted Greek equivalent of ready, steady, go.

I suspect that the concentrated attention on the forward end of the vessel was the reason that the problems at the aft end went unnoticed, at least for a little while. One end of the aft line was well secured to the deck cleat and the other end was safely attached to the quayside bollard; it did seem to be a pity that the middle bit was snagged around one of the ship's propellers. The spectators sensed that events had taken another turn when the officer in charge aft, threw his hat down onto the deck and stamped on it, whilst his young charges peered over the aft rail. The onlookers craned their necks to get a better view, thinking that perhaps someone had fallen overboard.

The captain no doubt would have preferred that, rather than having the warp being entangled around the ship's stern gear. Strictly speaking, according to the International Collision Regulations, his ship was now classed as a "vessel not under command".

I checked our British ensign and noted that it was flying proudly in the strong wind. I almost saluted it.

Some of you may seek to make allowances for the Greek Navy, claiming that similar things will have happened in our own Senior Service in the days when conscription swelled our armed forces. However, whilst I'm sure our conscripts could have been much the same as their Greek counterparts in most respects, I doubt that the same would apply to our naval officers. Frankly, I don't believe that any British naval officer would ever throw his hat on the deck and jump on it. No doubt he could be tempted to stamp on a rating, but never on his officer's hat. Unfortunately, our hapless crew hadn't yet finished displaying their blithe approach to their mariner's assignments in general and to discipline in particular.

The captain, no doubt smarting from the ignominy of his ship's docking performance, sanctioned fire drill for his unloved crew, thinking perhaps that the authorities would frown upon public flogging.

The conscripts approached fire drill with even less dedication than that afforded to any task since entering port, and displayed all the proficiency of a team in the first round of a Top Town competition. There was much shouting and aimless running around; officers and men were generally not as one. The water valves brought them all together in that none of them knew where they were. The fire hoses were laid out on the quayside in disarray; not yet connected to the water valves or to each other, they resembled a snakes and ladders board. Prior research by the officer in charge of the drill would have been advantageous, but all was resolved when the uniformed port authority officer arrived with slow and deliberate gait. Perhaps it would be more accurate to describe his gait as deliberately slow, as he clearly wished to demonstrate that whilst in port, no one in the services, whatever their rank, outranked the port authority. He drew chalk marks around the metal covers that protected from view the sought-after fire hydrants; their below-surface design leaned in favour of water preservation, rather than fire fighting assistance.

When at last a hose was fitted to the newly discovered hydrant and the valve opened, water gushed out of the end of a hose that was well removed and certainly not connected to the business end. Unbelievably, in true Buster Keaton fashion, someone actually peered down the nozzle in search of the missing water.

The happy-go-lucky approach of the conscripts, who were clearly enjoying themselves, was in stark contrast to the officers in charge, who looked angry and embarrassed. I kept a straight face; the officers had enough problems without any added frustration. Any country that has a conscription policy will have a number of conscripts who aren't selected as officer material yet possess a higher IQ than some of higher rank. Regrettably, those officers in possession of a lower IQ than their charges would probably never recognise the fact.

What was very clear, however, was that whilst the young Greeks were displaying a colossal ineptitude in everything they did, equally clear was that they weren't trying very hard. One sensed that whilst they had no other option than to be there, they didn't see their conscription period as central to any career plans they had for the future. Probably, most would view their compulsory service time as a student views a gap year and since flogging is now frowned upon, it's difficult to see what the officers could do to get their charges to take their tasks more seriously.

One thing was for certain; I was pleased that this particular ship's complement wasn't in charge of a lethal battleship or a vessel with nuclear warfare potential. No mugs the Greek naval personnel department, for you can't start a war with a minesweeper; that said I hoped they wouldn't have live mine-handling exercises whilst we were moored next door.

I'm not sure if the Sunday morning parade was a continuation of the disciplinary process or a regular weekly outing. I favour the disciplinary theory, for surely no one could be so incompetent if they had to do it every week.

The conscripts were lined up on the quayside in their smart uniforms and standing to a sort of attention. They were facing both their ship and a short rotund officer, resplendent in his ceremonial uniform complete with sword. He was puffed up to a degree that suggested he had looked forward to this event all week.

The iron railings at the back of the quay, which was now doubling as the parade ground, were the same railings that had held back the spectators during Saturday's mooring debacle; they now formed the demarcation line between the parade ground and a small but growing group of admiring young girls. They had no doubt become acquainted with the intrepid young mariners during the previous evening in Corfu's bars and discos.

The admired ones with their backs to the railings were as yet unaware of the presence of their followers, whilst the tubby one with sword was milking the situation in the misguided belief that the bevy of admirers had eyes only for him.

There was much strutting and shouting as he selected the tallest of his charges to bear the brunt of his remonstrations, which he followed with the very loud delivery of the Greek equivalent of: to the left, about-turn; to their credit, they all finished up facing in the same direction.

His Tubbyness with sword – who was now cooking on gas – took up his position at the head of his charges. He was standing ramrod straight, with his sword held vertically, its back edge one inch from his nose. He took a deep breath, expanded his chest almost in line with his stomach, and issued the order to quick march. He set forth, left arm pumping to shoulder height; it was a stirring display and would have been outstandingly so, had his entire platoon been following. Regrettably, only the front line and part of the second actually quick marched on the order and they ultimately proved not to be stayers.

It was the initial order to turn to the left that led to Tubby's undoing, for whilst the entire platoon finished up facing the same way, all but two achieved it with a quarter turn to the left. The wayward two, having initially turned to the right, completed a clockwise three-quarter turn, to be as one with their comrades. En route, so to speak, they spotted the female admirers clinging to the railings.

The bush telegraph informed all except those in the front row and part of the second row, who, having commenced marching on the order, slowly became aware that they were in a minority. The herding instinct proved to be a more powerful authority and they straggled to a halt in no-man's-land.

My stomach was now aching from the effort of containing audible laughter as I ran into the wheelhouse and slammed the door. I collapsed into the helmsman's chair, giggling with eyes streaming; my giggles became high-pitched moans when I looked at Jean, who was having difficulty drawing breath.

Mesmerised, we seemed to be witnessing the lead in to an inevitable accident. When I say we, I mean we in its full collective sense; that is, Jean and me, the crews of the four private boats moored on our port side, the officers watching from the deck of the minesweeper on our starboard side and of course, the spectators. Even the young conscripts had stopped waving to the girls, their eyes now focused on the lone marching swordsman; he was like a man with open trouser flies – no one wanted to tell him.

He didn't stop at the point when he first suspected that all was not as it should be, but his faltering steps gave the clue. Finally, that which he found difficulty in believing crystallised into reality. I think the majority of the audience were beginning to feel sorry for him, but men of his ilk are rarely able to fuel such emotion in others for long; he resorted to type, thus releasing observers from any need to display their sympathetic tendencies. With a face the colour of an overripe plum and wafting his sabre, he charged like an agitated baby rhino back towards his platoon, who were now intent on rearrangement as the front ranks sought sanctuary at the rear.

Whilst conscripts and observers alike were confident that he wouldn't go as far as to actually strike someone with his sword, there was a communal holding of breath as he approached his men now huddled like a group of rabbits caught in the headlight beam of an oncoming juggernaut. He was beside himself with anger and to my layman's eye, just a short step from insanity.

He loudly berated them as he paced before them, sword thrashing to underline a point, like an overacting Freddie Starr. As you would expect, he went on too long and lost the initiative; a growing number of his charges were tentatively renewing their interest in the camp followers.

A semblance of order was achieved when following a short discussion with a senior officer, the sword was sheathed and the platoon marched away from the gaze of their admirers to the shelter of the customs buildings. I could still feel the ache in my stomach the next day.

I doubted that any lessons would be learned, for the unfortunate man never was and never would be officer material. Calm under fire: inconceivable. Inspirational leader: never. Disliked but respected by his men: only half right.

So what's new? The same could apply to most uniformed Greeks. I make this statement in retrospect, having lived on board *Blue Skye C* in Greece for two years; an environment eminently suited to the study of the uniformed Greek psyche.

Perhaps I should confirm that when using the term uniformed Greeks, I refer to uniforms related to Greek authorities, such as customs officials, port captains and their officers, port police, immigration officers and all similar uniformed civil servants. You may add to that list, captains of ferries and Greek merchant vessels sailing the Ionian and Aegean seas that so often presume right of way over any vessel flying a foreign flag. They have been known to give way to another Greek vessel, but only when the other vessel was bigger; their version of the shipping regulations, whilst illegal, is easily understood.

Maybe I should make a distinction between Greek merchant vessel officers and officers of the Greek Navy. The officers of the minesweeper were the only serving Greek naval officers I have ever had contact with and whilst the happenings that I have just related don't show them off in a good light, they had my sympathy when considering the crew of conscripts that they had to control.

When speaking to them without the burden of their ship's company of raw recruits, they were both polite and friendly and didn't share the arrogance that the merchant boys generally possessed in spades.

I don't think that any of the ship's officers were overly embarrassed by their collective performance since arriving in port and I think that the conscripts viewed it all very much as the norm. Even his Tubbyness seemed to take things in his stride and he appeared not to hold any feelings of animosity towards the conscripts. So I warmed to the Greek Navy, acknowledging that their ways were different to ours, whilst being thankful that the Royal Navy protected the UK.

* * *

Our first guests on board were Mike Goodyear – GA's chief executive – and his wife Sally; both were, good fun, which helped Jean and me in our first week of looking after visitors other than GA.

I warmed to Mike when he saw me don overalls to carry out some maintenance in the engine room; he wouldn't rest until Jean had given him a pair to use for the week. There was no way that I could sneak into the engine room without him tagging on; he was in heaven if I gave him a spanner to wield. GA took to joining us, as he felt that we were having more fun than he was; such unsolicited assistance didn't help me to get jobs done.

The week went well, except for GA's injury, received when he fell off his motorbike whilst touring the island of Ithaca with Sally and Mike. His knee was quite swollen, but he had booked a table at the local restaurant and there was no way he would cancel. I went down into my engine room workshop and made him a crutch, along with Mike's assistance of course. GA was thrilled with it, but more so with the silk headband and eye patch that Jean had made for him – he not only paraded the deck in his pirate's garb, but he also limped to the restaurant in it. The locals thought he was wonderful.

Sally and Mike left *Blue Skye C* somewhat reluctantly. GA had offered them a fortnight, but they chose a week only, unsure that two weeks on a boat would suit them. Mike wondered if he could join us when we took *Blue Skye C* to the boatyard for her annual maintenance; he apparently had his own overalls. Sally left us to be known for evermore – owing to an error by the Greek transit log officials – as Housewife Norwich.

Jean lay awake worrying for most of the night before the group of GA's family and friends arrived. Strangely, just as I had assured her, none of them had two heads or sported horns. The party consisted of Mr Hubbard and wife Marjorie, their daughter Sandra, with her husband, Ivan, and Bob and Marita Dale. Bob was a director of one of GA's companies and was also a long-standing family friend. He was a large man carrying a considerable stomach and like many large men, he was a kind and gentle man, with never a bad word to say about anyone. Whilst Bob and GA were constantly arguing with each other, but with no animosity and much mickey-taking, they clearly liked and respected one another.

All in all, it generated a light and happy atmosphere on board, which helped to make our first serious cruise, despite my own qualms and Jean's considerable anxiety, into a satisfying endeavour and it generally set the tone for all future cruises.

We soon learned to change the atmosphere in small ways to suit differing personalities, but the first cruise highlighted that the main element required was a happy and worry-free atmosphere for all guests. I stress the worry-free element, for whilst I was aware that the first time on a boat can be unnerving for many, it wasn't until that first cruise that I realised just how apprehensive some can be once that link to shore has been severed.

We quickly learned that a guest's silence wasn't necessarily a mood following a tiff with their partner; more often than not, the cause was apprehension, triggered by something that – whilst basically offering no threat or danger – was in their eyes a definite cause for alarm. We became expert at reading the signs and didn't require the observation of white knuckles to recognise a guest's personal unease.

It was always a source of amazement to me that so many skippers, in their efforts to increase their imagined macho image, would sail a boat in such a cavalier manner that some guests were decidedly unhappy; such skippers appeared to derive a degree of perverse satisfaction on seeing the discomfort of others. Those wishing to employ such skippers can track them down in most quayside bars along the length and breadth of the Mediterranean; they are the loud ones, who know everyone and are between jobs.

Whilst I made every effort to ensure that all guests felt comfortable and safe, it wasn't always easy to do so when GA was on board. I'm not suggesting that GA didn't wish his guests to enjoy themselves, far from it, but as he himself never ever suffered the slightest concern whilst at sea, a guest would have to fall out of their chair white lipped and rigid with fear before he would notice their plight.

This shortcoming wasn't a problem in itself; it was more a matter of his view on how such nervousness should be eased that was difficult to align with. I don't argue that it's wrong to push fallen riders back onto their horses and I also recognise that a successful passage through stormy seas will increase confidence, but whilst ideal for the jockey and the sailor, I would submit that such remedies aren't ideal for apprehensive septuagenarians on holiday.

GA, whilst approaching seventy himself, had an appetite for living larger than most teenagers; he would dive from the deck, swim, eat and drink regardless of weather conditions, and thus he saw no reason why all others of similar age shouldn't be the same.

This was a little unfortunate for his wife Marjorie, who was not only a couple of years his senior but, it has to be said, didn't really like boating at all; no, that's not strictly true, for she enjoyed living on board *Blue Skye C* when it was tied to the quayside. She gained far more enjoyment going ashore to window shop and returning for afternoon tea on the aft deck, than actually going to sea. She enjoyed it when *Blue Skye C* was laid serenely at anchor in some secure and sheltered bay; it was that bit in the middle she hated. This became apparent on our first little cruise to Port Gaios on the west coast of the Isle of Paxos.

We had visited a few bays in Corfu, returning each night to Gouvia Marina that we had made into our Corfu base. As the guests were all happy and relaxed, I suggested that the following day, subject to favourable weather conditions, we did a mini cruise, staying overnight at Paxos, a beautiful little island 30 miles to the south. GA, who had been ready to take everyone there on day one and was of the opinion that I was being overly cautious with my guest acclimatisation plan, readily agreed to all except the weather condition bit.

The following day was perfect, with blue sky and not a cloud in sight; the sun was already hot as we cleared the breakfast dishes. We slipped between the town of Corfu and Vidha Island onto a south-easterly course between Corfu and mainland Greece three quarters of an hour later. All the guests were reclining on lounger chairs placed on the aft deck, except for Mrs Hubbard, always referred to by GA as Mother, who sat out of the sun at the dining table in the open-ended aft saloon concentrating on her crossword.

Jean was stretched out on the wheelhouse seat reading a book, whilst I recorded our exact position as we passed Vidha Island and then settled into the bolted-down helmsman's swivel chair and relaxed.

Unlike most motor yachts, *Blue Skye C* offered 360° vision from the wheelhouse and a spin around on my chair enabled me to easily monitor our surroundings. All was well and I was happy as the automatic pilot – every helmsman's superior in calm seas – nudged the teak and brass wheel back and forth, steering a course that left an arrow-straight wake in the blue waters astern.

An hour and a half later, with Prasoudhi Island a couple of miles to port, I was looking towards the three-mile stretch of water between the southern point of Corfu and the islands of Sivota and Nikolaos which, from our position seven miles to the north, appeared to be part of the mainland.

All was quiet on the aft deck; even those not asleep had their eyes closed, so I set a course to go through the centre of the gap, rather than a close-in sightseeing pass. Anyhow, it was perhaps as well, considering the low bank of fog or mist that appeared to have settled there.

How strange, a low bank of fog set exactly between two points of land, but with no overspill at the edges. Come on, Alwyne; sort yourself out, something's not quite right. I refocused my binoculars, to confirm what I thought I had glimpsed: waves, big ones, all with white tops, three miles of them, and we'd be there in about forty minutes. I swivelled round to look at the aft deck, all comfy and content. I spoke quietly.

'Jean, will you go batten down in the galley and deck anything movable in the saloon, we're going to rock a bit.' I added, 'In your own time, of course.'

Jean was down below in a shot; she'd heard what I said, but knew what I meant. I eased back on the throttles a couple of hundred revs, whilst all the guests dozed on, but GA, as expected, noticed the engine change and breezed into the wheelhouse.

'Problems, dear boy?' His eyes were searching the surrounding blue water for the cause of our sudden reduction in speed.

'Well, not right now, but in about half an hour we'll be in some nasty water. I'm not sure how long it will last, but it would be as well if we got everyone in from the aft deck until we sort it out.' I handed him the binoculars and pointed towards the horizon.

All small-boat sailors know the problems with highly magnified binoculars: it would be easy to read the name on the buoy, if only you could focus on it for long enough, but no, it flits in and out of your vision like an agitated mosquito. I had shelled out a ridiculous amount of money for my binoculars, but they were the business, well damped down with separate focusing for each eye and they were also able to make the darkest day into a bright one. GA, a racing man with more binoculars than you could carry, never seemed to get the hang of mine; he turned everything movable and then raised them to his eyes. Then he lowered them, checked to see if the lens covers had been removed and handed them back.

'Doesn't look too bad, does it?' he rubbed his nose.

'Well, we're not going to be in any danger, but we will have a few unhappy passengers if we don't warn them and bring them in off the aft deck. Mrs Hubbard will be particularly apprehensive.' I felt that the Mrs Hubbard bit would be the clincher.

'Oh, Mother will be fine; she's been in rough seas before.' He popped two fruit gums into his mouth, from a bag someone had left on the side table.

'Yes, she's told me and I think she was scared at the time.' He couldn't ignore that.

'She overreacts sometimes, that's why she's best not knowing.' He dismissed my point.

Recognising that I was on the wrong tack, I tried a different angle.

'Well, perhaps we should get all the recliners to the shelter of the aft saloon, to keep any spray off the mattresses and cushions,' I suggested.

'Good idea, dear boy, there's nothing worse than seawater for damaging things. I'll get them to move the chairs back a bit.'

To be strictly accurate, the chairs would have to be moved forwards and not back to get to the aft saloon, but this was no time to argue semantics. GA went outside to save the mattresses from getting wet, our passengers relocated and reoccupied the recliners and Mother kept her seat at the saloon table; spray didn't sound too alarming. There weren't any questions relating to the cause of the anticipated spray, for they were all well used to doing GA's bidding without question, as it was less hassle that way.

In any event, the sea was still blue and twinkling – when looking aft – with not a cloud in sight. Jean rejoined me, having stowed away movable objects in the galley and placed bowls of fruit and other unfixed objects onto the saloon floor. She eyed the confused water ahead of us through the binoculars.

'That looks horrible, wouldn't it be better to go somewhere else and miss it?'

'Well, we don't know how far it goes on for; we'll see what it's like when we get there.'

I checked the radar; the narrow strait was 3 miles ahead, eighteen minutes to go. I stood at the door and inspected our reposing charges. They were safe enough in that they were within the line of the aft saloon deck head supports.

Having cleared the chart table of all loose items, I settled back into the helmsman's chair and switched off the automatic pilot. The autopilot could maintain a more rigidly accurate course than I could in calm conditions, but in confused seas, it could never anticipate wave contact and would steer its course with no regard for the welfare of the ship and its passengers; it was best to take control of the helm at such times.

I could now see the waves in more detail less than a mile ahead, powering across from the mainland to the southern tip of Corfu; the wind must have been whipping down the foothills at some speed.

'OK, Jean, ensure that everyone is awake and aware that it's going to be a bit uncomfortable.'

'How's it going, dear boy?' GA breezed in. 'Looks a bit choppy.'

'It's going to be right on the beam, I'll lean into it a bit, but we'll know we're in it. Could you give Jean a hand if anyone gets really worried?'

As I looked back I saw that Ivan, now staring ahead, had spotted the waves; his mouth was clamped shut and three days' suntan had disappeared. GA had a wicked grin on his face as he went out to help Jean.

'Just something we've laid on for you all,' he proclaimed. 'It'll give you an appetite before lunch.'

Bob raised his recliner into a half-sitting position and resettled his comfortable 17 stone. Mother, who carried more weight than perhaps she should, moved at speed from her seat in the deck saloon to the one next to me; there were tears on her cheeks, she was petrified. My heart went out to her, for this wasn't what holidays were meant to be about. Over the years she took up this position whenever conditions scared her and I would prattle on about everything and anything, in an effort to damp down any real or imagined fears that plagued her at such times.

The first wave lifted *Blue Skye C* with some violence; fortunately, she leaned heavily to port on the way down, which enabled Bob's recliner to clear a space on deck for him to land on; however, it did meet up with him on its return journey. Marita, Bob's wife, kept letting out fairground-type screams, each one visibly increasing Mother's anxiety.

'Well, Marita seems to be enjoying herself, Mrs Hubbard.' I flashed a big, reassuring grin, but she didn't seem too reassured.

'Where are you going?' she almost shouted as I switched the autopilot back on and left the wheel.

'I'm not going away, Mrs Hubbard.' I tried another reassuring grin and then shouted through the door at Bob, who was clearly contemplating a bid to retrieve the recliner, which was now crashing across the aft deck from one side to the other. Although each thud against the mahogany handrail varnish work made me wince, I wasn't about to lose a passenger overboard.

'Bob, leave it.'

I stayed in the doorway until I was sure that he wouldn't attempt a chair rescue mission; he grabbed a hold on one of the stainless steel roof pillars just as the residue of a wave breaking against the hull topsides spewed across the deck. I think he recognised the prudence of leaving the rampant recliner to its own destiny.

With the autopilot re-engaged *Blue Skye C*, whilst dead on course, was now smacking down into troughs and sending shudders from stem to stern. I switched it off and took the helm again, easing the ship back into a slightly less violent motion. By now, Jean and GA had managed to corral the remaining chairs with a rope across the open end of the dining area.

I could see the waves easing some 400 yards ahead.

'Not long now, Mrs Hubbard, and then we can all have a cup of tea.'

She was still fiercely gripping the grab rail, but managed a wan smile.

The disturbed sea eased off quickly to a level that would enable the autopilot to take full control again and everyone began chattering like a group vacating the carriages after the Big Dipper ride; in retrospect, they all thought that they'd enjoyed it, but knew that they didn't want to do it again. The exception being Mother – she didn't think for one minute that she'd enjoyed it.

'Will it be like that on the way back, Alwyne?' She was still holding the grab rail until clear in her own mind that the waves had really gone.

'I don't think it will, but if it is, we won't go through it, we'll go the other way around Corfu and avoid it.'

That made her happy, she didn't leave the seat next to me until we arrived at Paxos, but she did take one hand off the grab rail.

With *Blue Skye C* moored stern-to in the Paxos Harbour in Gaios, all the guests went ashore to explore the town, while Jean and I set about clearing up the chaos in the saloon. One of the cupboard door catches had broken, allowing two-dozen bottles of wine and some stainless steel serving dishes free range.

Fortunately, only one bottle broke. Unfortunately, it was red and the saloon carpet was white; extra colour was added by the soil from the upturned pot-plant. The bowls of fruit and the nuts, sweets and nibblers that Jean had placed on the floor for safety had all overturned and the weighted chairs designed to remain upright – weren't.

An hour later and a bottle of white wine to neutralise the red wine stain and we were back in business. We sat back for five minutes with a cup of tea, whilst discussing dinner preparations; my input, as usual, aimed at reducing my washing-up chores to a minimum.

GA stuck his head down the companionway.

'Drink, dear boy? You as well, Jean; the gin and tonics are all ready on the aft deck. Forget about preparing dinner, I've booked a table at a delightful little restaurant. Looks a bit scruffy, but all the best places do out here.'

His head disappeared and then reappeared as he reached down to a dish on the bookshelf by the steps and collected a handful of dried prunes. I winked at Jean; owners could make life on board miserable or enjoyable.

Chapter Nine

Ferry skipper struts his stuff – could pride come before a fall? Maybe we over ordered.

We were fortunate in that we were cruising in the Corfu area in the late spring/early summer period and were able to get into small harbours like Port Gaios on the Island of Paxos. Later in the year it would have been impossible to manoeuvre in the narrow port without causing havoc amongst the large number of small flotilla yachts that pack the harbour in the summer months.

The start of the Port Gaios mooring quay has about 70m between it and the little island that blanks it off from the sea; then it increases to an average width of about 100m or so of navigable water, with an average depth of 3m. It only requires a few 10m and 15m boats moored along the quay with anchor warps stretched out ahead to concentrate the mind. Mooring in amongst small boats isn't easy: their hulls are below the level of *Blue Skye C*'s aft deck and cannot be seen from the wheelhouse when going astern. Skippers and crew of small sailing boats understandably appear alarmed as 80 tons of steel backs towards that tiny gap between them and the next boat.

A sharp 90-degree turn is required at the end of the narrow inlet from seaward, to gain entry into Port Gaios; only then could you determine the level of congestion along the quay. It was difficult not to look with envy when passing the prime mooring that was reserved for the daily Corfu ferryboat that brought supplies and visitors to the island.

The arrival of the ferry was something to see, for the skipper didn't follow the generally accepted approach to large-boat manoeuvring in constricted areas; namely, that whatever you do, do it slowly. For instance, if you're sitting on a moving mass of say 200 tons, travelling at 10 knots, then the absence of brakes increases the level of difficulty experienced in emergency-stop situations. More weight more difficulty; it's safer by far in tight situations, to do it slowly.

Bud Abbott – not the erstwhile American comedian, but a friend of mine who was the skipper of a much larger boat than *Blue Skye C* and had years of experience – insisted that the phrase "slowly, slowly catch a monkey" was rule number one in tight-situation manoeuvres. The Greeks scorn such a namby-pamby approach to boat handling and the Corfu ferry captain was Greek to the core.

I admit to some admiration when I witnessed the skilled but somewhat flamboyant mooring technique that he had perfected on a daily basis over the years. The ferry's entrance had become a daily attraction, rather like the changing of the guard at Buckingham Palace. Spectators would gather on the quay at the appointed hour and let out gasps of admiration as the skipper completed the equivalent of a handbrake turn to round the right-angled bend leading into port.

With a deft adjustment of throttles and gears, the skipper brought both props spinning full ahead to power his vessel at speed towards the mooring area. Noise was the thing; the skipper used noise rather like the orchestra's conductor at the last night of the proms inviting his audience to become fully engaged in the drama of the moment.

With engines roaring astern and the aft end of the boat engulfed in exhaust smoke, the vessel stopped inch-perfect over the anchor drop zone just feet from the shallows. Anchor and chain clanked noisily over the winch and out of the hawse pipe as thrashing propellers pulled the shuddering ship towards the quay; the harbour's clear water now turned into a brown soup of sand and silt.

After moving at speed towards the concrete ramp, the noise abated as the engines were cut and just as it seemed that the speeding ship would slam its stern up the ramp, the anchor chain took the strain and became bar tight over the water between ship and anchor. With its stern lines speedily and adeptly secured to the quayside bollards, the ferry's steel ramp dropped with a clang. Just minutes after clearing the tight entry into port, the delivery vans and passengers could disembark.

The skipper casually lit his cheroot and strolled from the wheelhouse, with the suspicion of a swagger, to take the applause from passengers and spectators alike; a masterly performance, albeit perhaps a tad hard on the ship's machinery.

It would sound like sour grapes, churlish even, if I were to suggest that whilst very impressive, his handling of the ship lacked the prudence one should expect from a professional seaman. So I maintained a discreet silence as our guests standing on the aft deck of *Blue Skye C* discussed the amazing performance they had just witnessed.

'That's got to be the best performance of boat handling you could ever see,' observed Ivan with a shake of the head. 'No reflection on you, Alwyne; you're good, but that, I mean that was incredible.' Ivan closed his eyes and slowly shook his head again, as if words couldn't do justice to such an astonishing display of virtuosity.

'Of course the Greeks are a seafaring nation, it's in their blood,' Ivan's wife Sandra added.

'You can tell that he does it every day.' Ivan again, it was turning into a double act.

GA breezed onto the aft deck and thrust a glass into my hand.

'Drink, dear boy?' Thank goodness for GA.

I saw the mooring show for the last time a couple of weeks before leaving the Corfu area bound for Athens. It's a pity Ivan wasn't there to witness the event. I was on my way back from the shops just as the ferry rounded the bend, so I joined the group of spectators on the quayside. I had always watched the performance at a distance from the deck of *Blue Skye C*, but from this new vantage point I was able to see in close-up detail just how inch-perfect the Greek maestro really was.

Full speed ahead from the entrance and then with engines roaring and stern enshrouded in exhaust smoke, the ferry slowed and then swung into position over the anchor zone. Full astern revs pulled the vessel back towards the quay and as it gathered speed, the clanking anchor chain could just be heard above the complaining engines. Something wasn't quite the same, though. Usually, the anchor chain left the winch in a controlled manner, but now it was clanking and banging out from the hawse pipe at speed; with a loud clunk and a splosh, the last link disappeared into the water: the Corfu ferry was now anchor-less.

The skipper, concentrating on the ship's stern, failed to see the crewman in charge of the foredeck frantically waving his arms in an attention-seeking fashion. There were clues there, but the skipper wasn't programmed to read them; no anchor chain noise was one clue and the fact that the vessel wasn't slowing down was a dead giveaway. I don't know at what precise moment the reality of the situation percolated into the skipper's consciousness, but when it did, the point of no return was long gone. He made an effort: his engines shrieking full ahead and props thrashing in the mud beneath the thick black exhaust smoke; there was noise, lots of noise.

The skipper's cause was a lost one; the ferry, now just 15m from the quay, couldn't be stopped. Relentlessly, the large ship mounted the ramp with props attacking the concrete like sharks in a feeding frenzy, accompanied by the most expensive sound I have ever heard. Then silence – a sort of embarrassed silence, in which no one quite knew what to say.

The skipper didn't appear for the ritual applause. He clearly thought that now was a good time for his crew to use their own initiative and he left them to fathom out how to get the supply vehicles down the ship's over-steep ramp that was still a metre short of reaching the ground. Bud's law – slowly, slowly catch a monkey – should be translated into Greek, but perhaps those sailors that have seamanship in their blood would ignore the slogan.

After the great levelling, we made our way back to Corfu; one of us on a high, I might add – I know, I know, very childish and immature.

GA and his last guests were returning to the UK, whilst Jean and I would prepare *Blue Skye C* for the passage to Athens. We would be sailing through the Ionian Islands and then between mainland Greece and Peloponnesus, via the Gulf of Corinth and the Corinth Canal. Whilst we were looking forward to the trip, our main excitement was that our daughter Lynne and her boyfriend Roy would be accompanying us on the journey. We hadn't been without guests or GA since leaving Cannes eight weeks earlier and whilst we had enjoyed that period, we were ready for a few days' rest before setting sail again.

We still had GA's hire car and decided to have dinner at a taverna some way along the coastal road on the outer limits of Corfu town. It was one of those places generally used by the locals and had been recommended by one of GA's friends.

You may wonder about that and it never ceased to amaze me that GA knew people in the most unlikely places. He was a great storyteller and he would keep Jean and me entertained for hours on long passages with tales of his travels. Some of his stories would seem, at times, to be a touch embellished, but more enjoyable for it

Incredibly, time and time again, some statement that we had taken with a pinch of salt proved later to be accurate in all detail. During the

Second World War that well-known travel agency Her Majesty's forces, activated his appetite for seeking out places of interest and in particular those venues not yet frequented by tourists.

He was a sergeant in the Royal Engineers, but whilst the majority of that regiment went about the business of building things such as roads, bridges and storage depots, GA was a member of a unit that went around blowing up such things as roads, bridges and storage depots.

The entrepreneurial trait that later turned him into such a successful businessman was underpinned by his aptitude for acquiring those things that were in such short supply that they were generally deemed to be unobtainable. Such men – whilst frowned upon by the top brass – were viewed as being indispensable by those officers who were a bit nearer the coalface, so to speak. These men possessed an aptitude for acquiring supplies that today's governmental procurement officers are unlikely to enjoy. To GA, the term "by the book" was merely a badly spelled method of obtaining reading matter.

Whenever we were about to move to a different venue or country in the Mediterranean, we would hear something like, 'I wonder if old so-and-so is still there, a lovely old boy, he used to get up to some tricks.'

I would wink at Jean and we would settle down, quite happily I might add, to listen to as entertaining a story as you could ever wish to hear. It didn't matter that we would never meet these people; his ability to paint the picture in your mind brought it all to life. It was on the passage from Italy to Corfu that Nikolus Coludas was mentioned.

'I wonder if we will see old Niky when we get to Corfu,' GA mused.

'Niky who?' I always had a ready riposte.

'Old Nikolus Coludas, he was a lovely old boy, you'd have liked old Niky.' There was a headshake followed by a chuckle.

'Oh, he died, then?' I asked, showing my concern for the old man.

'Oh, I shouldn't think so; he's younger than me and very fit.' He flexed his muscles to underline Niky's fitness.

'Ah, so you've seen him recently, then?' It was now becoming clear.

GA pursed his lips and gazed at the deckhead.

'Be about twenty-five years ago, business trip to Athens. Nipped over from there to see how he was, hadn't changed a bit. He has a blue fishing boat; we'll have to keep our eyes open, we may see it when we get a bit nearer to Corfu.'

There seemed to be no doubt in his mind that it was possible for us to meet on the high seas and even less room for doubt that given that Niky still had a boat, it would still be painted blue.

'What's the boat called?' This wasn't a sceptical query, but was intended to reassure that if I saw a blue boat, a full investigation would ensue.

'I'm not sure of the name, but it has an eye painted on the bow,' he confirmed.

I didn't enquire if the eye on Niky's boat was any different to the eyes that all Greek fishermen painted on the prow of their boats for good luck. Whilst I was aware that we would never meet GA's long-time acquaintance, I wasn't about to throw cold water onto his fantasy and I ensured that fishing boats of all colours were fully scrutinised through binoculars. GA maintained interest only if the boat was blue.

On that first family cruise, we lay at anchor in Ayios Stephanus, a small inlet just off the narrow North Channel that separates Corfu from Albania.

'What colour is that boat over there, dear boy?' GA was peering out to sea from our anchored position.

I focused the binoculars on the boat crossing the opening to the inlet.

'Blue.' I confirmed.

'That will be Niky, get after him; he'll be delighted to see me.' He was quite excited.

'We can't get after him quick enough to catch him, Mr Hubbard.' I became the professional skipper at such times of madness, pointing at Bob and Ivan, who were having a pre-lunch swim.

'We can come back for them later,' he beamed.

'The swimming ladder's still down and so is the dinghy; the anchor will take some time to get up.' I was squirming, so I played my trump card.

'Besides, Jean's just about to serve lunch, she'll not be too happy if we up anchor now.' That definitely checked his enthusiasm, but I could sense that the battle was not yet won.

'Bob and Ivan could catch them in the dinghy,' I suggested.

'Good idea, dear boy.' He shouted to Bob and Ivan, he was back on a roll.

Minutes later, with outboard at full throttle, Bob and Ivan disappeared around the headland in pursuit of the blue fishing boat. They arrived back about two hours later with a disconsolate air about them and looking like overdone lobsters.

The fishing boat had taken some catching on its way back to port and there had been some reluctance on the part of the crew to stop and talk. Not unnaturally, there had been a language problem, but there was no doubt that there was no one on board by the name of Nikolus. The rest of the day went by quietly by and we made our way back to Gouvia in the late afternoon.

''Ello, Meester Oobard,' the man on the quay shouted. 'My Capitan, 'e tell me you are 'ere.'

'Niky,' GA beamed 'come aboard and have a drink.'

'Close your mouth,' Jean whispered as I stared in astonishment.

I have to admit that Niky was a character. I presumed that they had met during the war, but GA was strangely unforthcoming when enquiries for such detail were made. They clearly had an affinity and I could well imagine what a formidable partnership they would have forged in the days when the outcome of the war was paramount and insider dealings were part and parcel of the game of acquisition.

They first met in the 1940s and not surprisingly, Niky's success level after the war hadn't gained parity with GA's achievements. I suppose that Corfu would have been an unlikely place to spawn such a level of industrial success. However, if the level of financial security and local influence is a measure of success, then Niky was successful. He employed a skipper and crew to run his fishing boat, and his motorbike and cycle-hire company didn't seem to require his presence, whilst several other interests were run from the corner table of his cafe. It seemed that the town mayor consulted Niky before making any decision of note.

It was on Niky's recommendation that Jean and I chose to eat at the taverna approximately 3 miles out of Corfu town. I apologise to all you Corfu-bound holidaymakers, for try as I might, I cannot remember the name of the taverna. If I manage to confirm the name and exact location before I finish this account, I will list the details at the end of the book. All that I can tell you, should you decide to look for it, is that you should take the coast road leading south-by-south-west from Corfu town and some 3 miles on you will find a residential area and that's the best I can do; if you're very hungry, you will search the area until you find a gate-like door set in a high stone wall, behind which you will find a very Greek taverna. Should you be seeking to quell your hunger pangs with convenience-type something and chips, then don't bother to enter, but go in search of an establishment displaying an "English food served here" sign. There, you'll be served chips that bear no resemblance to any chip you have ever tasted. For those stalwarts determined to track down this delightful little restaurant, there awaits a taverna with a little courtyard where Greek food is served on tables laid out beneath the stars and coloured lights are draped amongst the branches of gnarled old olive trees.

When Jean and I entered the courtyard, we were immediately taken by the ambience of it all, but were less impressed with the service, for the waiters quickly delivered a carafe of wine, a basket of bread and a dish of olives to our table and then ignored us completely.

Had it not been for a couple on a neighbouring table, we may well have left in high dudgeon after consuming all the bread, olives and wine; perhaps that's a bit unfair on Jean, as it was me who drank all the wine and ate the olives. The couple informed us that there was no actual menu and that the waiters would only serve the food after we had visited the kitchen and specified our choice. Somewhat chastened, we entered the kitchen, where someone who looked like the gardener lifted lids from a large range of big pans, to show us what dishes were on offer. We were spoiled for choice and finished up selecting from five different pans; it was perhaps a little greedy, but we thought that it would be nice for us to pick away between us at this tapas-type meal; wrong.

A couple of plates arrived piled high with meatballs, potatoes, onions and carrots, they had obviously made a mistake, for we had ordered only one dish of meatballs; clearly, we had someone else's order. The appetising dish we had ordered, having seen the strips of beef frying in olive oil with onions, peppers and mushrooms, arrived amidst two large helpings of potatoes, onions and carrots.

Potatoes, onions and carrots also accompanied our strips of fried liver and onions. The stuffed dumplings arrived generously garnished with potatoes, onions and carrots. We had been warned that the Greeks had a tendency to serve starters, main and sweet courses all at the same time; cleverly, we had sidestepped that problem and so were left with only one – what should we do with the eight workman-sized servings which totally covered our table for two? When we finally got over our fit of the giggles we picked away at what was by now becoming our lukewarm repast. We tried to do it justice, but the solids, now trapped by congealing gravy, had bested us. We had nonetheless generated some amusement for our fellow diners.

'Care to join us for a brandy?' a strong American accent enquired from the next table.

'You guys sure ain't got much room over there.' He could have left that bit out.

It was an offer we didn't want to refuse, for the waiters were showing no signs of clearing our table in the immediate future. I quickly pushed my chair back, lest the offer be rescinded.

'If you don't mind ridicule by association, we'd be delighted.'

We quickly vacated our table that still bore enough food to feed ten and joined the young American couple for drinks. A couple of hours shot past as we cemented Anglo–American relations. Our bill for wine and food was less than fifteen pounds; our American hosts insisted on paying for the brandy.

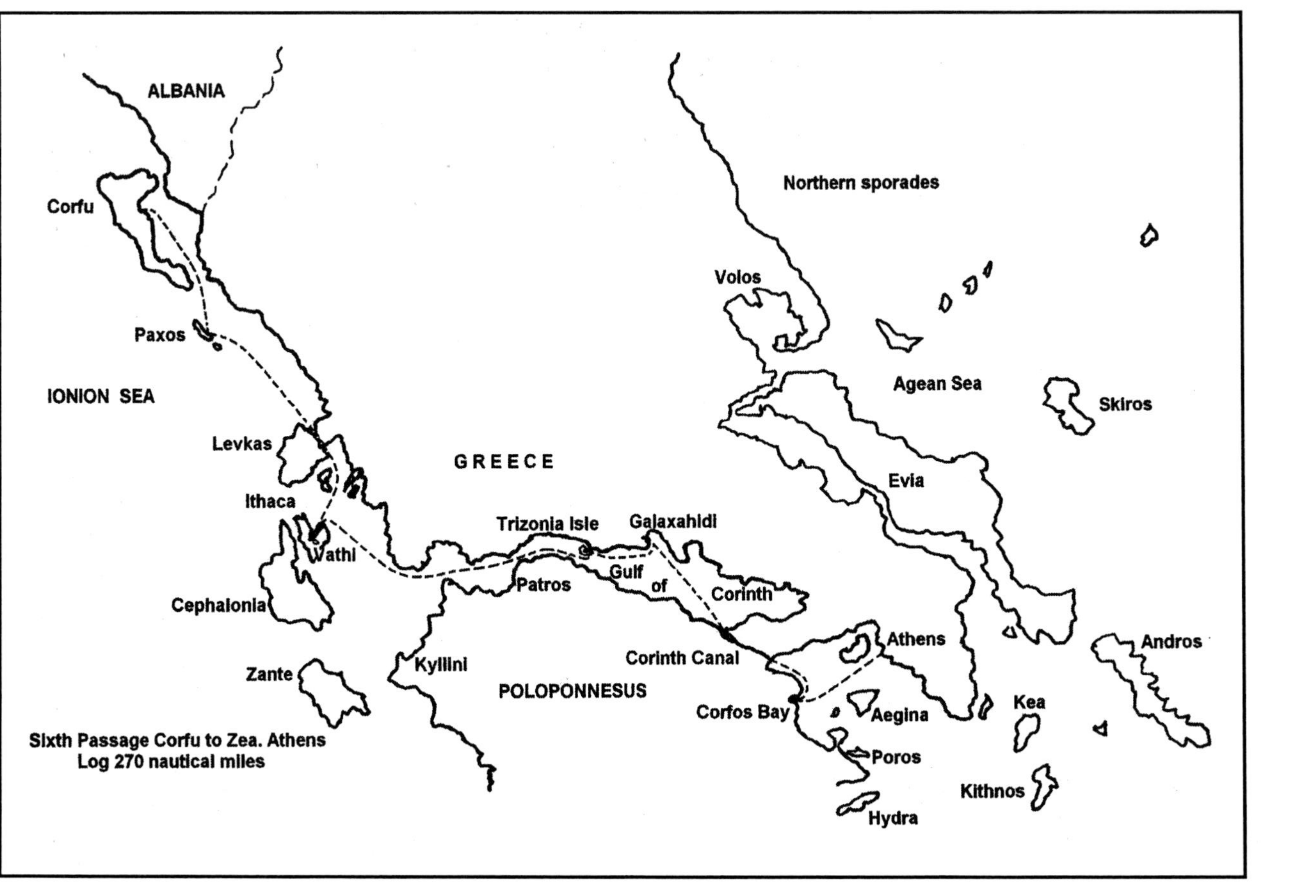

Sixth Passage Corfu to Zea. Athens
Log 270 nautical miles

Chapter Ten

A small yacht club and first through the Corinth Canal.

At last, the long-awaited day had arrived and we went to Corfu Airport to collect our daughter and boyfriend Roy. We hadn't seen them since the Christmas holidays and were excitedly looking forward to their company on the passage to Athens. Roy, however, was a little reticent; not surprising, really, considering that he'd never been on board so much as a ferry before and now he was to be trapped on board a vessel for two weeks with his girlfriend's parents. I mentioned to Lynne that he seemed a bit quiet and reserved.

'Oh, ignore him, he'll be right.' Lynne doesn't take after her mother.

The following day, 27 June 1985, we rounded Corfu Harbour and altered course for Paxos. The sky was, as usual, a deep, cloudless blue and I noted in the log that the sea was calm and flat, with not a breath of wind. The day was a first-time-sailor's dream, but Roy was hyper and judging by the way he hauled in the mooring warps when leaving the quay, his adrenaline was flowing and giving him that extra energy that young, fit men don't really need. In our youth, we take our athletic agility for granted and whilst we may think that we still have it twenty-five years on, our self-delusion becomes cruelly apparent when measured against the hyper- enthusiasm of youth in our own daily environment. The up side was that for the next two weeks I would have the fittest crew that had sailed on *Blue Skye C* for many a year.

It was a 230-nautica-mile sail from Corfu to Athens and weather permitting, we could complete the journey in a couple of days; however, I was determined to make this a relaxing cruise, for we had ample time to spare before Lynne and Roy were due to leave on their flight back to the UK.

As we moored in Gaios, I noted that the damaged ferry had been removed and I wondered if its skipper was helping with the repairs. The replacement supply ferry made a very conservative and workmanlike entrance into the harbour and docked with minimum fuss; I caught only a fleeting glimpse of the skipper, but I liked him.

We left Gaios at the civilised hour of 11.00 a.m. and headed for the Lefkas Canal, which bore no resemblance to a canal, for it had no banks. The canal was in fact a dredged channel and its waters merged with the surrounding water of the salt marshes that lie between mainland Greece and Lefkas Island. In the absence of an invitation to afternoon tea from the Onassis family, we passed by their private island, Skorpios, and anchored in a remote cove on the north-east coast of Meganisi, where we swam and relaxed in yet another remote and tranquil paradise. Yorkshire has many attractions, but Whitby, Scarborough and Bridlington don't boast such anchorages.

Life became particularly trying for Roy on the following evening at Port Vathi on the Isle of Ithaca. The pilot warned that northerly winds could be turned into severe downdraughts by the mountains adjacent to the Gulf of Molo. I don't know what strength the northerly wind achieved leading into the Gulf of Molo, but when it reached us in Vathi, it was gusting between 70 and 80 knots and our anchor couldn't secure a firm grip on the poor harbour bed. We had to move to the end of the inner basin to avoid being driven astern against a concrete quay.

Moving *Blue Skye C* to get alongside the inner basin quay demanded much rope work and Roy learned the hard way that half a turn around a bollard is insufficient. To his credit, he clung on to the mooring line as if his life depended on it and by the time I reached him to help get another turn on the warp, the pads of all his fingers and both thumbs had disappeared. His bandaged hands brought him much sympathy and even Lynne – who had taken every opportunity to display her superior knowledge of seagoing matters to the junior rating – accepted that he had earned his stripes for actions above and beyond the call of duty. The gale had blown out by the following morning, but we stayed another day for crew rest and relaxation.

"Roy the Bandage" took on a supervisory roll, while Lynne hauled in the warps as we left the Port Vathi Quay bound for Trizonia, an island in the Gulf of Corinth. Apparently, force five to six winds blow regularly through the Gulf of Patras and the Gulf of Corinth in the summer months, but we sailed on a flat, windless sea on our journey from Ithaca to the Island of Trizonia.

The north-eastern shoreline of Trizonia Island is within half a mile of mainland Greece and on that same shoreline is a 100-metre entrance leading into a superb bay, the hillside backdrop a profusion of lush green vegetation, olive trees and vines. Once anchored, the all-round view from on board was spectacular, but even more spectacular was the bay as viewed from between the trees as you climbed the surrounding slopes. Never was a more picturesque setting displayed on the front cover of a glossy sailing magazine or southern seas holiday brochure and there in the centre of it all lay *Blue Skye C* at anchor: wonderful.

As Roy and I sat in the little village square sipping an ice-cold beer and absorbing the serenity of it all, a man who introduced himself as Ion joined us. He established his status as an all-round good egg by replenishing our drinks and surprised us with the information that he was the owner of the Trizonia Island Yacht Club. Considering that *Blue Skye C* was lying at anchor in splendid isolation, one had to assume that the yacht-club membership enjoyed an element of exclusivity. It seemed that we had been exceptionally fortunate to arrive when we did, for on that very night the TIYC was serving a rather excellent curry. I suspect that the local taverna owner wouldn't be too happy with Ion's Westernised marketing technique.

Pre-dinner drinks were due to be served at around 7.30 p.m. and we duly rowed ashore and found the small, winding path worn into the hillside through a forest of greenery that we had been told would lead us up to the yacht club.

The building wasn't as big as the average yacht club; in fact, it wasn't as big as any yacht club, but it had the view that any yacht club in the world would be prepared to get into debt for. Ion and his partner Smiley were the perfect hosts and they clearly enjoyed their chosen lifestyle. One was English and the other was Greek, but as they both spoke with a cultured English accent and their appearance gave no clues as to their nationality, I wasn't sure who was what.

It would be churlish to suggest that the structure's features were strongly influenced by the architectural genius of Robinson Crusoe, but the place did have ambience. The sky was now inky black, displaying bright stars, like diamonds under spotlight on a jeweller's velvet cloth. We sat on the veranda and admired *Blue Skye C* from above, her lights now reflecting on the water's mirror-like surface as she lay serenely at anchor. I never tired of such magical moments. In addition, the wine had been good, the food excellent and I was sitting with my wife, my daughter and a young man who even I recognised would one day be part of my family; life doesn't get much better than that.

We must have slept in a little the next day, for I didn't blow the ship's horn to let Ion and Smiley know that we were leaving the bay until 10.50 a.m. Our destination was Galaxidhi, less than 20 miles away, a passage of a little under two hours. We were only about 60 miles from the Corinth Canal, but we decided to visit Galaxidhi and the Schooner Restaurant, which, we had been reliably informed, had the best fish menu in the Gulf of Corinth.

The problem with recommending restaurants is that you cannot guarantee with any confidence that the epicurean delight that you've described in mouth-watering terms is still available some months on. It's well known that chefs can be a touch temperamental from time to time and if the chef isn't the restaurant owner, then he or she may well have moved on within weeks, never mind months, since your well-intentioned recommendation. However, you can normally be reasonably confident that the restaurant will be open for business when the recipients of your enthusiastic recommendation arrive to sample the speciality of the house.

I'm not sure how long the Schooner Restaurant had been closed, but the dilapidated state of the building suggested that it would remain so for the foreseeable future; some other restaurant would have to take on the mantle of serving the best menu in the Gulf of Corinth.

I found the demise of the establishment unsurprising, for it would take more than a good restaurant to persuade me to revisit Galaxidhi. However, the island does have the distinction of being the venue where we persuaded Roy – a meat and Yorkshire pudding-eater to the core – to sample squid; of course, it was at a time when he was still trying to impress his future in-laws.

We arrived at the entrance to the Corinth Canal at 2.15 p.m. and anchored in the canal basin after a four-hour passage from Galaxidhi. There were about a dozen yachts moored to the quay, all of them waiting to make the short trip through to the Aegean. One of the skippers rowed out to us for a chat and I suspect it was to let it be known that some of them had been waiting there since 11.30 a.m. I caught his drift and reassured him that I was anchored off for the sake of convenience, rather than a desire to jump the queue.

'Is there a prize for the first one through?' I enquired.

He didn't stay long enough to answer, for the cause of the delay – a large cruise liner – was slowly edging its way out of the canal. He rowed like a maniac back to his boat, whilst his neighbours slipped their moorings and began circling like a group of agitated sharks, eager to be first into the canal; much in the same way that holidaymakers rush to board a plane that is most unlikely to take to the air without them.

We sat in the aft-deck saloon and drank our coffee, to show just how laid-back we were, whilst the cruise ship, looking far too big to navigate a canal, slowly emerged into full view, followed by an armada of assorted vessels. The fleet of agitated craft jockeying for position had been swelled in number by newcomers and to make matters worse for the British contingent – whose upbringing included the queuing code of practice – many of the newcomers were displaying French, Greek, Italian and German flags, all well known for their total disregard of queuing etiquette.

There was no way that I would enter the skirmish, I had worked too hard on Blue Skye C's paintwork to risk damage by a boat helmed by a skipper wearing a demented expression; had any of these vessels sported cannons, they would have been firing.

The pilot vessel gave a toot as it came alongside and paused long enough for a uniformed officer to board. I gave him the details he required to fill in his form and after some complicated-looking calculations, he presented a bill for 25,000 drachmas.

'We go now.' He pointed towards the canal entrance.

'What? Before everyone else?' I eyed the surrounding skippers, who by now, whilst not yet foaming at the mouth, were looking decidedly wild-eyed.

'Of course, you 'ave the ship is biggest, yes.' He spoke rapidly into his hand radio transmitter and the pilot boat began herding the fleet to one side in a manner that brooked no argument.

Roy looked a little embarrassed as he went forward to raise the anchor; Lynne went with him and enjoyed every minute as she smiled at our fellow passage makers; they glowered back, all united at last in common resentment. I gave them a cheery wave and led them towards the entrance.

The canal is some sight, for at just 25m wide, it looks alarmingly narrow; the limestone rock, through which the passage is cut, towers 76m above. The water has a strange, almost green, fluorescent hue to it, as if the canal didn't share the same water as the seas at either end. Even stranger was the fact that the canal linking two tideless seas had a 3-knot current. I was having difficulty steering a course, as we were moving between the sheer rock walls faster than the 3-mile-per-hour speed limit and my log was barely registering any speed at all. I glanced at the pilot as I rested my hands on the throttles and received a brief nod of permission; I gratefully increased our speed. As we left the waterway and entered the eastern canal basin, we were instantly buffeted by strong winds.

'Keep going, I jump,' the pilot assured.

I can't say that I was happy about it, for I would have to go at speed to ensure that the wind wouldn't force us against the quayside; I looked dubious.

'Is OK, no problem.' He shook my hand and left the wheelhouse.

If I closed to anything less than a metre from the concrete quay, it would be difficult to avoid being blown against it; the pilot jumped across a 1·5-metre gap and waved nonchalantly as I gunned the engines. Presumably, the pilot roster either takes note of weather conditions or the Corinth Canal pilots receive early retirement packages.

We blasted out into the Gulf of Kenkhreo, where the Meltemi was well into its stride and knocking up a nasty little short sea. I'd managed to keep salt water away from *Blue Skye C*'s shiny topsides and superstructure since leaving Corfu, so the sea state on the last leg came as no big surprise. We anchored in Frangolimani Bay, but the conditions were so uncomfortable that we moved and sailed around the headland to Korfos Bay, which offered excellent all-round shelter, and we anchored for the night.

'The anchor's bent, Dad,' Lynne informed me through the wheelhouse window.

'What do you mean the anchor's bent?' I like things to be clear.

'You know, that straight bit that fastens onto those two pointed bits.' She was a stickler for nautical jargon.

'You mean the shank that's connected to the flukes?' I corrected.

'I don't know which is a fluke and which is a shank; I just know that the straight bit's bent.' It is sometimes possible to follow Lynne's articulate descriptions.

'Jean, go and see to it, will you; it probably needs turning, there's no way it can be bent,' I assured.

Lynne, Roy and Jean peered over the bow as I manoeuvred *Blue Skye C* to the centre of the bay; we couldn't leave until the anchor was safely stowed.

'The anchor's bent,' Jean confirmed.

'How can it be bent? It's forged steel, it can't be bent. Turn it over and stow it, I'll sort it out later.' I was keen to get to Zea Marina by lunchtime, before all the spare moorings were taken up.

'It won't go into that pipe thing,' Jean shrugged.

I sighed as I left the wheelhouse to inspect the anchor.

'It's bent,' I affirmed, looking at the 70-degree bend in the last 50cm of the shank. 'There's no way that that will fit in the hawse pipe,' I assured everyone and ignored the raised eyebrows.

Fortunately, we had anchors port and starboard, so we stowed the bent one on deck and set off for Zea Marina, Piraeus–Athens.

I spotted an empty berth on the main quay and made a dash for it; the anchor was dropped and deftly, I might add, I manoeuvred into the slot. No one was impressed with my proficiency; to the contrary, it was as if I had started world war three. A couple of men on the quayside were shouting and waving their arms and a third was a little way off but making good speed on his bicycle, steering with one hand and waving the other; the body language suggested that he was a little upset. A couple more Greeks, definitely not bearing gifts, were approaching at speed in an important-looking craft.

'Well, it's nice not to be ignored.' My attempt at humour failed to alleviate the general fear that we were about to become political prisoners.

One of the men in the important-looking boat was holding on to our anchor chain with one hand and gesticulating wildly with the other; he nearly fell into the water on several occasions as the urge to gesticulate with both hands became too strong to ignore. At one such time, he held his left hand palm up and shrugged, whilst pointing the other hand towards the anchor chain. Then he assumed a look of disgust as he slapped his forehead with the palm of his right hand; each time, he nearly lost his balance. I was very concerned for his welfare, for I suspected that whatever I had done to generate such displeasure was unlikely to be excused should he take a ducking.

Whilst I couldn't understand a word he was saying, I had by now grasped that anchoring in this harbour was a no-no. A Greek gentleman on the next boat explained in good English that dire consequences would prevail should my anchor be hooked under the main mooring chain that ran along the harbour bed on a line approximately where I had dropped our anchor. Such a crime was punishable by a fine, plus the diver's charges for freeing the fouled anchor. I couldn't understand what he estimated our costs would be, but the look of horror on his face was enough to bring me out in a sweat. The crew and guests of neighbouring boats began to assemble on deck to witness our attempt to retrieve our anchor. Several officials were gathered on the quayside and, of course, the important-looking boat was standing by. Instructions had been given to the anchor detail; they were to take the chain in slowly as I eased out of the mooring and then speed up when we were directly over the drop zone. I nudged *Blue Skye C* cautiously forwards, carefully manoeuvring with throttles only; we had everyone's attention. You could almost hear the groan when the thumbs-up signal came back from the bow; we had escaped, much, it seemed, to the disappointment of the spectators.

We were allocated a mooring nearer to the port captain's office; it may well be that they wanted to keep an eye on us, but I prefer to think that they wanted our stay to be more comfortable away from the harbour entrance and its excessive traffic.

Whilst permanent mooring lines are frequently utilised in the Western Mediterranean, Zea was the first port that we had entered since arriving in Greece that had such a mooring system for larger boats. I presume that there are other Greek ports that use the system, but we never found one; normally, one has to put down an anchor. You would be right to suggest that if laying an anchor is the norm in Greece, why didn't the authorities put up a sign to inform newcomers to the port that anchors shouldn't be used; well, I have to confess that they had.

I saw the sign at the harbour entrance with all instructions in Greek, finished off with the picture of an anchor overprinted with a cross, but as the ship's pilot information for the port didn't mention the permanent mooring lines I interpreted the sign to mean that laying to a swinging anchor was prohibited and everything else was the norm. Well that's my excuse and I'm sticking to it.

Lynne and Roy had six days left before their flight back to the UK and I'm sure that many of you reading this chronicle would probably spend such free time exploring Athens and taking in its many historical sites. I personally prefer nature's structures to anything constructed by man centuries ago and now in desperate need of roof repairs. 'Philistine,' I hear you cry and it is your right to hold such an opinion. You're probably equally appalled that I have passed on similar traits to my offspring, hence Lynne, along with Roy, chose to spend those six remaining days swimming from the small beach nearby, sunbathing on the foredeck and lounging in the shade on the aft deck, whilst sipping whatever seemed appropriate for the time of day.

All too soon, Lynne and Roy's holiday was over and we sadly waved them off as their taxi left the quayside bound for the airport; we wouldn't see them again until the Christmas holidays. We had the usual day of moping and then got stuck into the preparations for GA and his family's next visit.

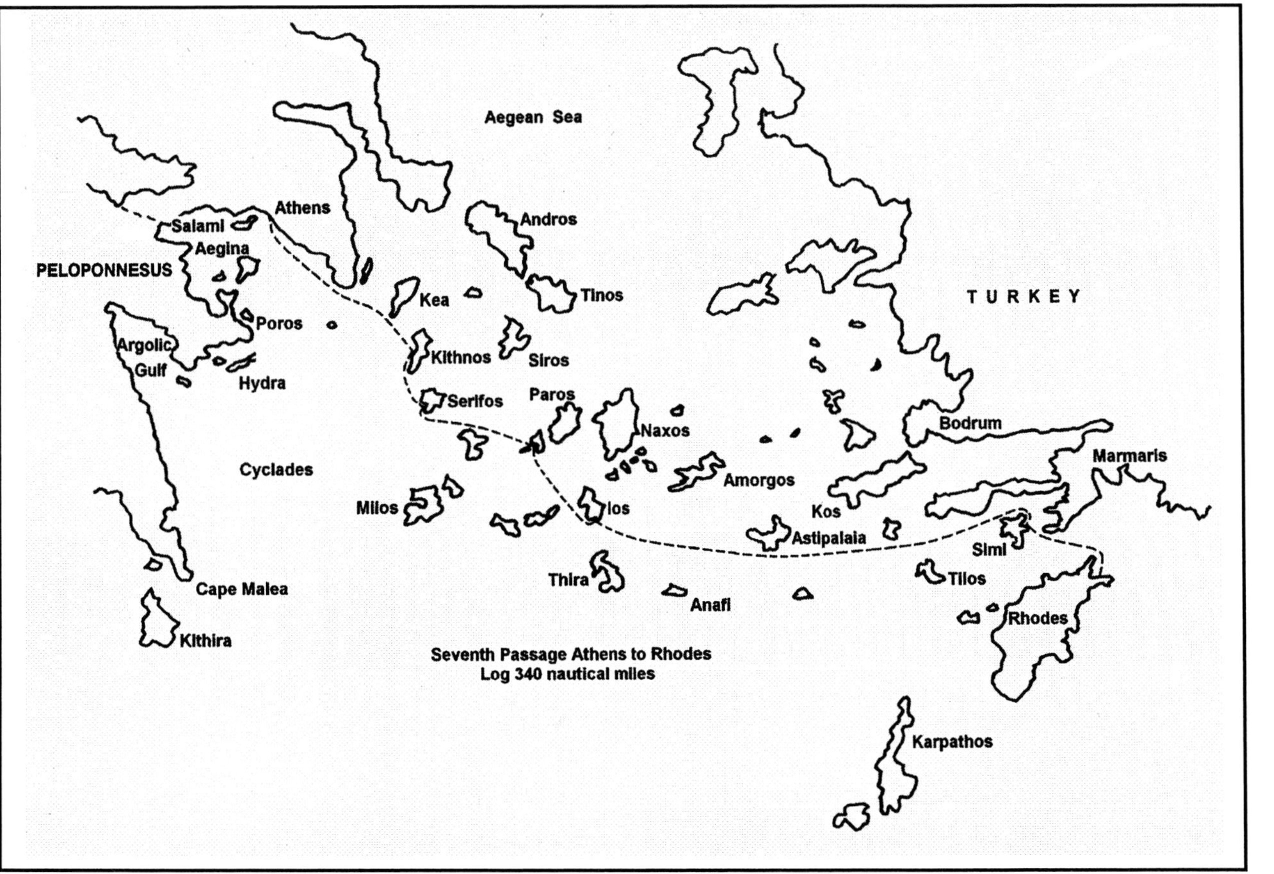

Seventh Passage Athens to Rhodes
Log 340 nautical miles

Chapter Eleven

Saronic Islands and Jean's impromptu swim. No short cut to Rhodes.

Zea Marina consists of a large outer harbour and a very large, purpose-built inner marina, which was scruffy when compared to the marinas and ports on the south coast of France. Wall-to-wall office blocks, commercial buildings and apartments surrounded the harbour and the circular-shaped marina. Boats and buildings are separated by a four-lane racetrack, which the citizens of Piraeus and its adjoining neighbour Athens convert into a six-lane race track at peak traffic periods between the hours of 6.00 a.m. and 1.00 a.m. The four lanes can just about cope with the traffic between 1.00 a.m. and 6.00 a.m. when a five-hour rush masquerades as the quiet period.

The environment I'm trying to portray here is round-the-clock, non-stop noise. Not the endless drone of traffic noise that can in time be ignored. It is a high-pitched motorbike engine-screaming, rubber-laying skid noise; mixed in with seemingly endless horn-blowing punctuated by the thump of front-ends meeting rear-ends. The inner city road has no double yellow lines, for no one in their right mind would contemplate stopping, let alone parking, unless a traffic light had been showing red for some considerable time; just slowing down would ensure a prod in the rear.

The contrast between Zea and Gouvia marina in Corfu couldn't have been more marked. Tranquillity is like fillet steak, if you have it every day then sausage and mash has a role to play and so the upside of our new location was that all those things difficult to find in Corfu were in plentiful supply in Piraeus. Maintenance materials, engine and equipment parts were within walking distance, along with a huge choice of restaurants, cafes and bars. All in all, it was a good place to be for preparing a boat for guests, so when GA and family arrived, *Blue Skye C* was shipshape and ready for the off.

GA's eldest daughter, Janet, and her three children accompanied him along with Mrs Hubbard. The plan was to cruise an area of the eastern Peloponnesus, namely the Saronic, the Hydra and the Argolic Gulfs. We completed the plan in eleven days, during which time we visited harbours and towns with magical names, such as Poros, Mandraki, Hydra, Ermioni, Spetsai, Khaidhari, Kheli and Aíyina. If you glance at a map to find these places, the spelling may well differ, for instance Aíyina on the admiralty chart becomes Egina on some Greek charts, whilst my Greek waters pilot refers to it as Aegina.

I have tried to avoid turning this account of our adventure, or opt-out as some of you may view it, into a form of travel guide. In my view, such a publication should always enjoy the opinion of at least three experts – I'm unsure how one becomes an expert in opinions – who hold differing views on most subjects. Having reached this stage of my manuscript, you will have decided what degree of similarity exists between our respective viewpoints. I can therefore suggest that if you share a similarity in preferences, you will not be overly stimulated by a tour of these locations.

Of all the areas that we have cruised in the Mediterranean, this one was the least memorable. If I were asked to choose the best of the above list I would pick Poros on the island of Poros, even though the most vivid memory is not one I recall with relish.

We anchored in Daskalia Bay on the south-east corner of Poros Island in time for a pre-lunch swim. GA had planned to take his grandsons out in the sailing dinghy after lunch, something he had looked forward to since its purchase in Cannes. This turned out to be the same let-down that all fathers and grandfathers have experienced from time to time. John, the eldest grandson, enjoyed snorkelling, driving the inflatable dinghy at maximum speed and chatting up the girls, but not necessarily in that order. Fairly standard teenage tastes, which most of us tend to forget when we get older. 'I would have given my eye teeth for the chance to do that when I was her/his age.' So goes the dialogue between grown-ups whenever the young fail to embrace enthusiastically that which we have decided they should like to do.

GA had purchased the sailing dinghy for his two youngest grandsons, convinced that the only problem would be getting them to leave it come mealtimes. Regrettably, the two of them weren't too young to notice the extreme tenderness of the craft; their regard for personal safety presumably had much to do with their lack of enthusiasm for the planned afternoon's water sport. GA spent a lone couple of hours dejectedly trying to coax some performance out of the dinghy in little or no wind. He eventually gave it up as a bad job and the dinghy was stowed on the foredeck for the remainder of the cruise.

It was decided that we should moor stern-to the quay in Poros town, so that everyone could spend some time ashore. John was operating the anchor winch and Jean was in charge of the stern mooring warps; everything looked in order as we slowly backed towards the quay and I concentrated on John, who was on anchor duty for the first time. I gave John the sign to stop letting out chain and then turned to check that the stern warps were being secured.

Normally, when backing towards a quay, there is an enthusiastic rush of people keen to be involved in the mooring process and they tend to jostle each other in their quest to be first to grab the warps when thrown ashore. In this instance, the quay was also the roadside pavement and passers-by stuck to that role. Consequently, when I turned, expecting to see Jean controlling the shoreline recruits from the aft deck, I was alarmed to note that the quay was lacking in volunteers and was miffed to note that the aft deck was lacking Jean's presence. Jean, always dependable in such situations, had deserted her post, so being a little put out I strode across the aft deck muttering that I would do the job myself and then for good measure offer to cook dinner tonight; might as well do everything whilst I'm at it.

'What are you doing down there?' I demanded crossly.

For some obscure reason Jean was swimming and whilst the water did look clear and inviting, her timing seemed to be inappropriate.

'I fell in,' gasped Jean.

Most people experience potentially disastrous situations at some point in their lives: a young child running off the pavement onto a road, or a near miss that could have been car crash. During such events time seems to slow down, but once the danger is over the mind pieces together all the available information in a split second and you break out into a cold sweat in recognition of what could have been. As I stared down at Jean in the water, the split-second thing wasn't working; there were big clues around, but they were taking their time to log in.

It should have been immediately obvious that Jean had fallen in because her hair was wet. Jean always enters the water via the swimming ladder and keeps her head above water at all times; wet hair is not her thing. It wasn't difficult to work out how both stern warps came to be dangling in the water, but I couldn't imagine how the heavy 4m teak grated gangplank came to be lying upside down on the pavement.

What actually happened was that as we were going astern towards the quay, Jean made the decision – as no one ashore had volunteered to take our warps – to lower the gangplank from its upright position to a horizontal one, sticking out from the stern rather like a diving board. Her plan was to walk across it and jump ashore when it was sufficiently close to the quay. Unfortunately, she hadn't lowered the dingy that hangs from the stern davits and when Jean approached the end of the gangplank clutching the warps, it pivoted on the dingy and did a somersault, pitching Jean into the water before crashing upside down onto the quay. Jean fell between the reversing boat and the harbour. My mind played out the nightmare scenarios: she would have been lucky to survive had the gangplank fallen on her, had the propellers been engaged she would have been horrifically mangled and had she been trapped between the quay and *Blue Skye C* she would undoubtedly have died. I broke out into a cold sweat and still do whenever I recall the incident.

Jean had swum clear of danger, when John jumped across to the quay and hauled her out of the water. She was bedraggled but happy; she hadn't had time to contemplate just how dangerous her situation had been.

'Drink, dear boy?'

GA handed me a whisky. 'You look as if you need one.'

The cup of tea that Janet gave to Jean rattled in the saucer from time to time as delayed shock took hold. Jean had started the preparation for dinner during the afternoon otherwise I doubt that she could have coped. She kept getting the shakes and it took some time for her to fully recover from the near disaster.

The last call on our return journey was to the island of Aegina, only 10 miles south-east of Zea Marina. Apparently, the island is very popular with the Athenians and tourists who wish to see the Temple of Aphia. In my opinion, the town lacked appeal and was historically remarkable only in that it apparently became uninhabited just after the total male population was butchered and 6,000 women and children were abducted by the pirate Barbarossa; compared to him, Blackbeard was just a pussycat.

Back in Piraeus with three days to fill before flying home, GA set up a deal with a young Greek named Costas, to act as the Greek agent for one of the companies in his group. Costas was manager of a local marine electronics equipment shop and he had done some work on our radar; not with any success I might add, but he did impress us with his politeness and his ability to speak almost perfect English. He also tracked down an engineering company prepared to straighten our bent anchor. This had been a big saving in time and money, as all the ones I had approached had offered to get me a new one, but had no interest in straightening our bent one.

GA loaned him the money to start up a business representing a drinks vending machine company that GA had recently bought. Costos was a likeable, thoughtful and considerate man, who played classical guitar and was a lover of the arts, so would he, you may enquire, be the right man to establish and dynamically drive forward the company's future success in Greece? Well no, actually; however, as it had been decided that *Blue Skye C* was going to remain in Greek waters for at least another year and as it would seem to be advantageous to have a bilingual contact in one's corner, the strategy behind GA's thinking was clear.

After the departure of GA and family, the port captain began enquiring as to how long we intended to stay; we had been allocated a short-stay mooring, but for a long-term mooring we would require a written statement from a resident who would act as a guarantor. Greek port captains seem to make up their own rules; we didn't have any such problem in Corfu and never encountered anything similar after leaving Zea Marina. Costas stepped into the breach and sorted out the problem; GA's special antenna had worked again.

We moved *Blue Skye C* to her new mooring in the inner marina that didn't have as much passing boat traffic and neither did it have the sea swell that plagued the outer harbour from time to time. Strangely, the inner marina was fitted out with floating timber pontoons, which were unusual in the Mediterranean as tidal movement was marginal. *Blue Skye C* was a large boat to be moored to the end of a timber pontoon; nonetheless, the move suited us and would make it more comfortable for Ian, who was due to arrive soon for his two-week holiday.

Ian was first out of the arrival exit at the airport, carrying his entire luggage in a small sports bag. Half of the contents were for Jean and me; he clearly didn't plan on attending too many social functions. Ian looked tired and in need of a holiday, though he managed to convince Jean that telling ICI that they were working him too hard wouldn't help his cause. However, she was happy, for she had two weeks in which to spoil him and it seemed that even between meals, food was always within arm's length.

However, at the same time that Ian was building up his reserves, people in Piraeus and Athens were dropping like flies. Athens is not the place to be in August and the Athenians leave the city in droves at that time of year when the place becomes a giant concrete and stone storage heater. Weeks and weeks of relentless sun is absorbed into the city's fabric and by August it's up to gas mark ten. The temperature seems to alter only marginally at night and whilst Ian would start the night in his cabin, by next morning he was fast asleep on the aft deck. Add to the heat an atmosphere that by comparison would make breathing in a London fog extremely beneficial, and you have a lethal combination which puts fear into the hearts of Athenian senior citizens.

Sleeping, swimming, eating and drinking for two weeks did the trick and as the end of Ian's holiday approached he was looking suntanned and fit; his fortnight seemed to be over in a flash. I'll not repeat the bit about feeling low after waving farewell to our family, for I may have mentioned it before.

Fortunately, we didn't have to stew in the heat for too long, as GA arrived with his friend Pat Betts, also a sailing man, who had a laid-back approach to most things in life. It was good to get away from the intense heat of the marina for a week's cruise to the nearby islands of the northern Cyclades. It was a refreshing and easy-going cruise, with the only periods of tension being the arguments between the two friendly millionaires over who should pay the bill for the meal or round of drinks; envisage two men trying to stuff money into the waiter's pocket, neither having scrutinised the bill.

It was late August when we arrived back in Zea Marina and we didn't have a lot of time to prepare for our next passage. GA wasn't too impressed with Athens and its immediate surroundings and so he wasn't keen to make it a permanent base. Several locations were considered and finally GA came down in favour of Rhodes, approximately 250 miles to the south-east; a base that would enable us to cruise the Dodecanese Islands and the Turkish coast.

Our youngest son, Stuart, and his girlfriend, Amanda, were due to arrive in September to assist us on the passage and we arranged to meet them at the airport at the ungodly hour of 1.00 a.m. However, we thought that the date we had been given was the flight take-off date and were nicely tucked up in bed when they finally – after having checked hundreds of boats – tracked us down at 3.00 a.m. We had been wishing the days away waiting for them to arrive and when they did we were fast asleep. What a mess! Though, Amanda and Stuart were too excited at being on board to consider our cock-up to be a problem.

We were looking forward to this trip and felt that we were fortunate indeed to have a job that enabled us to cruise through the Cyclades and Dodecanese islands with our son and future daughter-in-law as crew.

The prevailing wind in the summer is the Meltemi, which in July and August can blow for days at force seven or eight. Normally, the wind strength is less in September, though this September proved to be the exception to the norm and we got a very strong easterly. It had been my intention to sail a south-easterly course, taking in the islands of Paros and Naxos that I had been told were well worth the visit.

Whenever I have planned a cruise with deadlines I have been singularly unsuccessful and this cruise made no effort to break with tradition. Our deadline was, of course, Amanda and Stuart's flight out of Rhodes and I wanted to get there with a few days to spare, rather than arrive bedraggled and tired at the last moment.

We found that a course with anything easterly in it was difficult to maintain, for the easterly wind blew at force seven day after day and reduced our progress in that direction to a minimum. We holed up in Dhespotico Bay between Anti-Paros and Dhespotico Island for a day, sheltering from a force-eight blow; don't feel too sorry for us, as it was a delightful sanctuary and was well sheltered from the huge seas that we could see beyond the entrance to the bay.

The following day we made a quick dash down to Manganari Bay at the southern point of the island of Ios. We were now as far south as I wanted to go and had reached the halfway point in Amanda and Stuart's holiday, but we hadn't yet completed half the distance between Athens and Rhodes. For the remainder of the journey we had to be travelling east; so with a force eight still blowing east by north, we were forced to take shelter in Manganari Bay for another day. Not a big problem for Stuart, who hadn't taken long to discover that the sandy beach at the head of the bay was bedecked with top and bottomless sunbathers; apparently, they all make the trip each day from Ios town to get an all-over tan. For a man with a snorkel, Stuart seemed to spend a lot of time with his head up; I also noticed that on occasions Amanda took to viewing the scenery through binoculars.

By the evening the wind began to settle and we made preparations for an early start the next day. At 4.00 a.m. it was still dark and the bay was deserted and silent. I operated the winch and Stuart checked for snags with a torch as the anchor chain ascended through the dark water. It all seemed rather eerie and it sparked an involuntary little shudder between my shoulder blades; the story about Homer may have promoted the feeling of unease.

It is claimed that Homer died on a voyage from Samos to Athens and his body – thrown overboard – was washed ashore and buried by the sea on the beach of Ios. We didn't run back to the wheelhouse and neither did we dawdle; we were soon gunning *Blue Skye C* out of the bay.

Some twelve hours later we approached the isle of Simi's north-western coast. Its rugged features suggested that the island might be a rock climbers' paradise and it all looked rather barren, but it would do for a stopover before the final passage to Rhodes.

Whilst the wind was no longer gale force, it was now strengthening from the south-east. We were all a bit fed up with wind in general and were looking forward to a comfortable night in a port. The pilot gave Simi a good write-up, but we'd been disappointed many times before and from what we could see it didn't look very promising.

As we rounded the island of Nimos we could see across the bay into the deep cut that was Simi Harbour. The backdrop to the harbour was an amphitheatre of painted houses, seemingly one above the other, lining the steep-sided surround. Unlike many places we had visited, it didn't look as if the town mayor had bought a job lot of paint; almost every building was a different colour. The colours weren't starkly different but of soft natural colours of varying shades. It was all strikingly beautiful; no architect's hand here, for the streets were too narrow for town planners to have had a say. The developer's guidelines must have been clear: keep the streets shaded and cool and we'll make the fire engines smaller. Simi is one of the very few places that I have seen that looks better in reality than on a picture postcard.

We squeezed in amongst the fishing boats and went ashore for the first time since leaving Athens. Sitting at a pavement table outside one of the harbour tavernas we drank in the atmosphere, along with a few early sundowners.

Simi is buzzing with ferried visitors throughout the day, but by late afternoon when the ferries have left, the locals venture out to eat and drink in the cool of the evening. Even though the island no longer has a boat-building and sponge-diving industry, the locals seem to be some distance from being convinced that tourism is the way to go. By ten o'clock there's not much happening, unless that is, you happen upon Blondies Bar; two English girls – having sold up everything they owned in the UK – had selected Simi as the place to live out their dream.

We left Blondies Bar late enough for it to affect our waking time the next day and most of the fishing boats had left when we sat down to breakfast. Rhodes, our final destination, was two hours' sail away and we reluctantly left Simi at noon. The south-easterly that had started the day before had strengthened enough to make the last lap as uncomfortable as it could be; it had been par for the course so far, so why change now. I was pleased that we had only 20 miles to go and at least the sun was shining as always, which really does make a big difference; the same sea under layers of thunderclouds can be quite disconcerting.

The head sea had slowed us down considerably and we entered Mandraki Harbour at the north-eastern tip of Rhodes at 14.45 – this was to be our home base for at least the next twelve months. The harbour looked crowded but, fortunately, I had made arrangements when taking on fuel at Zea Marina to refuel with the same company on our arrival in Rhodes. My radio transmission to let them know we were on our way from Simi had apparently been received and understood, for there was a little man waving us into the only gap on the quay.

The last three days of Amanda and Stuart's holiday zipped past at speed and when the time for their departure arrived we were all, as usual, somewhat depressed. I won't say another word, other than to mention that we were now based on the last but one island in the eastern Mediterranean; only Cyprus left, beyond which we had the choice of Syria and Lebanon. Home did seem to be a very long way away.

Chapter Twelve

Answering questions at sea. Did that blanket move? Illegal geriatrics ashore.

Many sailing people I've met consider Rhodes to be too busy and touristy to enjoy and I suppose if you've spent much time cruising among the hundreds of small islands sprinkled the length and breadth of the Aegean Sea, then Rhodes by comparison is very busy. However, if you have recently lived for a period in Zea Marina in Piraeus, then Rhodes is a veritable Shangri-La.

There is no doubt that the island is beautiful, the air is clear and the buildings of the old and new town of Rhodes are impressive, so it's not surprising that Rhodes is one of the most popular islands in Greece for tourists. The tourist guide states that Rhodes has only two seasons: spring and summer. It enjoys 300 days of sunshine per year; furthermore, it claims that the chances of uninterrupted sunshine between April and October are virtually 100 per cent. The guide made no mention of the fact that there was hardly a street in Rhodes that had less than two umbrella shops; nowhere else have I seen as many such shops. Perhaps they started out as parasol shops and diversified, but how they managed to stay in business was always a mystery to me.

Mandraki Harbour was well placed, with the larger boats at the south-eastern end moored stern-to a quay adjoining a wide promenade. Across the promenade and adjacent road was the impressive new market building: a seven-sided, two-storey structure built around a shopping plaza. The entire ground floor housed shops, bars and restaurants, and large, intermittent arches gave access to the tree-lined plaza surrounding fruit, vegetable, meat and fresh fish market stalls; Jean loved it.

The Kon Tiki floating restaurant was moored at the end of the harbour and was backed by a large, open promenade with a bar and a dancing area, complete with a modern four-piece band and pianist singer, who sounded more like Lionel Richie than Lionel Richie. All in all, it wasn't a bad place to be based.

Every silver lining has an adjacent cloud and washing down the salt-layered superstructure of *Blue Skye C* highlighted the first. The problem was water: all the boats on the south-west quay were served by just one tap that was metered and padlocked. The water-man, who was also the diesel-man, came on duty at 9.00 a.m. and left at 5.00 p.m. He usually took a two-hour lunch break plus half an hour or more coffee or brandy break mid morning and afternoon.

The water pressure was equally relaxed, so much so that it took over six hours to top up *Blue Skye C*'s 8-ton water tank; those of you with a mathematical bent will have immediately calculated that six hours is longer than the water man's on-duty hours for the whole day. As we were just one user out of an average of twenty, all convinced that their need for water was greater than anyone else's, the saying "love thy neighbour" was merely a novel concept. At times, the arguments would turn quite nasty, particularly when a skipper tried to wash his boat whilst there was a queue of skippers waiting to fill their tanks.

I solved the problem by using my natural charm on the water-man, who clearly took to me and considered me to be an all-round good egg; so much so that he didn't take it as an insult when I offered a handful of drachma for the use of his padlock key during his off-duty hours. It was an arrangement that lasted for the whole of our stay in Rhodes.

One of the difficulties of sailing in Greek waters is the enormous number of regulations; made substantially worse by the disparate interpretation exercised by port officials throughout the Greek Islands. Greece must have more port and harbour officials per square mile than any other European country; most of the islands have them and they carry out their duties with varying degrees of efficiency and officiousness.

The Port captain on a small island – more often than not – would be a laid-back individual who worked on the theory that if he didn't look too hard for problems, he wouldn't find any. Naturally, there are some who find the power quite heady and like to strut their stuff; I didn't handle those so inclined very well.

Being a Yorkshireman, I had an aversion to tipping anyone who hadn't provided a service beyond just doing the job that they're being paid to do. I'm not averse to tipping someone who simply carries out their job in a cheerful and helpful manner, but those who expect a gratuity upfront, a sort of prerequisite to any action on their part, are simply wasting their time.

In retrospect, I acknowledge that I made life far more difficult for myself by not recognising that tipping upfront in order to smooth the path ahead is the way things are done in most Mediterranean countries. I could relate to paying the water-man for the overnight use of his key, but I baulked at tipping some self-important stuffed uniform for allowing me to moor in a place where I had every right to be.

Dealings with authority nosedived when – and this often happened in Greece – the uniformed official adopted an aggressive approach; then I found that I could no more offer the sought-after bottle of whisky or carton of cigarettes than fly. At such times I would allow my temper only a very short fuse before reacting with much anger and reciprocal aggressiveness. The usual outcome was that they left me alone and gave me no trouble, but as you may imagine, they gave me no assistance, either.

I recognised, of course, that my approach required me to observe rules and regulations to the letter. GA didn't always assist me in this particular, as his view of officialdom was, if anything, less tolerant than mine. So he was a bit grumpy when he wanted to leave Rhodes for a cruise to Turkey and I explained that we couldn't go until the port offices opened later in the afternoon, where I had to complete the appropriate documentation and officially surrender our transit log.

'Well, if we set off now, they won't know where we've gone.' GA looked at me with the expression of one who was surprised that I hadn't recognised how simple the solution was.

'We can't leave Greece without handing in our transit log,' I explained and held up my hands to show that they weren't in control of this matter.

'Well push it through the letter box.' Dear me, what a dumbo, his countenance suggested.

'They already have our transit log, they keep it whilst we're in port, but if we want to leave the country, we have to officially surrender it and sign the appropriate form.' Raised hands again.

GA's lips pursed. Mrs Hubbard and guests Walter and Barbara Hicks looked suitably uncomfortable as they sat around the dining table on the aft deck; they all knew the signs and particularly Walter, who you may remember was GA's financial director of many years.

'Alwyne, what's the worst they can do to us if we just leave?'

I noted the formality of Alwyne. I wasn't in favour enough to be "dear boy", but hadn't yet sunk low enough to be addressed as captain.

'Well, they will either refuse us re-entry on our return from Turkey or they will let us in and arrest me.' I hoped that he would view the latter possibility as a bad thing.

'Why can't we wait until tomorrow? I don't see why it's so important that we set off today.' Mrs Hubbard was never very keen to leave a port at the best of times, particularly one crammed with touristy shops and bazaars.

'It's the principle, Mother. Why should we have to remain in port just because they want a siesta?'

GA looked at Walter for a sign of agreement. Walter was scrutinising his wine glass with the intensity of a man who had just discovered a priceless antique.

'It's their culture to have a siesta in the afternoons, why should they change it just to suit us?' Mrs Hubbard's contributions to the discussion were delivered without looking up from her crossword puzzle.

'Well if they want to make it in the EU, they'll have to change their ways. Companies in the rest of Europe aren't going to piddle around trying to do business with them if they're fast asleep half the time.' GA looked at Walter.

'Are they, Walter?' No escape for Walter now.

'Perhaps they're different on the mainland, Geoff. I shouldn't imagine they export anything from Rhodes, its all tourist trade really.' Walter's expertise, honed over the years, assisted him in releasing the pressure that was building up.

'I'll go and check if there's anyone around at the office yet, Mr Hubbard.' I was on my way down the gangplank before he could answer. I knew that there wouldn't be anyone there yet, but a natural break wouldn't go amiss.

GA was leaning on the aft deck rail when I returned.

'No one there yet?' he beamed.

'No, I think it'll be another couple of hours before I'll be able to get all the paperwork completed.' I adopted a sympathetic tone.

'Well there's no rush for us to be off today, is there? Couldn't we set off in the morning, anchor in a bay for lunch somewhere?' He put this suggestion forwards in a hesitant manner as if fearing that I would be annoyed that my preference for leaving today was being thwarted.

'No, that's no problem; in fact, it's probably a good idea to set off in the morning,' I went along.

'Good, good. I know what! Tell Jean not to start preparing anything; we'll all eat out tonight. Now, what about a drink, dear boy?'

I queued at the port office with all the other skippers waiting to complete the mandatory paperwork. The Rhodes port office had a system of paperwork which had to be completed every time your vessel left port. Even if your plan was to go no further than a few yards off the harbour entrance for a swim and lunch, you still had to produce the ship's documents, crew and guests' passports and then complete reams of paperwork. The fact that we were bound for Turkey did not help matters; the officials became less helpful than normal and frostily produced even more documents to be completed.

Since we arrived in Rhodes and moored in the refuelling berth, *Blue Skye C* had been moving down the quay without having lifted anchor. When boats lower down the quay left port and other boats came in to refuel, each skipper had to readjust their stern warps to suit the new position they had been squeezed into. Anchors and anchor chains became entwined and no boat that had spent more than a day on this quay could expect to leave port without the ritual of untangling the cat's cradle of ground tackle. So it was late morning before we finally retrieved our anchor from the tangled mass of harbour ground tackle and left port bound for Turkey.

Many of the Dodecanese and Eastern Sporades Islands sit close to the Turkish coastline; the island of Samos lies only 2 miles off and seems to live amicably with its neighbour. About 20 miles of sea separates Rhodes from Turkey and you don't have to be too perceptive to recognise that the Greek resentment of the Turks runs deep within most Rhodians. Indeed, Yannis – the engineer I had hired to carry out some engine maintenance on *Blue Skye C* – was in no doubt that the only good Turk was a dead one.

Leaving Rhodes to visit Turkey is not actively encouraged by the Rhodians and when returning to the island from Turkey, you could be excused for thinking that the authorities suspected that you were on a spying mission. The distrustful manner adopted by the Greek officials contrasted with the relaxed approach of their Turkish neighbours.

Never having been to Turkey and never having met a Turk, I was unsure what to expect; I presumed that they wouldn't be wearing shoes with curled up toes and baggy satin trousers, but other than that I had no preconceived ideas. It turned out that my first meeting came sooner than expected.

We were anchored for lunch in Kumlu Bay about 5 miles from Marmaris, which would be our port of entry and was where we intended to spend a couple of days. Strictly speaking, we shouldn't be anchoring inshore until we had gone through the formalities of entering the country, but GA wanted to anchor for lunch and I wasn't about to get involved in another debate on rules and regulations.

My heart sank when I saw a fast-looking vessel about 2 miles away heading in our direction; through the binoculars, the grey hull and diagonal tiger stripes amidships gave the vessel a predatory look.

I sat in the wheelhouse and pretended to be reading a book and to my relief, the vessel passed us and dropped anchor about 80m away displaying no interest in *Blue Skye C.*

'What's he doing, dear boy? Looks like a police launch.'

GA reached for my binoculars and after much fiddling and refocusing, he scrutinised the newcomer; my simple ploy to display a large measure of unconcern in the arrival of a police launch was all for nought.

'I don't think we should look at them through the glasses, Mr Hubbard, we haven't officially entered Turkey yet and we shouldn't be at anchor; best keep a low profile,' I suggested.

'Ha, they're painting the boat; they've come out here to paint the boat.' GA turned and shouted to Walter.

'Walter, they're painting the boat.'

He passed the glasses to Walter as he entered the wheelhouse accompanied by Babs and Mother. The four of them stared intently at the police vessel; they were quite oblivious to the delicacy of our situation. The previously uniformed crew were now shirtless and wearing shorts as they sandpapered and painted the superstructure. I covered my face with my hands; short of blowing the ship's horn, I doubt we could have attracted more attention.

'Someone's waving,' Mother observed.

'It's the captain, he's not waving, he's pointing to his radio antenna, he wants us to speak to him on the radio.'

I said "us", but why did I feel that we were no longer a team. I switched our radio transmitter on to channel sixteen and heard the clear command.

'British vessel to my port, channel eight.'

I switched to channel eight.

'This is the captain of motor yacht *Blue Skye C.* Over.' I tried to sound friendly.

'You 'ave the small boat, captain. Please, you come with ship papers and passports.' As requests go, it was quite close to being an order.

I had realised that our undoing was my adherence to the rules in flying the Q flag, without which we would probably have been ignored on the assumption that we had already logged in at some other port of entry. To be fair to GA, he had suggested that I shouldn't bother with it when he saw me climbing on to the roof of the wheelhouse to fit the flag as we approached Turkish waters.

Walter and GA helped me lower the dinghy, but offers to accompany me were definitely thin on the ground.

The captain wore a very smart and well-pressed uniform and looked like a film version of a foreign police officer; he had black hair, black moustache and extremely black sunglasses. I observed that his arms were very suntanned, as were his hands, one of which I noticed was resting on his hip a little too closely, it seemed to me, to his gun holster; he had my full attention.

He shook my hand, which made it a little easier to resist the temptation to stand up straight and salute.

'You forget the Q flag, still it is flying.' He pointed towards *Blue Skye C*, where the yellow flag was flapping in the breeze above the wheelhouse, and the several faces that peered through the windscreen I hoped with some concern for my welfare.

'No, it's not forgotten. I thought that we weren't allowed to take it down until we had officially entered your country.' This was said with much surprise on my part as I strained to achieve my most innocent expression.

The sunglasses hid his eyes and I felt distinctly disadvantaged in my lightly shaded bifocals. He studied me for what seemed an eternity and then pointed to my briefcase and held out his hand.

'Papers.' He was neither impolite nor aggressive, but there was absolutely no doubt that he was in charge. He took the ship's registration book and the passports and sat down on a small seat attached to a bulkhead and began reading. Then, without looking up, he pointed to the seat opposite.

'Please, captain, you sit.'

The folder I had passed to him held every document pertaining to *Blue Skye C*, its crew and its passengers and after a detailed examination, he held up my Yachtmaster Certificate, a blue book with embossed gold lettering – and waggled it.

'What is the saying you 'ave in your country, captain? Pulling cloth over the eyes? You know about the Q flag, yes?' he waggled the blue book again.

I looked at his crew busily sandpapering and painting, none of them displaying the slightest interest in the embarrassed foreigner. Yes, their captain was in charge all right and he wasn't about to be fobbed off with surprised exclamations of innocence.

'Yes,' I confirmed, 'I know I shouldn't have anchored before clearance in Turkey, but the owner and his guests wanted to lunch in the bay and I thought I might get away with it.'

My toes scrunched up – I was glad that I had put shoes on for the visit. His English was very good, but I think my Yorkshire accent was giving him trouble. Strange, there are places in England where my accent gives people problems and yet to me, it all sounds perfectly clear.

'What do you mean, you get away?' He was suddenly wary.

'No, no, I'm sorry,' I apologised hastily and spoke at a slower rate and concentrated on not shouting.

'In England, to get away with it means that you did something wrong, but no one noticed, that is, no one saw you do it.' He remained silent.

'I thought no one would see us stop for lunch,' I added lamely.

I was aware that I had infringed the rules and that the man silently studying me had several options, most of which could prove extremely inconvenient; for me at least, if not for all on board *Blue Skye C.* Surely, I thought, my misdemeanour wasn't of the stuff that would attract international incident status; but then again ...

My mind went back to a story told by Bud Abbott – which I will relate later – in which he finished up in jail following a heated exchange with a Turkish customs official.

'You are not lucky, yes? I bring my boat to paint, I catch you with the red 'ands, yes?' He was smiling broadly now; he knew that he'd had me worried and I didn't doubt that he had sussed out the situation from the start. 'Next time you do all things right, yes?

As I vigorously nodded my head, he put the passports and papers back into the folder, which he then passed to me with one hand, whilst holding out the other. I dropped my briefcase and juggled with the folder whilst shaking his hand, all the while a picture of control.

'Welcome to my country,' he beamed and added as an afterthought, 'Passport police first, yes?'

There was a welcoming committee waiting on the aft deck as I approached *Blue Skye C*; everyone looked apprehensive except GA who, beaming broadly, called out.

'Everything all right, dear boy? Nice chap was he?' Never one to worry was GA.

'Yes, but we've got to go and complete the entrance procedures; like now.' I added the last bit in case GA was planning a different itinerary.

'Good, we can all go ashore then. You want to go ashore don't you, Mother?' The authority's requirements were fitting in nicely with his preferences.

All boats entering Turkey are required to visit the passport police, customs, health and port authorities and all the declarations are noted in the transit log. Once that is done, you don't have to submit the transit log to the authorities again until you are leaving the country; the Greeks could learn much from the Turks in this particular.

England is separated from France by just over 20 miles at the Channel's narrowest point and yet the French and the English, so close geographically, are far apart in attitude and manner. Why then should I expect the Turks to be similar to the Greeks in attitude and manner? Yet, I was surprised by the difference.

When visiting any country the first contact made is usually with an official of some sort; on a packaged holiday tour it will most likely be a nod from the passport official as you file through the airport. But if you enter the country from the sea on a private boat it's a different ball game altogether. The Greek officials were some way off adopting the ways of their European Union counterparts and I have to say that with the exception of a very few, those I came into contact with displayed an arrogance that I found irksome to a large degree. My expectation was that Turkey, not being a member of the European Union, would enforce very stringent rules in a manner in which delicacy played no part. Yannis, our Greek engineer, whilst waxing vehemently on the subject of the Turks' many failings, had primed me to expect nothing but the very worst.

The reality was like a breath of fresh air: passport police, immigration, customs, health and port officials alike were all polite and actually appeared to be pleased that we were visiting their country. They may well have been pleased to attract holidaymakers away from their neighbours the Greeks or they may have been instructed to make an effort to encourage tourism in their country; I know not, but I do know that it all appeared very genuine and even if some of it was manufactured, they get full marks for it in my book.

I liked the people, I liked their country and I liked their bread, which was soft with a light crust and unlike the bread of most Mediterranean countries, it remained fresh for longer than one day. The coastline is superb for cruising; it has safe anchorages amidst beautiful scenery and it would certainly be a good area to hire a boat or to take a flotilla sailing holiday.

We cruised westwards from Marmaris along the Carian coast, where harbours were few and far between, but there were many well-sheltered bays; the coastline was a bit wild and mountainous in some areas and thickly wooded with pine trees in others. We were now cruising in the Hisaronu Gulf and decided to log our exit from Turkey in the Port of Datça. It was late September and we found that we had it virtually to ourselves. We arrived around lunchtime and GA and Walter went ashore to explore the town and to choose a restaurant to dine in, for we had been at anchor for the past four nights.

I went ashore with them to get fresh bread rolls for lunch and left them nosing around the backstreets, one of GA's favourite pastimes. Datça looked to be a serene spot, with no apparent hustle and bustle in the town. I could smell the bakery before I saw the long wooden handle of the baker's spatula poking out of a window and into the street as he retrieved the golden hued cobs from the deep wood-burning brick oven. No doubt the baker's father and his father before him had baked bread in this way and I loved it: not a bread slicer or plastic wrapper in sight.

GA and Walter returned for lunch, though I suspected that they had visited a few bars, for they were both somewhat voluble.

'I think we'll eat on board tonight, Jean, we couldn't find a restaurant. Could we, Walter?' GA looked at Walter for confirmation.

'Well, we found some, but they weren't very good.' Walter didn't have GA's flare for exaggeration.

I resisted the temptation to point out that from our position on the aft deck, we could actually see several pleasant-looking restaurants. I said nothing because my relationship with GA had by now reached the stage that I can hear what he says but know what he means.

'Would you prefer to anchor out in the bay tonight, dear boy?' GA selected nonchalant mode.

'What do we want to anchor for?' Mrs Hubbard intervened.

'I've not seen the town yet.' Being tied to the quayside always beat anchoring in Mother's book.

'I could take you ashore in the dinghy.' GA tried to make that task sound easier than walking down the gangplank.

'I don't see the point,' she countered; and I confess that neither did I.

'Rats,' he said with the air of a man who had been forced into revealing that from which he had sought to protect us.

'Over there.' He pointed to a large drainage pipe that protruded from the quayside about 30 yards away.

'We've just seen them, big as rabbits, weren't they, Walter?'

Walter didn't seem to have a problem agreeing this time, which suggested that the rats were, indeed, well nourished.

'They won't come on board will they?' Mother's tone intimated that perhaps anchoring was no bad thing.

'Well, they can walk along the mooring warps. That's why ships sometimes have those metal cones fitted to their shorelines. Have we got some of those, dear boy?' he continued as I shook my head.

'That one that looked at us, Walter, that was big enough to climb up the swimming ladder.' He was really enjoying himself now.

'I'll pull out later and we can swing at anchor tonight,' I suggested, not that I was concerned, you understand; anyway, I like being at anchor.

Early the next day I went ashore in the dinghy to collect fresh bread for breakfast and to see if I could complete the documentation for leaving Turkey. The harbour master and customs shared the same building, which looked closed as I approached it; however, the unpainted door opened to my touch and I found myself in a small room with no furniture and badly in need of a lick of paint. There was a large portrait photograph of someone resplendent in a much-decorated uniform, displayed amidst the peeling paint and cracking plaster. I moved on through a panelled door into a larger room with a table, two chairs and a much-battered filing cabinet. The decoration and colour scheme was themed with that in reception. There was an unwashed cup on the desk, one of those small ones that the Turks use for coffee; I believe that Turkish coffee is best in small cups.

There was no bell to ring and no indication of what one should do, so I pressed on through the next door. Very big room this; two desks with chairs, several filing cabinets randomly situated and two piles of grubby-looking blankets on the floor against one wall.

I think the large portrait photograph taking pride of place above the table with the electric kettle was of the same man as the one displayed in reception. He appeared a little older in this portrait and I presumed that he had been promoted, for his proudly expanded chest displayed an extra row of medals and decorations.

The electric kettle, seemingly adapted from an old gas-hob model, had a frayed cable disappearing into a tangle of wires, plugs and adapters, all drawing power from one wall-mounted socket; 'elf and safety had yet to discover Turkey. There were several more unwashed coffee cups on desks, filing cabinets and windowsills, each saucer doubling as an ashtray; the room had its own distinctive aroma.

One of the blanket piles moved; I stared, transfixed. GA's story of rabbit-sized rats came to mind. The hairy hand and forearm – not spotted at first glance – moved the blankets to reveal a wrinkled and unshaven face; the man who comes at night to make your hair untidy had visited him with a vengeance. He was trying to open his eyes, but only one was obeying the order and as he propped himself up on one elbow, his none-too-clean string vest was displayed, sagging away from his bony chest.

His free hand located a previously half-smoked cigarette and a plastic lighter. Having filled his lungs with his first nicotine fix of the day, he was racked by a bout of gut-rending, eye-watering coughing. His cigarette, held between first finger and thumb, was never more than 5cm from his mouth as he waited for the coughing to ease and provide an opportunity to gulp down his second drag of the day.

The neighbouring blanket pile was suddenly thrown aside, revealing another man with bony chest but no vest; a vest would have been better. He wore underpants of similar design and colour to his partner's vest, which were either intended for a bigger man or he had lost weight. My back gave a little involuntary shudder as I noticed the colour of the mattress beneath him. He was speaking as he searched for his cigarettes, but his words didn't seem to be directed at me. I hadn't previously noticed the third pile of blankets just visible over the larger of the two desks; I moved to get a better view. The blankets looked cleaner and were atop a metal-framed camp bed and the moving arm was pyjama clad; I had clearly located the top man.

He didn't have the matching set, just the pyjama jacket over his vest and underpants, and as he spoke he pulled on his navy blue trousers; he was smiling, so I presumed that it was a general pleasantry. I nodded as if I fully understood.

'Yes, it's a beautiful day, I apologise for being so early.' I wore my biggest smile.

He spoke rapidly to the bare-chested one who had a hand-rolled cigarette, which was now dangling between his lips as he switched on the electric kettle and scratched the front of his underpants. Suddenly, it all became clear – I had been offered a cup of coffee and had inadvertently accepted. I felt a million miles away from Betty's Harrogate Teashop and their bonneted assistants, who donned plastic gloves to handle the pastry-serving tongs.

I think, for my benefit, yesterday's unwashed cups were being wiped – not washed, you understand, just wiped with a general-purpose towel of no discernible colour. Our caterer puffed, coughed and scratched as he waited for the coffee to brew; the drooping sag of his wide-legged Y-fronts making his thin legs look even thinner. I was mesmerised by his cigarette ash, now three quarters of an inch long and threatening to disengage at every cough; I willed it not to fall into my cup. The thick dark mixture was poured with precision from a long-spouted pot, followed by more sugar than could possibly be dissolved in such a tiny cup.

The port captain – now fully dressed in his uniform – looked smart and authoritative as he handed me the small cup and saucer, cigarette burns still on the latter; I tried to look grateful.

'К ... Ч ...' He was a man after my own heart; he knew that if he spoke loudly I would understand his every word. 'Ж ... ф,' he added.

'We are leaving Turkey today and sailing back to Rhodes. Our guests have to fly back to England.' My statement was accompanied with detailed sign language, completed with vigorous arm flapping.

'Ah, И ...Ψ.' He nodded his understanding and confirmed it with a little arm flap.

I produced all the relevant documentation from my briefcase and spread it out on the largest and tidiest desk. Bare Chest and String Vest were now dressed in uniform and looking somehow younger as they joined the port captain and scrutinised the documents. I wondered how I could empty the coffee cup without actually drinking it. Bare Chest indicated that

I should follow him into the next room and as I followed I couldn't help wondering how he got those huge underpants into such tight trousers.

He took an ink pad and a handful of rubber stamps from the desk drawer and having carefully selected three, he missed all the paperwork's designated stamp boxes by a considerable margin and thus conveyed to any scrutinising higher authority, just what pressure this department was under.

Back in the main office the port captain looked concerned and nodded towards the second desk.

'Ω … ΣΣ.'

I realised that he was concerned that my coffee was going cold. I gulped it down like unwanted medicine: medicine's better.

'No, no,' I squeaked, pausing to lower the pitch an octave. 'I'd love another coffee, but I must get back to the boat. But thank you for your kind offer; Turkish coffee is the best, yes?'

I pointed to my empty cup and loudly kissed the tips of my fingers. Then I formed a circle with finger and thumb. They all nodded vigorously; I was getting the hang of the language. I departed after much hand-shaking and arm-slapping and went to collect the bread.

'Everything all right, dear boy, no problems?' GA enquired as I handed the bread to him from the dinghy.

'Well, I had to have a coffee with them,' I grimaced.

'How nice, lovely people, aren't they?' he said.

The rat sighting had prompted us to leave Datça a day earlier than originally planned and so it came as no surprise when GA suggested that we stop for a night at Simi before returning to Rhodes. I knew that I would have a problem convincing him that we had to go to Rhodes first to re-enter Greece officially, even though we would have to pass close to Simi to get to Rhodes some 30 miles distant.

'Why can't we enter Greece at Simi, then?' GA's tone left no doubt as to how stupid he thought the whole thing was.

'Everyone entering Greece by sea has to do so at an official port of entry.' My tone suggested dire consequences for anyone failing to comply.

'Well how will they know that we haven't arrived in Rhodes direct from Turkey?' Answer that one, his tone suggested.

'They probably wouldn't,' I agreed, 'but the port captain at Simi has no authority to allow us into Greece and as we have no transit log, he won't.' My tone suggested that there was absolutely no way around the problem.

'Well, if we try, what's the worst they can do to us?' His tone suggested that he was getting fed up with my tone.

I had to admit to myself that the main issue on my mind was to operate strictly within the rules and not give the authorities the chance of making my life a misery; a chance I was convinced the Rhodes immigration authorities would jump at. I decided to try one last pitch and if that failed, well, it was all part of the adventure and I wouldn't be paying the fines.

'I suppose the worst they could do is refuse us entry into Greece or impound the boat and deport us all.' Actually, when I thought about it, such a possibility didn't fill me with alarm.

'Oh well, that's no problem, then; if they don't want us in Greece, we'll spend our money in another country. The Turks would be delighted if we took our business there.' He beamed, all problems solved.

GA's approach to life in general was along the straight lines of commerce. Sometimes you are a seller and sometimes a buyer, but unless the seller has a monopoly, the customer is always right. As far as GA was concerned, Greece didn't have the monopoly of sunshine and blue sea and had much to learn about customer relations.

I had about me a sense of unease as I paused before entering the harbour master's office in Simi. My first meeting with the port captain hadn't been a great success; my reluctance to pave the way with handouts hadn't helped my cause. I wasn't anticipating any favours. A touch out of breath from running up the steep external stone steps to the office, I took a deep breath and entered.

'Good evening, captain.' I gave him my best smile.

I think I can say that he wasn't captivated by it and without returning my greeting, he held out his hand for the transit log.

'Ah, well now, we have a bit of a problem here, I don't actually have a transit log. Now as you know, we used to have one, but I don't have one right now, as of this moment ... so to speak.' I felt that I was winning him over.

'The transit log, you 'ave lost the transit log?' Hands open, palms up, his shoulders by his ears, he was a picture of consternation and was having trouble breathing.

'Rhodes,' he pointed easterly, 'you go back to Rhodes now.'

I was about to mention that he'd been pointing in the wrong direction and then felt that perhaps no good would come of it.

'No, no' I assured him, 'we haven't come from Rhodes; we've just come over from Datça.'

His look suggested that he hadn't fully understood. I pointed; making sure the direction was accurate and added,

'Datça in Turkey.'

I thought that he was about to have a heart attack; he said a lot of words I didn't understand and I sensed that he was a bit upset.

'You go to Rhodes. Much problems to stay here, no stay here, you go to Rhodes.' His hands flapped me towards the door.

'That's where we have the problem, we can't go; we have engine trouble.' My tone was apologetic.

'What is this engine trouble?' he said guardedly.

'I'm not sure; I think it's a fuel problem. I'll have to check and clean all the filters,' I shrugged.

''Ow long this problem?' He really wasn't happy.

'If I start as soon as I leave here, hopefully we shall be able to leave tomorrow.' I tried to imply that I would work throughout the night if necessary.

'You go when problem OK, everyone stays on boat.' He waved his hand in dismissal.

This wasn't going well, staying on board wasn't what GA had in mind; in fact, everyone would already be ashore wandering around the shops or having a drink in one of the harbour-side tavernas.

'Everyone will already be ashore and they will all want to go to a taverna for dinner tonight.' I was beginning to bristle a bit.

'Everyone stays on boat, no go tavernas, everyone stay on boat,' he ordered testily.

'Now come on, they just want to go ashore for a meal, it's no big deal,' I pleaded.

'Everyone stay on boat.' Then, underlining the point, he repeated,

'Everyone stay on boat.' Flexibility was out of the question.

'Hell's teeth!' I shouted and I slammed my briefcase onto his desk.

'I've had it up to here with your rules and regulations.' I wafted my hand above my head as a level indicator.

'The European Union is about free trade and passage for its members, unless of course you're in Greece. Your rules seem a bit more relaxed when it comes to EU grants for olive trees.' I paused to assess the effect of my outburst.

He looked totally taken aback, hurt almost. Maybe he thought I was accusing him of olive tree grant fraud.

'Why you so angry?' he questioned, in stark contrast to his previous demeanour.

'I'll tell you why. We've sailed in Greek waters for months now and every time we have changed location, port captains have changed the rules. None, I might add, in line with any embraced by the rest of the European Union. In the past five months the owner of my boat has put thousands of pounds into your economy and now he and his geriatric guests wish to go ashore to eat. What's the problem? Are you expecting them to plant a bomb?'

There was a period of silence, broken only by an occasional tap of the port captain's pencil on his desktop.

'You go ask port police if yes.' He held his shrug with his hands out, palms uppermost.

I thanked him profusely for his help and shook his hand, all very polite as if we had just passed the time of day discussing the weather. Then I departed with haste, lest he had a change of heart.

I slowly descended the steep steps whilst trying to formulate the approach I should adopt for my meeting with the police. I knew that there was often some rivalry between port police and the harbour master's office and I wondered why the port captain had passed the buck. Was he just covering his back or was there something else that I should worry about?

I paused outside the unpainted door; it crossed my mind that a department with a budget that couldn't stand a paint job for the front door may have a few disgruntled employees. I stepped into a large dark and dingy room. The two windows facing out onto the quay were glazed with grimy, discoloured glass; the police were certainly not too interested in what went on directly outside their front door. The room was empty, so I closed the door loudly enough to let interested parties know that they had a customer. There was a large desk and chair at one end of the room and an open staircase abutting the wall; I presumed that the man descending the stairs tucking his vest into navy blue trousers wasn't the caretaker. In all other aspects, he resembled a caretaker as he scratched his unshaven chin and let the ash fall from his cigarette onto his vest. He slumped into his chair, making little effort to assume an official guise.

'Do you speak English?' I enquired with deference.

He closed his eyes and gave a half nod, a royal gesture suggesting that I should proceed. I had decided that my statement should be short and to the point.

'I've called in to Simi with engine trouble on my way from Datça to Rhodes. Can the owner of the boat take his guests ashore to eat?' I held my breath.

'Yes,' he nodded as he pushed back his chair and went back upstairs.

'Everything all right, dear boy, no problems?' GA greeted me on the aft deck.

'Port captain isn't too happy, but we can stay for one night.' I left out the detail.

'Good, good, I thought it would be all right,' he beamed.

Re-entry into Greece was a farce, for it took over five hours to complete the same paperwork that took about half an hour when we originally entered in Corfu. If they weren't actually admonishing me for visiting Turkey, then a touch of retraining wouldn't have gone amiss for the employees of the department responsible for processing the entry formalities.

Blue Skye C had travelled more miles in the last five months than she'd covered in the previous five years and it came as no surprise that keeping all the equipment and machinery functional throughout the season hadn't been an easy task; the boat was in need of extensive maintenance. I was therefore not best pleased when GA informed me that he had agreed to let a business friend of his have a holiday on *Blue Sky C* in mid October, delaying the maintenance start date by nearly a month.

Having wound down from leisure-industry-host mode, into overall-wearing maintenance mode, I could appreciate how small-hotel owners appear a little tetchy at the end of a busy season. However, as we couldn't start on maintenance work, we would just have to lounge in the sun on the aft deck for a couple of weeks; I don't know what it's like to run a hotel, but I suspect boats are better.

The two weeks' rest we'd had before the guests arrived proved to be a godsend. Don Rastrick, his wife Jill and four friends, Ken, Pam, Martin and Jane, arrived ready to have a good time and it soon became obvious that they wanted Jean and me to have a good time as well; any attempt by Jean and me to sneak away for a rest was immediately thwarted.

Other than our own children, this was the youngest group of guests that we'd had on board and as they only had one week, they weren't about to hang around. Swimming, windsurfing, dinghy sailing, waterskiing, overeating and drinking and never going to bed on the same day that we had risen left Jean and me completely shattered; we hoped that they felt a little tired, too.

The impromptu barbecue was special. We had anchored close in to a small beach on the west coast of Simi. The bay was protected from the west by a narrow spit of land, but was open to the south. It wasn't marked on the charts as an anchorage and whilst it wasn't a bay in which you would normally seek to spend the night, the weather was settled and it was certainly attractive, surrounded as it was by steep, rocky cliffs and a pebble beach. Finding the beach littered with driftwood, it was decided that instead of eating on board, we would have a barbecue.

We dropped two anchors and laid out a shoreline, which enabled us to move easily by dinghy between boat and beach. We had sundowners on board and when darkness came, we went ashore with food and drink and lit the barbecue fire.

The population of Simi would struggle to reach 2,000 and none of them lived on this part of the island; we are talking isolation here. There was no moon, but the stars were incredibly bright in a black sky. *Blue Skye C* sat motionless on glasslike, still water with the flames from our beach fire reflecting on her stern; it was easy to imagine that we were the only life left on the planet. In a way, it was quite eerie and it came as no surprise to find that I was pleased that I wasn't there alone. Perhaps everyone had similar feelings, because I noticed that whilst we were on an isolated beach in an isolated bay, the portable music centre had the volume turned down and we were all speaking in whispers.

There was a population increase when a small fishing boat entered the bay and began trawling. There seemed little pattern to the boat's movements, its erratic course causing the beam of the bright light – mounted on the stern of the boat to attract fish – to disappear and then reappear unexpectedly. So quiet was the engine that the boat would appear quite close in as if from thin air; the fisherman sitting in that dark area behind the lamp couldn't be seen. I doubted that he normally fished so close to shore and I couldn't help thinking that a professional fisherman wouldn't waste his time watching us. Scepticism is my middle name and I wondered if I should sleep in the wheelhouse just to be on the safe side.

Don, a larger-than-life character whom I'm sure never entertained such negative thoughts, rowed off at midnight, to see if he could cut out the middleman and purchase some fresh fish for breakfast. Sadly, two hours of trawling hadn't been successful for the lone fisherman, and Don returned empty-handed. However, he proclaimed that the fisherman would be trawling all night and would personally deliver fresh fish before he left the bay at 6.00 a.m. It was generally agreed that having set the whole thing up, Don should be the man to complete the transaction at dawn; we had bacon and egg for breakfast. Our hapless fisherman didn't catch one fish in eight hours' trawling; not so professional, after all.

We waved goodbye from the aft deck as the two taxis carrying our last guests of the season sped off to the airport. Jean and I, without a word spoken, laid back on sunloungers and didn't move for three hours.

I reflected on the happenings since taking on the job of running *Blue Skye C* and concluded that our first season had been reasonably successful. No one had complained and *Blue Skye C* was still afloat. Furthermore, Jean and I were enjoying the life and that, after all, was the whole point of the exercise.

The next five months would be taken up with maintenance work and whilst there is always much more maintenance work to be done on a boat than on a house, it would be for me a daily task and not something one had to do at weekends after the day job. The added bonus was the location; there can't be many better places in the world to lead such a life than the Mediterranean.

When we had sailed off from Troon sixteen months ago, such a life was the stuff of daydreams; now, the daydream was reality and the lifestyle most definitely fulfilling, for I hadn't done any daydreaming for quite some time. There were, of course, thoughts for the future, as few things remain the same throughout a lifetime, but for now, what we had would do nicely.

Chapter Thirteen

A Greek engineer, painting monks and the prize-fighting Agapitos.

It had become apparent before we left Athens that we would require the services of a skilled engineer at Rhodes, with the specialised tooling and expertise to carry out major maintenance on our main engines and stabilisers. Costas had phoned from Athens and arranged for an engineer he knew to contact us when we arrived in Rhodes.

Yannis Lagos had the perfect build for a marine engineer; he was about 1·7m tall, very sinewy and was able to work easily in the confined spaces that are the norm in most small ship's engine rooms. He had a big smile, wore large steel-framed glasses and had very large hands; they looked as if they should belong to a much bigger man. His were even more noticeable because they were never clean. Black engine oil was trapped beneath fingernails, ingrained in calluses and the splits in the tough skin of his fingers and thumbs. It came as no surprise that he could remove difficult-to-get-at nuts and bolts with his fingers and thumb, which most of us would struggle to loosen with the aid of a spanner.

For some reason I never thought of Yannis as a married man and when he invited Jean and me out for dinner at a nightclub, we were surprised when the incredibly attractive woman accompanying him was introduced as his wife, Anna. She was slim, about 1·5m tall and was wearing a stunning white dress, which showed off her trim figure and jet black hair. In addition to the perfect packaging, she had a bubbly personality and spoke fluent English with a cultured accent. Her family had owned a large piece of Cyprus until the Turks had claimed it; which explained Yannis' hatred of all things Turkish. In his quest for her hand in marriage, he had beaten off several high-profile suitors. She looked so young that I was amazed to learn that they had been married for twelve years and had two children. He was clearly very proud of her as he stood in his dark suit and crisp white shirt, his arm around her slim white-silk-clad waist, highlighting in detail every contour of his large, black-oil-impregnated hand.

He had a few other things going for him: he seemed to know everyone who had clout, he was an excellent engineer and his cousin was an import agent. Now that last detail may not seem to you to be of any significance; however, I can assure you that any boat owner who has tried to get equipment or spares from outside Greece in general and Rhodes in particular, will confirm that without a smart import agent in your corner, you may as well learn to do without.

Yannis was a fixer, be it mechanical or otherwise. A year in the Mediterranean had taught me that anyone wanting to achieve anything in a country differing in culture and language from their own really needs a Yannis Lagos.

The date of our flight home for Christmas had been booked six weeks earlier and we had been counting the days ever since. When the day finally arrived we set off for the airport, leaving *Blue Skye C* in chaos. The main engines and main generator were stripped down and the service battery banks had been removed from their housing awaiting replacements. The saloon, main corridor and wheelhouse carpets were lifted and all furniture and electronic gizmos were sheeted over; everything was left ready for the arrival of engineers and decorators. Yannis had arranged for the painting to be carried out whilst we were away by – would you believe – two monks. I'd heard of singing monks, but never of painting ones; it was a shame that we would miss them.

GA's chauffeur had met us at Gatwick and he whisked us away in a large Mercedes. He actually apologised to us for not using the Rolls Royce, because he found the Mercedes less stressful to drive in heavy traffic. I set his mind at rest, suggesting that I fully understood how stressful driving a Rolls Royce must be. We sank back into the large back seat and watched the disappointment on the faces of those who strained to see if we were famous VIPs.

We had planned to hire a car at Gatwick for the drive up north, but GA would have none of it – he had a spare car we could use after spending a couple of nights at Worlingworth Hall. We were received as if we were royalty and looked after as such; none of which figured in our contract of employment. The spare car turned out to be a large red Jaguar coupe and even though it had a full tank of petrol at the start, it required a top-up before we reached home. I planned to stay in a lot over Christmas.

Our welcome home was wonderful; having dinner with all our children at the same table was one of the family joys that we really missed. Whilst Ian, Stuart and Lynne had everything under control, they didn't seem to be too unhappy to arrive home from work to find the washing and ironing done and the evening meals prepared. Jean was in her element, but nonetheless there were some problems.

'This will be the third night in a row that you have been out,' Lynne accused.

'But last week you said that you'd had lots of calls asking when we'd be home and you stressed that we should visit everyone,' I defended.

'Well, you could go during the day when we're at work,' Lynne offered in a simple-as-that tone.

Ian and Stuart nodded in agreement; this was a new twist: I remembered similar conversations a few years earlier but with me laying the ground rules.

That night things got even worse. We had been invited to dinner with Alan and Bette Chadwick; I had known Alan as a boy and he had been my best man at our wedding, so whenever we met there was much to talk about. We'd not seen each other for over a year and so the conversation flowed and we were surprised when the phone rang at 1.30 a.m. It was Lynne checking to see if we were OK. We'd been expected home earlier and they were all worried – why hadn't we let them know that we were going to be late and why had we not phoned to put their minds at rest? Our wrists, perhaps quite rightly, had been slapped.

It was less than two years since we had sailed away and in that time it seemed the clock had turned full circle. How well I remembered lying awake listening for the sound of a car returning or keys rattling in locks. I could never go to sleep until all our offspring were in bed. Now, here we were putting our offspring through the same mental agony that Jean and I had found so distressing. One is never too old to learn.

It's strange how one's perception of age and where one stands in the overall scheme of things can be changed by just a few words or a small act. I think I first recognised the shortening of the gap between my sons and me when they stopped expecting me to pay for every round of drinks. There were sufficient words and acts on this holiday to make Jean and me realise that our children had matured considerably in our absence.

We met Ian's new girlfriend, Mary, for the first time and Jean, with that special antenna available only to the female of the species, was able to inform me that Mary would become one of our daughters-in-law; Ian of course, did not yet know this.

Jean's antenna was in action again when Lynne and Roy invited us to meet them in Wetherby for lunch.

'They're going to tell us that they want to get engaged.'

'How do you work that out?' I challenged; the notion had never entered my head.

'Lynne's fingernails, they're longer than she normally wears them and she's wearing nail varnish, it's to show off the ring.'

That seemed to me to be a big leap in the dark, but her tone left no room for doubt. During lunch my eyes kept locking on to Lynne's fingernails, which looked the same as always to me, but then I don't think that men place women's fingernails all that high on their important best features list.

We were having coffee when Roy cleared his throat.

'Alwyne,' he sounded a little nervous, 'I er ... I wanted to ask if Lynne and I could get married.' The bit after the "I er ..." came rushing out at speed.

'No!' I applied my sternest expression, 'and I'll tell you why.' I pointed my finger at him to underline the severity of the situation.

The poor lad looked stunned. His face drained of colour and he looked too upset and confused for me to keep it going any longer. Relief showed on his face as I smiled, shook his hand and congratulated him. None of my little act came as any surprise to Lynne, who was already showing off her ring to Jean. The wedding was to be a year in October, twenty-two months hence; no need to worry about arrangements yet.

It did cross my mind that arranging a wedding required a hands-on approach to smooth out the inevitable glitches; I wondered where we would be in eighteen months time. I didn't fancy Greece as a command base for arranging a UK wedding.

All too quickly our holiday was over; once again the sad goodbyes, but hey, cheer up, there are worse things than living in Rhodes.

We left Worlingworth Hall earlier than planned, as the overnight snow was now 20cm deep. Our early start enabled us to arrive at Gatwick just thirty minutes after the scheduled flight time; fortunately, the plane had had to be de-iced and was delayed by an hour.

The flight wasn't direct, so naturally we missed our Rhodes connection flight at Athens. It was dark when the taxi drew up by *Blue*

Skye C and we were pleased to see her, but I was a bit irritated to note that the workmen had left the lights on.

Irritation changed to real annoyance as I looked around the wheelhouse – not a lick of new paintwork to be seen. I rushed down the little staircase to the main corridor, maybe they had worked here; I hoped that they hadn't splashed any paint on to the very expensive wallpaper that was GA's pride and joy. I felt around for the corridor light switch and froze, something didn't feel right and the lights came on, to reveal a corridor stripped bare of wallpaper!

I was coming nicely to the boil as I jumped down the four steps into the saloon: not so much as a touch of undercoat, with the carpet and underfelt all rolled up just as we had left them. Amidst this disorder two chairs had been placed, one occupied by a woman that I can only describe as questionable and the other by Yannis Lagos' brother-in-law John. They were drinking the ship's brandy from cut-glass goblets, whilst stubbing out their cigarette ends on the floor.

John was a complete waste of space and I had already refused to pay Yannis the hourly rate that he had billed for John's work, the majority of which – I pointed out to Yannis – had been spent smoking in the engine room; hours that on the invoice had been erroneously recorded as labour.

Yannis employed him because he was family, although it was difficult to accept that Yannis' wife and her brother shared the same parents. Other than being taller than the average Greek, he was overweight and lazy with it. Yannis employed him as a labourer and gofer: he displayed no aptitude for either.

Maybe one of their parents had English connections, for like his sister he also spoke fluent English with a cultured accent; it was that which gave one the impression that he was a capable man fallen on hard times. A cultured accent is a big advantage to those with the personality and brains to utilise it, but a much bigger advantage for those with little wit.

'You weren't expected back yet,' he jabbered.

He backed against the wall when I walked towards him and looked relieved when I picked up the brandy bottle and the half-full glasses.

'That hadn't escaped my notice,' I replied as I handed the bottle and glasses down to Jean in the galley.

'Have you been sleeping on board?' I demanded.

'No, no, no,' he said, then offered as a plus point, 'I've just been looking after the boat in the evenings.'

'Working during the day would have been better,' I pointed out.

'I have been, I've stripped off the wallpaper,' he said with some pride.

'Tell Yannis that I would appreciate him calling to see me in the morning.' I stood aside, allowing him and his companion to leave. 'First thing,' I added.

The woman, who didn't understand what was being said, quickly grasped that it was time to go and the two of them almost jammed in the doorway in their haste to leave.

It was a depressing return and morale was a little low as Jean and I set about preparing a bed in our bare cabin that had been left stripped down ready for decorating.

The next day I was up early and had just sat down for breakfast after a full inspection of the ship, when Yannis knocked on the wheelhouse door. It was a quiet knock and his demeanour suggested that he didn't really want me to hear it. He replaced his worried countenance with a large, confident grin.

'Welcome back to Rhodes, my wishes for the New Year.' His calloused hand vigorously pumped mine in the hope that it would crank up a smile on my disgruntled countenance.

'I 'ave sacked 'im, 'e is no good, 'e is gone; I wash my 'ands.' He slapped his hands across each other twice, to make the point.

'Yannis, I don't care what you do with him as long as he's not on *Blue Skye C.* But you, you were supposed to be. The engine room is as it was when we left and what about the monks? Praying won't get the paintwork finished and by the way, why the hell did you tell that idiot to strip off the wallpaper? He's too bloody lazy to come up with the idea himself. He's been too busy entertaining women and drinking GA's brandy.' I paused for breath before adding, 'And how many times has he been on board at night?'

'Never, never before. He was no more nights on board. I make im pay for brandy.' He tried to smile in the hope that all had been solved.

'Never mind the bloody brandy, when I've deducted the wallpaper cost from your bill, you won't be able to afford brandy.'

As I was beginning to feel better, Yannis was beginning to look decidedly glum.

I thought it time to raise morale and get things moving a bit. There were no engineers around that were better than Yannis and there wasn't one who wasn't steeped in the Mediterranean tradition of telling you what they thought you wanted to hear rather than the truth; besides, I actually liked him.

'Right, Yannis,' I was all business, 'when are these monks coming? Tomorrow?'

'Yes, tomorrow, no problem, they finish soon, no problem.' He dismissed the problem with the usual Mediterranean hand swiping.

'Engines, Yannis, you may have noticed that this is supposed to be a motor yacht, what we have here is a houseboat. You'll be starting tomorrow as well, I take it?' It was more a demand than a question.

'Yes, tomorrow, I start finishing tomorrow, no problem ... on my mother's grave.' One large hand rested on his chest over his heart.

One monk in brown habit arrived three days later, followed shortly after by Yannis. For workmen to arrive within a week of an agreed date is recognised in Greece as the epitome of customer service.

Yannis assured me that one monk was better than two, as two monks could get in each other's way, thereby slowing things down and furthermore, the monk that had arrived was the better painter of the two. Yannis gravely doubted that the absent monk would have been capable of achieving the high standard of finish required.

'Why did you originally organise for two monks to paint if you knew that one of them was no good?' I wasn't going to ask, but it slipped out.

'You wanted the work it should be finished quickly. I do it for you.' He looked pleased that the matter had been satisfactorily clarified.

The next day two monks arrived; don't ask.

The saloon walls and ceiling were painted white and on completion it looked like a spray-paint finish; I have never seen a better brush-painted surface. These men were painting monks, rather than monks that painted. Yannis had a smug "I told you so" expression for days after the painting was completed.

We'd had some heavy rains in the first half of December and January was proving equally wet. When it rained it did it well, no wondering if it would or wouldn't. First, a few large drops and then millions of them hammering on the roof: Rhodes' rain is very noisy. The claim that Rhodes has only two seasons – spring and summer – is just as well, for hail as big as their raindrops would be a threat to life and limb.

My biggest task after a rainstorm was removing the stray dogs that huddled together for shelter under the aft-deck awning. There were about six or seven regulars that I had to drag, legs and paws stuck out rigidly in front of them, skidding over the deck and down the gangplank; they left most unwillingly. There were such large numbers of stray dogs and cats in Rhodes that you showed kindness to one at your peril; a saucer of milk and your boat would make Noah's Ark look short on guests.

By March we had finished everything planned for completion before going to Simi, with the exception of the work on the starboard stabilisers that had seized. The engineer sent from the UK to sort out the problem lived with us for a week and then flew back home with a good tan, but left the stabiliser fins still well and truly jammed. They would have to be removed and refitted before we anti-fouled the hull; we could be out of the water for some time.

By the last week in March, when the time came for us to set sail for Simi, we hadn't been out of Mandraki Harbour for five months and during that time our only movement had been sideways; each time a boat left or a new boat arrived we adjusted our stern warps, but our anchor remained in the same place. The majority of the boats, however, had wintered in Rhodes and we had become a friendly community, so when we pulled away from the quay and found that our anchor was well and truly jammed, we had an armada of dinghies around us and advice wasn't in short supply.

Anchors fouled with the ground tackle of other boats can usually be freed in time without too much trouble, but this time was different. Whatever we were caught by wasn't letting go and our powerful hydraulic winch was beginning to pull the bow down, when suddenly the pressure released and the chain came in, minus the anchor. I radioed Yannis to arrange for a diver to retrieve our anchor, but it was never found, or so the diver said; we're not talking small anchors here, its shank was 1·2m long. Such custom-made anchors are very expensive and I had hoped that a thorough search would have been successful; there I go again, it's not easy being cynical.

The fouled anchor delayed our start and so we were an hour overdue when we arrived in Simi. As we came alongside the quay in front of Blondies Bar, Agapitos, the owner of the boatyard, and his two sons came out to greet us and to take our warps. It was our first meeting and having heard so many stories from Yannis about the man I was surprised, for he didn't fit the mental picture that I had formed: I'd expected him to be bigger.

He wore a woollen hat that may have been red at some time in the distant past; years of sunshine and grubby hands had turned it into something best left alone, but it did match his shirt and trousers. The dark eyes below the grubby hat seemed to be set in creased brown leather; in fact, all his skin looked like tough-grained leather: face, neck, arms, hands and his bare feet, which looked tougher than any old boot and just as much in need of a clean.

More creases were formed around the mouth that often opened in a gap-toothed grin. He was sinewy, sun-dried and his age was difficult to estimate, but whatever age he was, one got the impression that he would be just as tough and little changed a few decades on.

He invited me into Blondies for a drink whilst his sons put on diving gear and jumped into the water to take details of *Blue Skye C's* underwater configuration. Agapitos and I sat in Blondies Bar and drank ouzo for the rest of the afternoon; neither could speak the other's language and yet we talked non-stop with the aid of sign language. The more we drank, the better we understood each other. By early evening we were patting each other on the back and nodding enthusiastically in agreement with anything the other said. Once again, I answered in the affirmative as Agapitos' tone suggested that he had asked a question. 'Yes,' I nodded compliantly, not realising that I had just agreed to stop drinking ouzo and move on to whisky.

I have to say that the full credit for the accuracy of detail covering that afternoon and evening must go to Jean. There is nothing more tiresome for anyone who has been the worse for drink, than to have the whole episode related in detail by a witness who was stone cold sober at the time. I certainly have no intention of punishing myself yet again by committing the details to print.

Jean, however, does acknowledge that she cannot account for every detail, for it seems that even she has no idea how I managed to climb from the quay and onto the boat without falling overboard. When I awoke the next day I was able to work out, without help, why it was that I was lying on the settee face down and fully clothed.

Mediterranean countries have two widely used systems for taking boats out of the water: the most efficient being the four-legged gantry crane that can straddle a water inlet and hoist a boat out of the water and carry it slung between its legs to any part of a boatyard. The second system is to sail a boat into a steel cradle that supports the boat in an upright position between steel posts. The cradle, with its wheels sitting on rails, is then hauled out of the water and up a ramp to dry land.

There is also a third – tried and tested throughout the ages – system, still used by Agapitos and Sons Plc. They'd had a lifetime of success hauling fishing boats from the water but, they admitted, never a boat as big as *Blue Skye C.* Their system consisted of two huge baulks of timber about 45cm square and 12m in length, bolted in parallel with timber blocks between, forming a 12m x 1·2m timber sledge. The sledge, weighted down to stop it from floating, was positioned in line with a row of cross timbers, set into the ground in similar fashion to railway sleepers, running from under the water and up the beach.

My job this fine morning was to position *Blue Skye C* accurately over the submerged sledge, whilst the two brothers dived underwater to fit some timber wedges in appropriate positions between keel and sledge. The whole lot would then be hauled ashore over the timber sleepers, courtesy of a steel hawser and large, powerful winch.

I admit to feeling a little delicate and given the choice I would have chosen a different task, but I expected no sympathy from any quarter and so at 8.00 a.m. we slipped our moorings and made our way around the end of the quay towards the boatyard. Fortunately, I managed to manoeuvre *Blue Skye C* into the correct position at the first attempt; I'm sure that had I missed on the first run it would have all been downhill thereafter.

There was some juddering as *Blue Sky C*'s weight began to bear down on the sledge as it was hauled along the sleepers; there was much screeching and groaning as the winch strained to get everything moving. The steel hawser became bar tight and as the screeching noise intensified, the spectators that had gathered to witness the event backed away as one, ready to flee should the complaining steel rope rupture under the strain.

Slowly, the sledge eased its way over the well-greased sleepers. Jean and I – now high above the ground – were acutely aware that there were no posts or props to stop the boat from toppling over. We took up a central position on deck, absurdly seeking to ensure that our weight distribution didn't adversely affect the balance of the ship's 80 tons.

Inch by inch, the sledge bearing *Blue Skye C* was hauled up the beach until her stern was clear of the water's edge. My toes slowly uncurled when I heard the sound of the supporting props being hammered into position under the hull. Gradually, my pulse eased back to normal; a sit down and a cup of coffee was at this moment my dearest wish.

The top of a ladder appeared against the side deck and a moment later, Agapitos' wide, gap-toothed grin came into view; I groaned – he had brought me a glass of ouzo.

The most uncomfortable time that Jean and I spent on *Blue Skye C* was always the annual two-week visit to a boatyard; a ship out of water is like a fish out of water, nothing works. Engines and generators are seawater cooled and there is no electricity. Lavatories won't function without access to seawater and you can't get water out of a tap or shower when electric pumps are disconnected from battery power. There are boatyards in the Mediterranean that supply mains power to vessels ashore, but Agapitos' on the isle of Simi wasn't one of them.

Mediterranean boatyard shower and toilet facilities had one common denominator in that they were all situated in the remotest and dirtiest work area. All such facilities were out of bounds for cleaners; Agapitos' boatyard differed in that there were no facilities whatsoever.

However, there was a delightful little hotel open out of season for bed and breakfast close to the boatyard and overlooking the bay. If Agapitos had been a true entrepreneur, he could have had the most successful boatyard in the Aegean; but perhaps that was the last thing he wanted.

A couple of weeks to polish the propellers, fit new anodes, clean and anti-foul the hull and repaint the topsides is the shortest time that I could complete the job if I worked from 6.30 a.m. until 10.00 p.m. each day. Boatyard costs are based on the number days the vessel is ashore, so every owner seeks to keep the time spent there to a minimum. However, it wouldn't be possible in Simi, as the stabiliser repair work was an unknown quantity, added to which, Yannis had to make frequent ferry trips back to Rhodes for spares. It looked as if we would be in the boatyard for about a month; in this instance it wasn't an unpleasant prospect and, indeed, it turned out to be a period that we look back on with much fondness.

We soon settled into a daily ritual and when work was finished it was back to the hotel to shower and change, then along the quay to Blondies for sundowners. A short walk around the harbour brought us to a little backstreet restaurant with outside tables where we ate every night.

The proprietor Nikos and his wife Anna were a delightful couple who could never do too much to please; they prepared all the food in a small kitchen, where each customer had to visit to make their choice of the dishes on offer. Nikos, who was proud of his culinary skills, removed pan lids with the flourish of an illusionist.

'This one good for you,' he would declare as he revealed a particular dish, 'that one no good for you.' The statement was whispered in a conspiratorial manner. What it was that wasn't good for me he never disclosed, but there was always one that fell into that category.

Saggi viewed himself as the headwaiter and he appeared confident that if there had been two waiters, he would still have held that title. Parents really should give much thought when choosing a name for their pride and joy. Hereditary traits were probably ignored by the parents of the very short, very fat and totally bald baker, who delivered fresh bread every evening to Nikos' restaurant; his mum and dad had been a tad optimistic when they saddled him with the name Adonis.

The name Saggi conjures a mental picture of a slightly overweight man of droopy appearance; he was in fact the opposite: he was slim, quick and witty. Always immaculate in his waiter's uniform, half an inch of pristine white cuff showing below the sleeves of his black jacket and a white napkin folded over the crook of his left arm. Saggi was proud of his skills and bustled around the tables set on the pavement of this backstreet restaurant as though it were the Waldorf.

Generally, waiters in Mediterranean countries, unlike many of their counterparts in the UK, don't view their trade as a demeaning one. They serve each dish with a flourish and recognise that restaurants are a part of the leisure industry in which they play an important role. Good waiters make customers feel like valued clientele and Saggi was a good waiter; he bustled between tables but never missed a signal and you didn't have to trip him up to attract his attention. He assured me that he had served at the tables of several of Athens' top restaurants; his stay in Simi, he confided, was only of a temporary nature.

Athens isn't a place to be in the heat of summer, which may have accounted for the fact that Saggi was still in Simi at the end of the season. On the other hand, he was Simi's star waiter; perhaps he enjoyed being a big fish in a small pool and pools don't come smaller or more tranquil than Simi.

We usually finished off our evenings with a nightcap in Blondies Bar; there, we would listen to the latest escapades of big Sue and little Sue, the two Birmingham blondes. Big Sue was escaping from her job as manager of a branch of an American bank and had joined forces with little Sue, who was escaping from an ardent lover who refused to accept rejection. A holiday visit to Simi set the wheels in motion and their dreams became a reality when their offer for the quayside property was accepted.

You won't require a huge imagination to gauge the effect that the arrival of two attractive, bar-owning blondes would have on such a small, parochial community. As far as all the female Simiots were concerned, the BB of Blondies Bar was an acronym for Blondies Bordello; the male side of the equation rather wished that it were.

The bar was ideally placed to catch the tourists as they disgorged from the Rhodes ferries and again whilst they waited to embark for the return journey. However, at night, when all the ferries had departed, the bar was quiet and was patronised only by one or two of the few tourists staying on the island and a handful of young locals, whose declarations of undying love for the two blondes was correctly identified by the bar owners as lust.

The only local married man that I saw at ease in Blondies was, as you may have guessed, Agapitos. Not really surprising, for Agapitos wasn't your everyday man; he was without doubt a one off. Agapitos' lifetime of working in the sun by the water's edge had effectively baked him nail hard. He walked around the boatyard barefooted on its carpet of old nails, screws and sharp pieces of metal, mixed amongst the wood shavings that had accumulated over many years. A walk around the yard usually left me with half a dozen assorted nails and tacks embedded into the soles and heels of my shoes.

What I'm trying to depict here is the picture of one very tough old man. The stories about him were legion – there were other Simiots of note, past and present town mayors and local officials, but Agapitos' fame was legendary.

A long time ago, way before the invasion by packaged-tour holidaymakers, the Dodecanese had an inter-island competition. It dated back longer than anyone could remember; the competition's longevity was probably a result of its simplicity and the considerable kudos that the champion island enjoyed. Boxing was the name of the game or, to be more accurate, the less sanitised form of boxing known as bare-knuckle fighting.

Each island had its own champion and if that champion felt that he was better than the overall champion, he threw out a challenge. There were no divisions separating heavy, middle and lightweights, there were just fighters. There were no promoters, agents, referees or rules; the winner was the one left standing and rematches were few and far between.

Simi provided, for some considerable time, a champion of much repute: a young man named Agapitos. This achievement alone was sufficient to make him a local hero, but it was the war that catapulted him into the status of a legend.

The Dodecanese islands were under Turkish rule until they were awarded to the Italians after the 1911/1912 Italian–Turkish war; they didn't officially become part of Greece until 1947. During the Second World War, the Germans patrolled the islands in small, fast gunboats, arriving without warning, to nip in the bud anything that might be regarded as an anti-German uprising.

On one such trip, a German gunboat's entry into Simi Harbour was being watched by a group of small children sitting with their legs dangling over the quayside. It isn't known if the German helmsman was over arrogant or simply inept, but his catastrophic mooring attempt severed the legs from one of the small boys. The child's mortal injury drew little apparent remorse from the crew, which changed the Simiots' shock and grief into simmering hatred.

It was standard practice for Agapitos and his friends to take to the hills whenever the German gunboat was sighted, but when the young men were informed of the tragedy, they stealthily filtered back into the town. At this point, the story lacks detail, but the outcome was that the gunboat and its crew disappeared. The Germans searched the area for signs of the missing boat and crew, but the seas around the Dodecanese islands can be treacherous. However, the perilous seas at the time that the German boat went missing failed to stop Agapitos and his friends rowing a small boat to Turkey; they didn't return to Simi until Germany surrendered to the Allies.

Such stories relating to that Second World War period abound in Greece, although documentary evidence is thin on the ground; but then it would be, wouldn't it. If only half the stories about Agapitos are true, he stands out as a man not to be trifled with; even his wedding day couldn't pass without drama.

Historically, the Simiots were famous in the Dodecanese for their boat-building and sponge-diving; Agapitos and his boatyard is all that is left of an industry that was famed for building fast galleys for the Knights of St John, whilst sponges have been fished out to extinction.

I know that a sponge is a marine animal, but I'm not sure what terminology a sponge diver would use to describe his work. I sense that "fished out" isn't the correct one, but then again, harvested, gathered or collected to extinction doesn't seem to do it either. It seems to lack the descriptive dramatisation that would be appropriate when referring to the demise of the Simiot sponges.

The death of the sponge-diving industry in Simi prompted many of the divers to emigrate, seeking a new life in America. It is claimed that some made the trip in their small fishing boats; which says much for their bravery and perhaps more about their despair.

Many years later, a young Simiot woman, who was related to one of the families that journeyed to America, became engaged to Agapitos. The wedding would naturally follow the age-old traditions passed down over the years and would involve the whole community. One of the special guests – the cousin of the bride to be – travelled all the way from America to be present at the ceremony and not unnaturally brought with him his American ways. The tradition so acceptable in the West was evidently not the norm in Simi and when the American cousin exercised the tradition of kissing the bride, he had unwittingly got it wrong ... big time!

Agapitos, as I'm sure you have all surmised, wasn't into rhetoric and immediately after the cousin had completed his traditional kiss, Agapitos decked him, laying him out cold with just one punch – honour and face was the issue. Perhaps other men would have turned a blind eye; Agapitos, however, wasn't like other men and he underlined that fact when he turned to his wife of less than one hour and announced to her and the gathered guests that this was the last occasion that the two of them would ever be seen together in public.

I didn't know where their family home was and in the four weeks that we worked in the boatyard I only saw the unfortunate lady once; dressed head to foot in black as is the fashion for the older generation of Simiot women. Agapitos wasn't at the yard when she called to speak to her sons, so maybe the veto still applies to this day.

A month of cloudless skies enabled me to complete all the external jobs: topsides and superstructure was gleaming white and the mahogany handrails were stripped to bare wood and treated with eight coats of yacht varnish; *Blue Skye C* looked a picture.

During the four weeks we had got on well with Agapitos and his sons, apart from one argument that left them not speaking to me for a day. I was busy rubbing down the handrail around the aft deck, when I heard a discussion going on below me. I became intrigued when I heard metal being tapped and decided that it was time to investigate.

Agapitos and his two sons appeared to be discussing some aspect of *Blue Skye C's* stern gear – two things set the alarm bells ringing: the first was the chalk marks on the rudders and the second was the welding torch and the gas bottles.

'Morning, gentlemen, is there anything going on that I should know about?' I smiled thinly at Agapitos.

He expounded eloquently, 'Σ … ŷ 'Ω.'

I feel that in this instance it's acceptable for me to utilise the phrase "it was all Greek to me", but I did understand very clearly the sign language and exaggerated gestures, yet I was having difficulty believing it.

'You've got to be joking. No, not a chance, *okhi, okhi, okhi.*'

I repeated one of the Greek words that I'm fluent in; the other three, *Ne* strangely meaning yes, *Moussaka* and *Ouzo* couldn't be worked in at this stage.

The problem was that *Blue Skye C* was occupying space for longer than they had anticipated and they wanted to bring in another vessel to work on. No big deal that, except that to do it they needed the timber sledge that *Blue Skye C* was sitting on. To achieve this, it would require a series of complicated jacking and blocking manoeuvres for every metre withdrawal of the sledge, plus a reverse of the process, to get the sledge back under the boat for our re-launch. At best, we would escape with dented hull plates and if they got it wrong and the boat toppled, then *Blue Skye C* would as like as not be a write-off; I wasn't prepared to take that risk.

Oh, and by the way, there was another little factor: to enable them to withdraw the sledge from under *Blue Skye C*, they had brought the gas torch equipment to cut 10cm from the bottom of her two rudders.

This was one of those times when fluency in the appropriate language would have been most useful. In the absence of that ability, I had to rely solely on sign and body language. I'm almost certain that they got the message, but just in case they didn't, I took the precaution of dragging the cutting gear to the far end of the boatyard.

We didn't communicate again until Yannis arrived on the next ferry from Rhodes; the matter was finally resolved when I offered to let them carry out all the underwater preparation and antifouling to our hull as compensation for delaying their – what seemed to me – very dubious schedule.

We were all friends again and later that day, as I was treating some metal fixings with rust inhibitor – a liquid that looks just like water – Agapitos offered me what I took to be the Greek equivalent, in a dirty, paint-stained plastic container. He threw up his hands up in horror as I dipped my brush into it; his olive branch was ouzo.

The next day, whilst Jean was shopping, the yard was quiet and I was precariously balanced on rickety scaffolding and a single plank, carefully painting around a porthole, when suddenly from above a shout was heard.

'There you are.' GA, whisky glass in hand, beamed down on me from the deck above; he had arrived on the morning ferry. 'Weather's terrible back home, horses can't run, thought I'd pop over for a couple of days.' He took a gulp of his whisky. 'I was surprised when I looked over the rail and saw you working there. Why don't you come up and have a drink, dear boy?'

I didn't get any more painting done that day. Unlike most employers, who naturally like to see their employees being productive, GA was a positive barrier to my productivity. I knew that for the rest of his visit my progress would be hampered.

'Nearly finished, dear boy?' This first enquiry of the day was at around 4.00 to 4.30 p.m. and was thereafter repeated at approximately half-hourly intervals, until I finished for the day.

GA enjoyed the ritual that Jean and I had settled into, in particular the sundowners and the nightcaps at Blondies. GA, of course, got on like a house on fire with both the Sues; he enjoyed an attractive female audience and they enjoyed listening to his stories.

Much as I would have preferred to stay, I had deadlines to work to and so my early morning starts forced me into leaving Blondies before midnight. I doubt that GA ever noticed our departure each night, just as he was getting his second wind. He stayed for five days and left a few tired people behind. I liked to think that whenever he returned home from the boat he took a few days' rest; it stopped me feeling physically inferior.

On the last day of our stay, Jean presented Agapitos with a new woollen hat that she had made for him. He proudly wore it when I took a family photograph; there were no womenfolk on it.

On the journey back to Rhodes, *Blue Skye C* sailed like a dream, with fully operating stabilisers and a super-clean hull; we hit 12 knots with ease, all ready for the new season.

Chapter Fourteen

Onassis would turn in his grave. The demon butcher of Patmos and pretend police.

Following the success of the first season, I'd heard that many people wanted to spend a fortnight on board *Blue Skye C.* Jean and I began gearing up for a very hard summer; all we asked was for GA to ensure that new guests didn't arrive on the same day that the previous guests were leaving.

It wasn't good for guests to feel pushed out at the end of a holiday and neither was it good for new guests to arrive before the boat had been prepared for their welcome. Most of all, however, it wasn't good for Jean and myself, who required at least one full day to clean the boat, prepare the cabins, take on water, refuel and purchase provisions; not to mention girding our loins, in an effort to look fresh, keen and welcoming for the next holidaymakers.

Having ensured that GA was aware of the need to leave a gap between bookings, naturally we weren't surprised to learn that our first holiday group would depart on the same date that the second group arrived. They, in turn, would leave on the same day that the third group arrived. This would mean six weeks of non-stop sixteen-hour days – a bit hard for a crew of two.

GA had an aversion to committing himself to anything in advance other than race meetings. The consequence was that those who knew GA and his spur of the moment tendencies were apt to grab at the first dates available and as GA didn't do long-term holiday planning, those dates tended to be bunched up and separated by long gaps. So whilst the concentrated work period was harder for us, the advantage was that our family could fit their holidays easily into the gaps.

Mary and Ian arrived for a holiday four weeks before GA's first guests were due and after a few days in Rhodes, we decided to spend a week on the isle of Simi. We received a great welcome back from everyone except the port captain; I was beginning to think that he didn't like me overmuch and our business was conducted with exaggerated courtesy.

Both Mary and Ian fell in love with Simi, not a difficult thing to do. After a lazy day swimming and sunbathing, we would stroll to Blondies for sundowners, followed by a saunter through the backstreets for dinner at Nikos'. Then it was back to Blondies, to see how far we could get down the cocktail list; we usually finished off with a Mississippi Mud and walked back to *Blue Skye C* with a gait that suggested we were up to the ankles in it: Ian and me that is; Jean and Mary can be a bit boring.

On our last night in Simi, we sat at our usual table outside Nikos' restaurant, whilst Saggi bustled around exchanging conspiratorial glances with Mary and Ian. We drank wine and nibbled at bread and olives, whilst waiting to be invited to the kitchen to choose our main course.

Just as I was making some comment about the degree of laxity that was creeping into the service, Saggi appeared, bearing a huge grin and four large lobsters; he was followed by Nikos and his wife, who had come to see our reaction to the surprise dish.

It transpired that Mary and Ian had ordered the lobsters three days earlier – to enable Nikos to obtain good ones – for the last meal of our stay: I think that our reaction was everything that they had all wished for.

It was a super holiday with memories for us all, one of which will always pinpoint the time that Mary stopped smoking, not that she smoked much, but like so many at university she didn't want to be different from her fellow students. There were three of us on the aft deck enjoying pre-Blondies sundowners whilst waiting for Mary, who was still down in her cabin getting ready for the evening.

'Have you been smoking, Mary?' Ian casually asked as she joined us on the aft deck.

'No,' she said defensively.

'Mary, are you sure you've not been smoking?' His countenance suggested scepticism.

'Well, just a bit,' she reluctantly admitted, 'what made you think I'd been smoking?,' clearly bemused as to how Ian could possibly have known. He pointed to one of the handrail stanchions close by.

'Your cabin porthole is just below there and it gave us a clue when you blew smoke through it. Sticking your hand out to flick the ash more or less confirmed it.'

'I didn't know that my cabin was just under there,' she complained, as though it was a most unreasonable location for a cabin. 'I'm stopping smoking anyway,' she concluded with some irritation.

To my knowledge, that surreptitious drag was the last one she ever had.

A couple of weeks later we were on our way with Walter and Babs Hicks and their friends Alan and Maisie Lewis, who were more interested in Greek history than swimming and sunbathing. They particularly wanted to visit the Aesculapion terraces on Kos, an island famed, as I'm sure you all know, for being the home of Hippocrates and sticky-uppy lettuce.

They were also keen to visit Patmos, one of the most northern Dodecanese islands, to see the monastery of St John the Divine high above the harbour of Skala. The other attraction between the monastery and Skala was the Church of the Apocalypse and the Cave of St Anne, where it is claimed that St John wrote the Apocalypse.

As you may imagine, I couldn't wait to get there. Regrettably, I was unable to accompany them on their site trips owing to maintenance jobs that kept cropping up. Jean's accusations of my Philistinism seemed to ignore her concentrated culinary activities, which usually coincided with our guests' sightseeing departure time.

Sightseeing, as you may have gathered, is not my thing. There are many man-made structures throughout the world, breathtaking in sheer size and engineering skills, which would definitely grab my attention. Nature, be it the Matterhorn or a magnificent sunset, can get my pulse racing, but a historically famous cave that can claim no individual feature that separates it from all other caves, leads me to the conclusion that if you've seen one you've seen the lot.

Naturally, historians investigate such sites shrouded in myths and legends and because they are historians, they perceive things through different eyes. However, the average holidaymaker drawn by the descriptive official area guidebook can be excused, if after examining some must-see historical feature – usually after a climb that would have taxed Sherpa Tenzing – they feel slightly disappointed. Mind you, their disappointment is never evident when you're obliged to listen to their rhetoric and inspect endless photographic evidence of their epic holiday, retracing the route trekked so many years before by Genghis Khan.

Of much greater interest to me was *Christina*, a large ship with traditional lines, which owed much of its fame to its first owner, Aristotle Onassis, who named the ship after his daughter: the new owner now hires it out on charter.

The large ship lay at anchor in the harbour approaches of Skala as we entered the bay. We also had to anchor off, as the moorings to one side of the ferry quay were full. I decided to try and get a mooring on the main quay as soon as the last ferry left, and tied up alongside whilst I made my request to the harbour master. My request was refused but as I manoeuvred away from the quay, one of the adjacent moorings became free and as the vacating boat left I was ideally placed to nip into the empty space; much to the chagrin of all the skippers still anchored off.

On my way to the harbour office after mooring *Blue Sky C* I passed *Christina*'s highly polished liberty boat and its two smartly uniformed crew waiting by the quayside steps. As I dealt with the entry procedures in the general office, the sound of loud talking and laughter came from another room off to one side.

The door opened and the captain of *Christina* emerged, resplendently uniformed like an admiral of the fleet; he was red-faced, stiff, short and stocky. He also had difficulty holding his stomach in. The port captain fussed around his strutting visitor and escorted him back to the waiting liberty boat. After much hand-shaking, the illustrious one took up his position amidships, ramrod straight, legs apart and hands clasped behind his back; in his mind's eye, he was the spit of Lord Nelson. Both crewmen emulated his braced, open-legged stance; one held a highly polished boat hook horizontally at hip level, whilst the other helmed the boat at speed back to the anchored *Christina*.

The captain had clearly been more successful than I had in negotiating a mooring on the now empty ferry quay and quite rightly so, for *Christina* was far too big to moor in amongst the rest of us. Furthermore, if the Greek captain of a famous Greek ship couldn't get preferential treatment in a Greek harbour, then what chance had the rest of us? I'm a great believer in exploiting any edge you may have in such circumstances.

Even though *Christina* was anchored well off, the clanking sound of her heavy anchor chain being taken in could be clearly heard on shore. Like most captains, I always pay attention to manoeuvring boats, for you can learn much from watching differing techniques and I duly settled myself in the wheelhouse with my binoculars at the ready.

The large ship turned and brought its stern to face the quay. As it moved slowly towards the mooring, the anchor splashed into the water. They were a long way out, so the captain was laying plenty of chain; he certainly didn't intend to risk anchor-dragging problems.

The crew on the aft deck readied the stern gangplank by lowering it to the horizontal as *Christina* edged towards the quay; the final lowering would take place when the ship was near enough to allow the end of the gangplank to rest on the quayside.

The two thin heaving lines, each with a weighted monkey's fist knot on the end, were hurled through the air an impressive distance from the aft deck to shore; two waiting crewmen collected and hauled them in, ensuring that the heavy warps attached to the heaving lines didn't trail in the water, thus removing the risk of them fouling the propellers. The stern warps were looped over bollards, completing a successful operation by the shore and aft deck crew.

'Let out more chain,' I urged as I noticed the anchor chain tightening and as if my telepathic message had been received, the captain could be seen talking into his hand-held radio transmitter from the bridge wing deck. Rephrase that – he was shouting into his transmitter, he definitely appeared to be extremely agitated.

The man on the foredeck standing beside the anchor windlass was also talking into a hand-held radio transmitter; no, his body language suggested that he too was shouting. He was wearing smart blue trousers and a short-sleeved blue shirt with some type of insignia on his epaulettes; the fact that he had matched his captain, fist shake for fist shake, suggested that he was probably the chief engineer.

Meanwhile, *Christina* had stopped with the end of the gangplank some 10m short of the quay; she had run out of anchor chain, with not a link more to spare; there would be no going ashore for anyone just yet.

There was no way the captain could extricate himself from the embarrassment of such a cock-up. His shouting and gesticulations did nothing to evoke sympathy from the growing number of onlookers. The port captain – having waited on the quayside ready to offer some sort of an official welcome – had retreated to the sanctuary of the harbour master's office, presumably not wishing to be tainted by association.

Christina sat stranded in no-man's-land for some ten minutes, as if the captain sought to convince us all that he was exactly where he wanted to be. Some find it hard to acknowledge that they have made a mistake, whilst others find it extremely difficult. *Christina*'s captain was finding it impossible. There is a fair chance that if you concentrate too hard on trying to avoid blame when you should be concentrating on the problem at hand, the position will deteriorate.

Having berated everyone in sight – even the crew on the aft deck, who up to now had carried out their duties in exemplary fashion – he adjudged that the guests now recognised that he was personally blameless in this unfortunate episode. He gave the order to cast off astern and pompously made his way back up to the bridge.

Christina began drifting away from the quay as the stern warps were released from the bollards and hauled aboard. No one, including the skipper, gave a thought to the heaving lines, both neatly rolled up on the quayside; when things go wrong, they can usually get worse.

The anchor was raised and Christina repositioned on a slightly different line. Back she came again, with anchor chain clanking.

There were shouts from the aft deck as the two strong-armed crewmen charged with throwing the heaving lines suddenly realised that they didn't have any. There was no way that they could get the heavy stern warps ashore without the heaving lines. Their decision to wait until the ship was closer in and let the crewmen on the quay throw the lines back on deck was no doubt an easier one than notifying the captain of their little problem.

It will come as no surprise that all attempts by the unfortunate duo on the quay, to land a line on *Christina*'s aft deck, came to nought. After several attempts, accompanied by the vocal encouragement of a growing number of spectators, had splashed well short, the heaving lines were ferried out to the waiting ship by dinghy. Needless to say, the face of the illustrious one was in the dark sector of puce as he watched from the bridge wing.

I would like to report that at last events took a turn for the better, but I can't. Things did seem to be going well, the lines were successfully thrown ashore, stern warps were successfully secured and the gangplank was lowered towards the quay: oops …about half a metre short.

Winches groaned as they applied more tension on the warps in an effort to pull the big ship closer to the quay; anchor chain and stern warps were now bar tight. *Christina*, the centrepiece in the tug of war, now had her gangplank 60cm above, but only just level with edge of the quay; to lower it would be to miss it.

The admiral, his face now in the dark purplish-brown sector of puce, was losing it; so far, he had blamed everyone except the guests and whilst there was every possibility that they too may not come out of this shambles entirely blameless, it was clear that the prime culprit as far as the admiral was concerned was the chief engineer.

The engineer was having none of it and the two of them confronted each other nose to nose and with arms wafting, they screamed and shouted abuse at each other; parting and then coming together, they resembled a couple of insects in a mating ritual.

At times the captain strode angrily from the foredeck as if the confrontation was over, only to return and start his shouting all over again. On the third flare-up the engineer stormed off the ship, jumping off the end of the gangplank, which was still raised above the quay, but now resting precariously on two boxes. As he made his way along the quay he received a sympathetic and supportive cheer from the spectators; I suspect that had the captain shown himself at that time they would have booed.

One doesn't expect such an inept display on all fronts from the captain of such a large ship; indeed, the crew, guests and even some of the spectators experienced a degree of embarrassment.

That night the ship was lit up from stem to stern like a Christmas tree and a dining table was set for a banquet on the deck overlooking the aft deck. Music blared and guests in their finery sipped cocktails and displayed themselves for the benefit of the watching grockles. The captain circulated in his white dress uniform; at last he was doing something he was good at, the earlier embarrassments cleared from his mind.

Well, perhaps not totally, for when Jean and I laid the breakfast table the next morning, *Christina* was long gone.

Whilst our guests went in search of things historical, Jean and I went in search of meat for that night's dinner. We asked around for directions and having followed several false leads, we happened upon a butcher's shop of sorts.

Anyone taking a self-catering holiday on some of the lesser-known Greek islands could be in for a culture shock. Those EU directives demanding totally sterile meat-purveying emporiums have as yet failed to be embraced in the backstreets of remote Greek islands.

Through a small opening in the wall, we stepped down into a stone-floored dark room; the one small dingy window didn't help our eyes to adjust from the ultra brightness we had left outside. I was pleased that I couldn't see the floor in clearer detail, for it had a disturbingly tacky feel underfoot. There was no gleaming counter and electronic scales, the dark room revealed only a weighing device hanging from a ceiling beam and a circular end-grained wooden butcher's block sitting on three legs in the centre of the room. I couldn't take my eyes off the block – it looked centuries old, its surface cut, gouged and hacked; alarmingly, it was dark red-brown in colour.

Jean smiled at the butcher – or at least we presumed he was the butcher, as he came from within; he had materialised from a far dark corner, where there must have been a door. There was no blue-and-white striped apron; in fact, there was no apron of any colour – perhaps it was in the wash. I presumed that the stubble on his chin was more the "I can't be bothered to shave" stubble than the designer type favoured by celebrities; I personally have difficulty differentiating between the two. His welcoming smile was short on teeth and the few he had on display lacked that healthy sparkle.

'Do you have any lamb chops?' Jean enquired.

'Ŧ … ǖ,' he replied helpfully.

'I don't think he has any, let's leave it shall we?' I couldn't take my eyes off the two large flies walking around on the butcher's block.

'We can't leave it; I need meat for tonight's dinner.' Jean smiled again at the butcher, lest he thought that we doubted his reputation as a purveyor of fine meats.

'Ǐ … Ǽ.' He held a finger in the air, indicating that he had just the thing for us.

He disappeared into the dark corner and through the wall. No, I could make it out now, it was an opening covered by a curtain of fine metal chains. Many shops had them – they allowed one to walk through an opening whilst keeping the flies out, unless of course they were already in, in which case they barred any escape route. At least our local butcher was trying to keep up with the latest technology.

'Look at that block,' I whispered. 'It's never been washed in years, let's go.'

The butcher returned with a large piece of meat draped over one arm and he brushed the chopping block with a small besom that must have been infected with every germ known to man. He threw the meat over the block with the flourish of a silk trader displaying his wares;

indeed, textiles weren't far off the mark, for the meat resembled a piece of old lace curtain.

'Let's go, Jean,' I whispered urgently but Jean ignored me.

'Do you have any lamb chops?' she smiled patiently.

The master butcher looked confused, so Jean dug her finger into the side of my chest and ran it up and down my ribs.

'Baah, baah,' I mimicked.

Greek sheep speak must be similar to their British cousins, for immediately his face lit up. He grabbed the piece of lace curtain and disappeared into the dark corner, reappearing triumphantly bearing a whole rib of lamb.

'That's it, I'll take the whole piece.' Jean clapped her hands and further confirmed that it was just what she wanted by sign language.

He gently laid the lamb ribs on the block as if they were made of porcelain. Yet again, he disappeared, returning this time with a large meat cleaver, which he held questioningly over ribs. Jean nodded – she wanted it cutting into chops, as her plan for dinner was rack of lamb with all the trimmings.

We were treated to a display of master butchering at its finest. He may have looked dubious at the start, but there was no doubt that he could handle a cleaver. Had the room been lighter, the blade would have flashed, but in the darkness it was merely a blur. It seemed to have taken only seconds to reduce the rib of lamb into a pile of broken bones and misshapen lumps of meat. He hadn't cut down between the bones but across, three times for each chop. Triumphantly, he lifted up the mutilated side of lamb held precariously together by strands of meat and broken bone.

'We can't take that, he's ruined it.' I stared at the mangled mess in disbelief.

Jean, who unlike me never wasted time getting angry, was thinking of a way to utilise the demon butcher's handiwork.

'I think I can do something with it,' she mused as she smiled at the butcher and opened her purse.

'Thank you, Jean, that was a superb dinner.' Walter sat back from the table, brandy glass in hand.

'We never seem to be able to get lamb like that back home.'

Everyone nodded in accord.

'You're right, Walter, the butcher's shops are different back home,' I confirmed.

'Where was the shop, Alwyne? I might call tomorrow and tell them how much we enjoyed their meat.' He sipped his brandy.

'I wouldn't know where to start, Walter. We only found it by chance.' I helped Jean collect some dishes from the table. 'Anyway, I don't think there will be time, Walter, we need to be leaving straight after breakfast tomorrow if we're to find a nice bay to stop in for lunch before they get there.' I nodded towards the boats packing the moorings around us.

'Pity,' said Walter, 'it's nice for a shopkeeper to hear from satisfied customers.'

A mental picture of Walter flashed into my mind, an accountant from head to toe entering the demon butcher's dungeon, his sandals sticking to the floor as he stood by the flyblown chopping block. Bear in mind that this was a man who would only brush his teeth with bottled water; it would be best if Walter didn't see every ancient monument on the island of Patmos.

It had been our intention to visit Port Lakki and Platanos on the island of Leros, surrounded, according to the tourist brochures, by a mass of hibiscus, jasmine, bougainvillea and oleander. The island was apparently associated with the cult of Artemis – the worship of the mother goddess – and in a country where the male rules supreme, this little Greek island has a local law which decrees that all property passes down through the female line; surely an island worth a visit.

It may be that this law was responsible for the behavioural pattern of the two uniformed officials who boarded *Blue Skye C* whilst we were at anchor in Partheni Bay at the northern end of the island. It was a beautiful, desolate and well-sheltered bay, a perfect anchorage to spend the night before our visit to Port Lakki. We were enjoying gin and tonics, when a fishing boat came alongside and two men in uniform boarded us without so much as a by your leave. They had an arrogant and aggressive manner; without trying really hard, they had already pissed me off.

'You no stay 'ere,' the small one affirmed.

'Where you from?' the other small one demanded.

'Why not?' I enquired, ignoring the second question. I continued whilst they thought of a suitable answer.

'And whilst we're at it, I don't remember you asking permission to come aboard.'

They looked uncertain as my reaction was presumably not as expected. Walter joined us, for he saw the conciliatory approach as the way to go.

'Good evening, gentlemen, would you care for a drink?' He held his hand towards two chairs and they looked keen to join him.

I ignored Walter and blocked the way to the chairs. Walter's wife, Babs, who had picked up on the vibes immediately, spoke sharply.

'Walter, leave it to Alwyne.'

Like most long-married couples, tone counted far more than words and Walter retreated.

'You 'ave papers to be 'ere?' The pushy one of the two scribbled on the palm of his hand with a finger.

'Torpedoes,' he said. 'Torpedoes,' he repeated, waggling his hand to simulate the course of a torpedo passing right through our present position.

'The torpedo range is in the other side of the bay; it's marked on the chart. We're nowhere near it and furthermore, the pilot for this area, sold in Greece, by the way, shows no anchoring restrictions in this position.'

I paused as they exchanged glances and sensing their uncertainty, I pushed on.

'All our paperwork is in order and we have every right to anchor here.' I paused once more, wondering about the fishing boat, it was certainly short on official presence.

'Papers? Do you have any official identification papers?' I finger scribbled on the palm of my hand. 'You know, like those papers you were talking about.'

They were definitely looking unsure of their ground and the less confident one edged towards the waiting fishing boat; their cover was blown.

'Best you both leave,' I pointed to the fishing boat, 'now would be a good time.' The nervous one was already back on board, whilst his partner, reluctant to admit defeat, continued to threaten angrily.

'We will come back, you will 'ave to leave.' Then he jumped back onto the fishing boat and the scruffy-looking helmsman swung the boat in a wide arc away from *Blue Skye C.*

As I watched the boat head towards shore, I wondered how many cigarettes and bottles of booze their scam brought them each week. I have to admit that they had me going for a while there. They blew it by starting off too aggressively. I really don't like being threatened, but presumably it was a tried and tested technique.

Just as I experienced a little pang of doubt, wondering if they would actually return with reinforcements in a police launch, a 9m sloop sailed into the bay and anchored off our port bow. It was followed by another identical sloop and as it anchored, a third, fourth and fifth entered the bay.

Half an hour later we were surrounded by ten German flotilla yachts all lying serenely at anchor, it was clearly a regular anchorage for the flotilla leader; our uniformed friends would not be back as promised. Nevertheless, we gave Port Lakki a miss on our return journey to Rhodes.

We rounded the Turkish peninsula of Knidos in thick fog, the one and only time we experienced such sea conditions in the eastern Mediterranean. After an overnight stop in Panormittis Bay at the southern end of Simi, we arrived back in Rhodes to find Mandraki Harbour full to bursting.

We tied up to the ferry quay, the only empty space in the harbour. The next guests were due to arrive on the same plane that would return Walter and party to the UK; it left us with little time to prepare for the changeover.

Chapter Fifteen

Kon Tiki restaurant magnetism, Panormittis Bay magic and Jacques Cousteau style.

We would have to move from the ferry quay in a few hours when the ferryboats returned. Then we would have to drop anchor and go stern-to the most suitable boat moored to the general quay, which would provide us with access to the shore.

Mandraki Harbour has moorings on both its sides and when all are full, incoming boats double up and tie on to the bows of those already moored. Easy enough for 8m crafts, but the problems increase for larger vessels.

The only boat that I could tie up to with *Blue Skye C*, without running the risk of ripping cleats from their decks, was an old three-masted schooner. I had to tie up off centre, as she had a huge bowsprit, complete with sail and crew-catching net beneath. Our combined length put our anchor in amongst the ground tackle of the yachts on the other side of the harbour and the floating Kon Tiki restaurant, which was only 15m from our starboard bow; I was not a happy man.

GA enjoyed sailing and loved boats, particularly the older ones with classic lines, but his love of boats came a poor second, when compared to his passion for horses and horse racing. At this particular time, he owned about fifty or sixty of them, all trained at his Worlingworth Hall stables.

Ferdy Murphy was GA's trainer who hails, as you may have guessed, from Ireland. The National Hunt racing season had just ended and it had been a successful one for GA's stable, a large part of it owing to Ferdy's hard work, and so he and his family were our next guests: a fortnight's holiday as a thank you for his efforts.

I took to Ferdy on sight; he was an ex-jockey and like most of them tend to be, he looked tough and lean. He was bigger than the average jockey, probably the cause of his change from riding to training earlier than the norm; keeping his weight down had become a problem. He was a laid-back character with a touch of the rascal about him; he loved horses and he was quite partial to whisky – as a trainer he didn't have to give up either.

GA had told us that we had three guests on the way, Ferdy, his partner Janet Morgan and her mother Maggie, but four arrived. The extra one was Daphne a long-standing friend of Ferdy's, who I understand had agreed to her joining the party when in flamboyant mood in a racecourse bar. He seemed particularly vague about the detail, though Janet and Maggie, who appeared somewhat miffed with her presence, didn't allow his embarrassment to fade.

Janet, although several months pregnant, made light of traversing the net below the schooner's bowsprit, to climb on board *Blue Skye C*; Janet's mother Maggie did likewise. The extra guest unfortunately made very heavy weather of it and a considerable amount of effort was required from Ferdy and me, to ensure that she didn't go for an early swim. Regrettably, she was a difficult person to please. We were all regaled at regular intervals, with the minutiae of her previous holiday on a cruise ship.

A *Blue Skye C* holiday was about the freedom to go where you wanted and when you wanted, freedom to stop in a small bay and swim in crystal-clear water. Bays that a cruise ship couldn't even see, let alone anchor in. Accommodation for *Blue Skye C*'s guests was free of charge, as was the food and wine, always served as far as I can remember with a smile by the captain and his lovely wife.

A plate by plate description of her cruise ship's six-course banquets wasn't what anyone wanted to hear whilst sipping their after-dinner brandy; and certainly there was nowhere in my job description that suggested that I should provide evening entertainment. I suspect that on her next cruise-ship holiday, she would regale some poor unfortunate fellow shipmates, with details of why such a holiday fell short when compared to her previous holiday on a private motor yacht.

I was keen to leave Rhodes as soon as possible, for I hated being so close to the southern end of the crowded harbour. Also, being moored to the end of another ship left us vulnerable to the prevailing summer north-westerly winds. I hoped that our anchor was still firmly in place up wind of us; my hopes were dashed.

The wind had pushed us further down the harbour and the mooring lines of some small fishing boats at the southern end were uncomfortably close to our starboard propeller.

My plan to use our anchor to pull us round into the wind came to nought, as it must have been dislodged by another boat when raising its anchor. Our chain came in slackly, with no anchor restraint, and our propellers were now too close to the mooring lines of the small fishing boats for me to engage them. We swung slowly but surely to starboard and nestled gently but hard up against the floating Kon Tiki restaurant.

Surely this for Daphne would be a new experience; it would never have been in the itinerary of a cruise ship. I was also quite certain that diners occupying the Kon Tiki's window-side tables have rarely experienced the sight of 80 tons of steel coming to rest within 60cm of their moussaka.

I could understand their alarm, for the Kon Tiki restaurant, a single-storey wooden structure sitting on a floating raft, sat quite low on the water and *Blue Skye C* was blocking out their light. The normally much-sought-after window-side tables were now there for the taking.

The whole restaurant will have lurched a little when we initially leaned against it, but the waiters did seem to be overreacting. Those brave enough to approach the open windows were very explicit with their advice. Ferdy and I managed, with much pushing against the roof of the building, to ease *Blue Skye C* forwards by the several feet required to clear our propellers away from the fishing boats' mooring lines.

I knew that when I gunned our starboard engine in reverse, to kick our stern away from danger, I would have to give our port propeller some forward thrust to cancel out astern momentum, which would in turn press our bow harder onto the Kon Tiki. All aboard the restaurant would certainly feel the force, but pussyfooting around wouldn't help anyone.

I had asked Ferdy to stay on the foredeck, knowing there was little chance that his pushing against the Kon Tiki would even slightly reduce the load being exerted on the restaurant. I had hoped that it would be seen as a demonstration of our concern; there was a lack of feedback to suggest that our concern was appreciated.

The Kon Tiki groaned and creaked as *Blue Skye C* pushed hard against it and as the stern began to move out, I cut the port engine and increased the revs to the starboard engine; the bass rumble changed to a baritone roar with tenor aspirations.

We were now the main attraction in Mandraki Harbour; little groups on the quayside were expanding into big groups and a ranting waiter was now out of control; his little fist kept poking out of the window perilously close to Ferdy's ear as Ferdy strained every sinew to help move our bow away from the floating restaurant. *Blue Skye C* was now shuddering and the restaurant tables were moving with the vibration. The queue of hungry patrons had noticeably reduced, as prospective diners of a more timid disposition joined the quayside spectators; only the brave and the very hungry remained holding on to their mobile tables.

Just as I was about to abort the attempt to break free from our trap and accept the ignominy that a tow-away would induce, our bow began to move, putting distance between Ferdy and the avenging fist. The waiter would never know what fate had saved him from had Ferdy's hands been free.

Slowly at first but gathering speed, we swung into clear water and turned through 180 degrees. Easing the throttles to both engines ahead, *Blue Skye C* moved gracefully out of the harbour; I wouldn't be mooring at the southern end of Mandraki Harbour again.

Panormittis Bay is situated at the south-western corner of Simi. There is a windmill to the left of the narrow entrance leading into a sheltered bay that offers a safe anchorage whatever the weather. Ashore, there are some large monastery buildings, a small shop with very limited provisions, a very small taverna that only opens if a local ferry calls in and that's your lot.

The monastery buildings have some very basic rooms, which can be rented by visitors seeking complete peace and tranquillity – the very attributes that Jean and I craved following a fortnight's cruise and a same-day changeover. Ferdy and his team were all for it and we dropped anchor two hours after leaving Rhodes.

The fortnight's cruise was to be easy-going; relaxation seemed to be the main goal of our guests and if you couldn't relax in Panormittis Bay, you had a major problem.

That evening at anchor will always stick in my memory. We were the only boat in the bay and the densely wooded slopes rose steeply from the surrounding shoreline and monastery buildings; like a giant amphitheatre around an arena of sheet glass. We dined in the open aft deck saloon as the sun was setting and by the time brandy was being served, *Blue Skye C* sat motionless in such impenetrable darkness that it seemed almost touchable.

The light from the table lamps appeared to be absorbed by the darkness before reaching the aft rail, but we could just discern a small, flickering lamp in the distance; it was the only indication that there was such a thing as a shoreline. A walk around the deck revealed the reflection of the anchor light on the flat surface of the water, which thankfully assured us that we weren't, as feared, suspended in space.

We sat silently around the table, where conversation seemed out of place, listening to a Louis Armstrong tape of spiritual song classics. Maggie, quite mesmerised by it all, was a lone dancer on the aft deck, swaying to the slow beat of "Let My People Go". The volume was turned down low, to ensure that those seeking tranquillity ashore weren't disturbed, but in such conditions, even the smallest sound will travel long distances. As the tape ended with the haunting sound of Louis' trumpet, followed by his gravelly chuckle, there was a period of absolute silence. Then, from over the water, came the sound of hand clapping and the flickering light on shore was moved from side to side to signal whence it came. It was a magical experience, an ethereal moment, and one I doubt that any of us would ever forget.

The following day, when Jean went ashore, she met the couple that had been clapping. They had been sitting on the balcony of their monastery room listening to the music floating over the water from *Blue Sky C.* Jean apologised, saying that we had kept the music down low, hoping not to cause annoyance. But far from being annoyed, it had been, they assured Jean, the most enjoyable evening of their holiday.

'Quite magical,' they affirmed.

Compared to most evenings spent at the monastery, we had provided a veritable hoedown.

Ferdy and his team departed to the airport looking relaxed and suntanned, just four days before GA was due to arrive for his first cruise of the season.

GA, as always, arrived in good spirits with Mother, and Bob and Marita Dale. Also, as always seemed to be the case when Mother was on board, we had a cruise with more than its fair share of high winds and disturbed seas. We sailed back to Rhodes to spend the last four days of the holiday in harbour, well within walking distance of the many shops and markets, where Mother was in her element. It was a fortuitous early return to Rhodes, as it enabled Jean and me to meet some friends of long standing.

Peter Tomlinson, a friend dating back to our junior school days, had left the UK with his wife Pat some twenty-five years ago, bound for South Africa. Since then, our only communication had been via Christmas cards and infrequent letters. This year, they were on a tour of Europe that took in Athens, from where they made a detour and flew over to Rhodes to have dinner with us. It seemed incredible that not having seen each other for so many years, we were able to meet on one of the most far-flung islands of Greece.

It was now the end of June and when GA and party left us, he hadn't planned any other guests for the July and August. Our only visitors in that period would be Stuart and Amanda, followed by Lynne on her own. Roy had to stay at home to look after the family business during his father's illness.

We had acquired a good central mooring next to the schooner, owned and chartered by a Jacques Cousteau look-alike who – being very well aware of the resemblance – promoted the image by always wearing an identical woolly hat to the one sported by the famous diver. Our French neighbour really did appear identical in all respects of build, looks and accent. Passers-by rarely failed to do a double take and he wasn't averse to signing autographs. There was no doubt that he had a touch of the showman in him and like most showmen, he was a charmer and like most charmers, he was more at home with women than he was with men.

When he offered a lady his hand to assist them ashore, he did it with gentlemanly style, a style that I certainly couldn't match. Had they stumbled, however, I'm not sure that he would have caught them, or so I like to imagine. It therefore came as no surprise that when Stuart and Amanda announced their engagement during their holiday on board, Jacques presented Stuart with a bottle of champagne and Amanda with a single red rose. His toast was delivered in his strongly French-accented English and oozed Gallic charm; Stuart and I stood by like a couple of carthorses in the presence of a thoroughbred.

We didn't take *Blue Skye C* out for any trips during Stuart and Amanda's holiday, for at this time of the year, one day away from the harbour and it could take a week to get a quayside mooring back again; unless you were going on a cruise, it wasn't worth the hassle. We settled for a lazy, late-breakfasting, sunbathing, swimming and eating-out holiday.

All too quickly it came to an end, Amanda shed tears and Jean shed tears; Stuart and I would have openly scoffed at such weakness, had it not been for the lump in our throats.

An hour after they left in the taxi, Amanda and Stuart arrived back on board – their plane was still in the UK and their departure was delayed until the following morning. We had an extra night with them and an extra teary farewell.

It was now July and with Roy unable to take a holiday at this time, Lynne arrived on her own for a much-needed break. Due to be married the following year, the two of them had bought one of those properties which estate agents describe as needing a little attention. They'd been working on it every night and every weekend for months and had reached that stage where there was more work still to do than there had been when they'd first started. We'd not seen Lynne for six months and she was in need of some parental cosseting.

Lynne was a little distressed when we met her at the airport, as there had been a considerable deterioration to Roy's father's condition and it was accepted that he only had a few weeks left to live. On top of all this, she had been held up at customs whilst a smirking officer, no older than Lynne, searched and emptied her case item by item. The ego-driven Greek authority's personnel were displaying yet again their propensity for distressing some and stoking up fist-clenching anger in others.

We sent Lynne back home looking a lot happier, fitter and much more relaxed. The only time that Jean didn't pander to her every whim was on the return ferry trip from Simi. After quite some time spent in Blondies Bar, where Lynne had sampled many of their lethal cocktails, the trip back on the lurching ferry wasn't a happy one. Jean had no sympathy for those with such self-inflicted illnesses, whilst I, a kindred spirit, sought to administer to her every need.

My reference regarding the Greek uniformed authorities was by no means a throwaway remark; they were indeed beginning to get to me. In fact, my dislike of them was no longer limited to the uniformed species, for Greek authorities in any guise were failing to gain high marks on my toleration chart. Please don't think that I seek to deter you from holidaying in Greece; indeed, one of our best family memories is of a two-week Greek flotilla sailing holiday. However, a Greek holiday is one thing – running a boat there is quite another; to do so in anything approaching an efficient manner is an almost impossible task.

Clearing goods from customs was a nightmare. You cannot get anything out of customs without an agent, but having one doesn't guarantee that you will get what is yours within four weeks of its arrival in Rhodes. Even though you hold shipping documentation that states that your goods have arrived, the strutting shed manager knows, without so much as a perfunctory check, that they haven't.

Blue Skye C's service batteries and engine parts had arrived from the UK in a 1·5m x 1·5m x1m wooden crate. Generally, goods imported for *Blue Skye C* were stacked in some obscure corner of the dockyard or languished in a container that no one was bothering to open. But in this case I could clearly see the sturdy wooden structure through the open shed doors: M/Y *Blue Skye C* was stencilled on the sides of the crate in large black letters. I was therefore surprised when my agent told me that it hadn't yet arrived.

'What do you mean it's not arrived? I've seen it; it's too big to miss.' I held my arms out to signify the size of the crate we were discussing.

'Maybe you make the mistake, yes?' My agent shrugged his shoulders.

'No, there's no mistake, it's in that shed over there.' I pointed to the shed behind him.

'Ah, then the papers, they are not finished.' He held up his hands as if all had become clear.

I had spent morning after morning in this dark old building, where groups of agents smoked and drank coffee from plastic cups, all waiting for papers to be "finished". Other groups stood around tall wooden desks, from where the daily business was conducted – a Dickensian scene but less efficient.

'When,' I said, 'will I get the batteries?'

'Tomorrow or the next day, no problem,' he assured.

'Tomorrow's Saturday,' I pointed out.

'Ah, yes, OK. Wednesday, we have them Wednesday, no problem.' He dashed off to attend to some important business in the canteen.

The shed manager continued to claim that my shipment hadn't arrived, but at least my agent had the good grace to show embarrassment. He confirmed that such delays were a regular feature when non-Greek boats had goods shipped over from their home countries. It should be noted that the batteries from the UK were replacements for the Greek batteries that we had newly installed during the winter maintenance work. I wouldn't be having this hassle had the Greek batteries been fit for purpose.

Import taxes and agents' fees were high and no doubt the shed managers felt they were entitled to some of the action; a bung would have heralded the miraculous arrival of delayed goods, even if the docks were totally free of ships at the time. Whilst I can claim never to have acquiesced in their unsubtle requests for bungs, I cannot claim to have wholly beaten the system, for the delays did cause considerable difficulties for me.

The world abounds in diverse systems that allow certain people the power to act in such a manner that falls little short of criminality and who are seemingly accountable to no one. It will always be so whilst ever there is a majority of people who won't accept the inconvenience that ensues as a consequence of taking a stance against such practices. Tip of the day: send it by air. It's more expensive, but it's faster and devoid of ransom demands.

The banks in Rhodes didn't need to demand extra payments, they took it without a by your leave. In fairness to them, they claimed that it was all down to the main bank in Athens, but who knows how the spoils were divided.

Boat bills are big ones and the readiness shown by some skippers to leave port overnight without paying their debts surprisingly hasn't fostered a no-cash, no-deal approach by traders. Such unscrupulous skippers are nothing less than criminals, but how does one describe the actions of a major Greek bank, which regularly withheld average sums of £10,000 from *Blue Skye C*'s account. Such sums destined for *Blue Skye C*'s account were transferred from the UK to the Greek bank in Athens in a maximum three-day transaction, yet that same bank never managed to transfer those sums to its own Rhodes branch in less than four weeks. Each time I claimed reimbursement of interest for the periods in question, I was reliably informed that the matter was being dealt with at head office.

'But,' and at this point there would be a shake of the head, suggesting mysteries that no foreigner could possibly understand, 'they are very busy at head office.'

It would be wrong of me to suggest that all Rhodians supported Gadaffi's terrorist activities, but they were certainly very anti-American after the USA carried out retribution bombings in North Africa. Rhodes being situated nearly as close to Libya as it is to Athens could well have had something to do with their views. However, whatever the reasoning, when an American warship made a request for one of its crew to be transferred to a hospital in Rhodes, several hundred protesting Rhodians marched to the harbour.

As the port police vessel made ready to leave the far end of the quay, one policeman, who wanted to be on board but not enough to run the gauntlet of protesters, marched on board *Blue Skye C* as if he had every right to do so. He stomped imperiously along our beautiful teak deck in his leather shoes – a no-no even for GA and his invited guests. He had chosen us because our bow was forward of all the other vessels on the quay and therefore offered the best location from which to hail his lift.

In an age when the British police must guard against hurting the feelings of muggers and rapists when arresting them, the sheer arrogance of their Greek counterparts stands out in stark relief. He was aware enough to recognise that I was annoyed and making him wait for the police launch in his socks nibbled a bit at his ego. Unfortunately, the episode did nothing to help me in future dealings with the harbour authority.

To make matters worse, the protesters deemed that our role in allowing the authorities free passage over *Blue Skye C* stamped us as police sympathisers, pro-American and anti-Greek; I had to raise our gangplank to deter the more aggressive protesters from attempting to board us.

You will recognise that generally our Greek experiences are of a type unlikely to affect the average holidaymaker; therefore, you will no doubt have gained some insight as to why Jean and I were so pleased when GA asked how we felt about leaving Greece to winter in Malta.

GA had popped over from Athens to stay with us for four days. His suggestion over dinner that we move to Malta for the winter and then cruise the area in the summer was like music to our ears. I tried not to over enthuse, for GA wasn't averse to changing his mind if he thought that any of his unexpected decisions met with universal approval. There were two more cruises to do, one in September and one in early October, so we planned to leave Rhodes as soon after that as the weather permitted.

Don and Jill Rastrick's second visit wasn't as boisterous as their first, for this time they were accompanied by Don's mother and stepfather, who clearly wanted a holiday with the accent on relaxation. The cruise was therefore only memorable to me for the lesson it taught. Virtually every cruise we made from Rhodes included at least one visit to Simi and never once did I moor against the empty ferry quay without a confrontation with the port captain.

'You not stay 'ere, only ferries. You move' So went the port captain's regular welcome.

'There's nowhere else to go and the first ferry isn't due until eleven tomorrow,' I repeated time and time again.

'Thees place, it ees clear at all times, you go.' At this point, he usually stood to attention, indicating that the matter had become official.

'No, it's not clear at all times. By tonight, like every other night, there will be another six or seven boats on this quay. I'll move when you make them move.' Always the same words, but I changed the sequence from time to time.

'You bring papers to my office.' Then he'd leave, happy to have issued an order that I must obey.

I'm aware that each time I present myself in his office, he will scrutinise the ship's documentation as if he has never seen *Blue Skye C* before. He will also check my passport number against a list on his desk, hoping against hope that this time my number, so to speak, would be up.

We moored alongside the ferry quay and I left Don tidying the mooring lines whilst I went down to the engine room to switch on the generator. Back on deck, I prepared for my regular contretemps with the port captain and was surprised see him cheerily conversing with Don on the quayside. On spotting me he hailed.

''Ello, captain, you are back again yes, you stay 'ere tonight?' He waved his cigar expansively.

Jean confirms that in my astonishment my mouth actually dropped open. Guardedly, I nodded affirmation, unsure of the new strategy he was employing.

He pointed to my briefcase. 'Papers no problem, tomorrow is OK.' He left with a spring in his step.

'Seems a nice chap,' Don mused.

'The man's been a pain in the backside for over a year,' I complained. 'What on earth did you say to him?'

'Not much, I was lighting a cigar when he came over, so I gave him one. Well, four actually. I gave him the packet I'd just opened.' He puffed on his cigar.

If ever there had been a lesson for me in handling such situations that was it. I comforted myself with the thought that it wouldn't have been as easy had Don been a non-smoker.

GA arrived for the last cruise with his friend Pat Betts and his wife Judy. Mrs Hubbard wasn't well at the time and was unable to make the journey. The trip was only for a week, so we lost no time in setting out for Turkey.

We were moving into October now and whilst the skies were still blue, the winds were strengthening. We headed for the Bay of Fethiye, which offered many anchorages in a relatively concentrated area. Strong winds had forced us to leave Wall Bay, GA and Pat going ashore in the dinghy to collect our hurriedly discarded stern warps, whilst I had to motor into the wind at quarter revs just to remain in the same place. They wasted no time getting out of the dinghy on their return.

We moored stern-to at Fethiye and for those of you interested in Lycian rock tombs, this is the place to be, but not in a force nine north-easterly gale. We soon had to move away from the quay, as neighbouring boats with dragging anchors were getting tangled with each other. I made for shelter in the lea of a large ship that was moored at the other side of the bay. The ship – which had the word "HOTEL" painted on its side – was permanently moored close in to land; someone had clearly lost money on the venture, for it looked sad and derelict.

I laid out two anchors and I think that our guests were impressed with the way I did it, for we never moved a centimetre throughout the gale. I spent the night in the wheelhouse watching boats motoring in circles, their anchors failing to hold them against the howling wind.

The wind had abated by morning and the sky was cloudless when I fired up the engines ready for the off. The hydraulic windlass was labouring a bit when pulling in the starboard anchor chain, so I altered position and took in the port anchor first.

Having repositioned directly over the starboard anchor, the loose chain came in easily at first and then again the windlass was complaining. Centimetre by slow centimetre, the powerful hydraulic system raised the anchor, but the resistance became so great that I had to lock the brake, to prevent damage to the windlass. The anchor was within a metre of the surface and the flukes could be clearly seen with their catch: the huge ground chain that was holding the permanently moored hotel ship in position.

The ground chain, attached at intervals to embedded concrete blocks, had held us securely and prevented any anchor slip during the overnight gale. I looped a rope around the chain and secured it to our foredeck cleats. Then we lowered the anchor until it was free of the chain and released one end of the rope that was looped around it. *Blue Skye C* breathed a sigh of relief as the huge ground chain sank in an instant. Whilst our guests could no longer claim that their undisturbed night was down to their skipper's anchoring skills, they could take huge comfort from the knowledge that skill or no skill, their skipper was a lucky one.

Dolphins accompanied us on our trip from Fethiye to Skopea Liman; dolphins never fail to make people at sea feel happy and so everyone was smiling when we anchored in the well-sheltered Tersane Bay.

Pat's smile faded a little after four hours of non-stop effort on – but more often off – the sailboard. Judy put the valiant effort down to Pat's determination to succeed, but GA was of the opinion that Pat wouldn't have lasted half an hour, had it not been for the assistance he was receiving from a shapely young German girl with long blonde hair.

That night the few boats anchored in the bay could easily be seen by moonlight. On the deck of one of them, a lone trumpet player entertained all with some slow jazz solos; the impromptu performance sounded professional, but I doubt that such atmosphere could be recreated on stage.

It was our last night as I leant on the handrail and took in the scene – the chances of our ever anchoring in this bay again would be extremely unlikely; as the strains of the trumpet faded into the night I felt quite moved.

'Drink, dear boy?' GA was never one to allow emotion to get in the way of practicalities.

I took the offered whisky, grateful for GA's intervention; for a moment there I was forgetting how much I wanted to journey westwards.

On our return from Turkey I was subjected to the usual unsubtle and petty delays that the Greek officials took such delight in inflicting. However, this would be the last transit log I would be made to wait for and I felt quite relaxed about the whole thing, which I think took some of the fun out of it for the pitiable bureaucrats, to the point that they lost interest and reduced the four-hour process down to two.

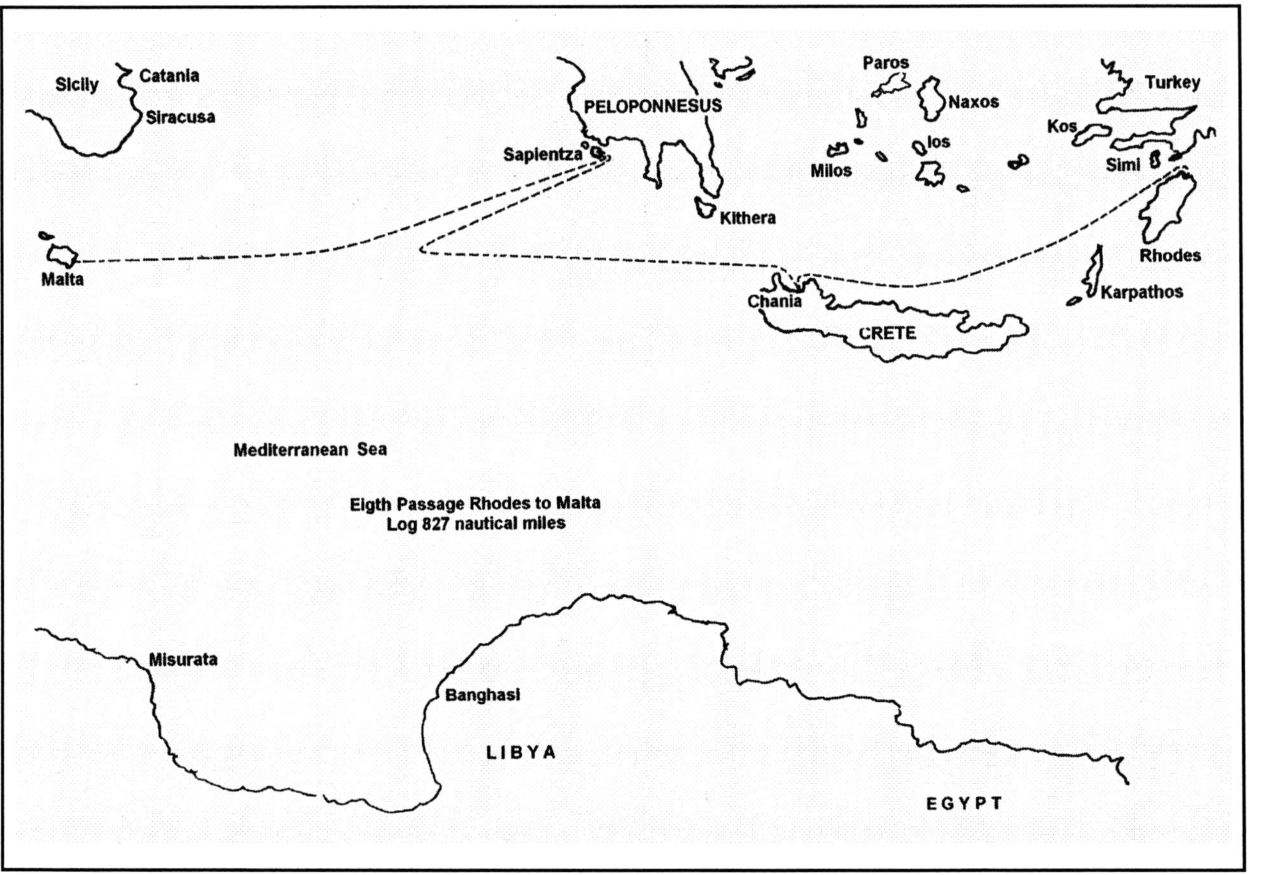
Sicily
Catania
Siracusa
PELOPONNESUS
Sapientza
Kithera
Paros
Naxos
Milos
Ios
Turkey
Kos
Simi
Rhodes
Karpathos
Malta
Chania
CRETE
Mediterranean Sea
Eigth Passage Rhodes to Malta
Log 827 nautical miles
Misurata
Banghasi
LIBYA
EGYPT

Chapter Sixteen

Trumped-up charges and stormy seas, but we reach Malta and Spindrift.

We were excited now and eager to be off. Our water and fuel tanks were full and anything that required tying down, oiling or greasing had been dealt with and only simple provisions had been stored; with only the two of us making the journey there would be no time and little inclination to prepare or partake of gourmet dishes.

We said our goodbyes to all the friends we had made whilst living in Rhodes. Yannis became quite emotional, as did some of our neighbours; at such times, it's worse for the ones being left behind than for those leaving for pastures new. All we required now was the appropriate weather.

Malta is approximately 700 nautical miles from Rhodes and once we cleared Crete there would be nowhere to seek shelter. I would have preferred a period of settled weather but my desire to be away from Greece took preference. Having extricated our anchor for the last time from Mandraki's tangle of ground tackle, we left harbour to the sound of many ships' horns, at 4.00 p.m. 23 October 1986. Darkness and a sea swell arrived hand in hand three hours later.

Just before midnight we were 2 miles off the Island of Sofrano. The signal from the island lighthouse would have been flashing a white light every six seconds had it been lit: why was I not surprised.

By 2.00 a.m. the next day, *Blue Skye C* was about 30 miles off the north-eastern coast of Crete, pounding noisily into a big swell. After another bruising fourteen hours' sail off the coast of Crete with its mountainous backdrop, I decided to put in to Chania for a rest; Malta, some 475 nautical miles to the east, would have to wait.

I would have preferred to carry on to Malta. Another stay on Greek soil wasn't in my plan but the passage from Rhodes had been hard work and Chania was the last refuge on offer before Malta: big mistake.

Chania reads quite well in the Greek pilot, but of course we weren't there for the market, the mosques and minarets; all we required was a resting place to await better weather conditions.

We moored alongside a rather rusty fishing trawler, recently purchased, the new owner informed us, as a diversification exercise. He owned several jewellery shops; strangely, he recognised some obscure compatibility between his shops and the fishing industry. My initial scepticism turned to admiration when, after many conversations, it dawned on me that I was talking to one of those men who are always ahead of the game. Here was a man who had done his homework on the European Union small print. Whatever benefits awaited the owners of clapped-out fishing trawlers, he would be at the head of the queue. I have no doubt that olive-tree ownership beckoned as another suitably compatible offshoot to the jewellery business.

Naturally, he could speak excellent English, don't they all? Well, not all, because the port captain didn't know a word of English, which is perfectly understandable, but, alarmingly, he was also totally uneducated in the science of sign language.

After two days of waiting for a weather improvement, I was summoned to the captain's office and thirty minutes later, I still had no idea what point he was trying to make. Even my well-honed sign language failed to impart my intention to return with an interpreter.

It was little wonder that I couldn't understand what the captain had been saying, because even when all had been explained to me I still had difficulty understanding the situation; I was speechless. Apparently, sixteen months earlier, *Blue Skye C* had been placed on a blacklist. You may remember that when we arrived in Athens, I had been surprised by the difference in the interpretation of the regulations to that which we had become accustomed to in Corfu.

Unwittingly, we had committed the crime of having left Zea Marina for our first cruise, without notifying the port officials of our intentions, and we were subsequently placed onto a blacklist. We returned to Zea Marina and were based there for a further two months, paying our mooring fees on a weekly basis and paying in advance to secure that mooring whilst away cruising.

It seemed to me particularly Greek that the Zea authorities could put *Blue Skye C*'s name on a blacklist, to be circulated to all entry ports, and then allow us to moor there whilst sailing in and out for over two months without noticing. Furthermore, we had cruised around the Dodecanese islands for a further fourteen months, during which time we had officially left and re-entered the country on several occasions.

My jeweller friend explained all this to the captain, who sat impassively stroking and tugging at his jet-black beard, all of course to no avail. The captain instructed me to submit a full and detailed report written in Greek – it was all getting farcical. Had I not been so desperate to get away from, what in my mind fell well short of the overused term "the idyllic Greek Islands", I would have made an issue of it. My fishing jeweller recommended a solicitor, but the thought of becoming involved with the Greek legal system filled me with horror; I opted for the written report.

It was a good report, a comprehensive report, a report packed with accurately detailed movement, complete with dates and times; my friend kindly rewrote the report in Greek. I have to say that I was a little surprised that the rewritten report was two pages shorter than the original, but perhaps the Greeks use only one word for our two.

It could be that the Greek version lost something in translation; certainly, the captain lost no time in bringing in a guilty verdict. He'd conducted the trial, found us guilty and proclaimed the punishment, a fine of 70,000 drachmas, which was about £300 at that time; I really did want to leave Greece.

November brought no particular improvement to the weather pattern, but it was slightly brighter than my mood, which I knew was unlikely to change whilst ever we remained in Crete.

Yet again, I completed the formalities for leaving Greece, I thanked the port captain for his kind hospitality and if he recognised the heavy sarcasm he didn't show it. I tried to convey the utter contempt I felt for him and his Greek counterparts; I didn't succeed, sign language just doesn't do it.

We cleared harbour just before 1.00 p.m. on 2 November and pitched into the easterly swell. By 5.00 p.m. the swell was getting bigger and by 7.00 p.m. it had got bigger. Just to help matters, the wind changed from north-westerly force three, to westerly force five, in other words right on the nose.

I learned later that the cause of our discomfort was a deep depression that had been centred over Malta, which had then decided to track the big seas its winds had produced. As the waves increased in size and crashed onto our foredeck, I reduced speed down to eight knots and then to six.

Heading directly into an oncoming sea isn't *Blue Skye C*'s strongest point of sailing. The pitch-black night wasn't helping, either, and each time one of the bigger waves crashed against the wheelhouse windows, it did so without any warning.

One hand for the boat and one hand for you is the general rule. In other words, whatever you're doing, do it with one hand, and use the other for hanging on to anything strong enough to bear your weight. Stupidly I had been adjusting the radar with both hands twiddling knobs, when *Blue Skye C* informed me that no one was steering her. I was flung across the wheelhouse like a rag doll and crashed against the wall-mounted, drop-leaf table, which was fortunately in its drop-leaf position. As I clambered to my feet and staggered on the pitching deck back to the wheel, I realised that we were broadside on to the waves. I tried to pull the wheel for a turn to port, but it wouldn't budge, it was locked solid. I strained every muscle to turn the wheel, but it remained immovable and we were rolling dangerously. I heard a little voice from the far corner of the wheelhouse.

'Are you all right, darling, can I help?'

I could just see Jean in the darkness, hanging on to the balustrade guarding the aft quarter's staircase. Having made up a bed on the wheelhouse floor, she had been rolled against something she could hang on to.

Jean's voice added a touch of reality to the situation and prompted me to engage my brain before I did some damage to the steering mechanism. The simple action of turning the automatic pilot on switch to off brought the helm back under my control. With my legs clamped around the pilot chair, I hung onto the wheel and very, very slowly, *Blue Skye C* swung back on to a compass course of 270 degrees.

Jean and I had developed a watch system of four hours on, four hours off throughout the daylight period, whilst I did all the night watch; if I became drowsy, Jean would take over, so that I could have a catnap for half an hour or so.

Tonight, I didn't feel drowsy, which was just as well, for whilst Jean can steer a compass course in normal conditions, there was no way she could control the wheel in such turbulent seas be it day or night.

I had hoped that daylight would hail friendlier conditions, but I was disappointed; all it did was highlight the fact that everything was as bad as we had thought it was when it was dark. I had now been on watch for over sixteen hours, with nine of them spent tussling with the wheel. At our present speed, it would take over two more days to reach Malta and the conditions were clearly getting worse. There wasn't much choice, we would have to go back; it seemed that Greece was reluctant to part with us.

There was an uncomfortable moment as we wallowed broadside on to the waves before swinging onto a new course of 050 degrees; as if released from heavy chains, *Blue Skye C* flew at 12 knots with not a care in the world. It always amazes me that one's well being at sea can be so much improved simply by changing direction.

I was happy to be rid of the constant pounding, vibrating and shuddering that we'd suffered for the past twenty-two hours, but I wasn't happy to give up any of the 175 miles we had worked so hard to cover. Worse even than that was the prospect of re-entering Greece. Any port in a storm is a valid adage, but at this time I felt that if it had to be a Greek port, the storm would have to be a very big one.

I found what I was looking for marked on the chart – it was tiny island with no town name and not a mention of it in the pilot book. A small island that may well be uninhabited, just off the south-west corner of Peloponnesus, namely Sapientza Island. It was situated about 65 miles north-east of our present position. We dropped anchor in its little sheltered bay at 4.00 p.m. Jean made me a cup of tea, but I didn't stay awake long enough to drink it.

You don't have to have experienced the elation that grips you to appreciate what it feels like when, having taken apart an electronic gizmo – about which you know nothing – in the vain hope that you will find a broken wire, you actually find one.

When I opened the box that controls the automatic pilot my heart sank, for it had balanced spinning wheels that I assumed spun and it had a fine wire as thin as a hair, connected from one thing to another thing, its purpose I couldn't begin to imagine. It also had, like any self-respecting electronic gizmo, far more wires than it could possibly make use of; in addition, it had lots of other things.

I studied it from many angles and even unfixed things that didn't look too important, things that I thought I might, with luck, manage to re-fix. I realised that I had no chance of achieving any kind of repair, the technology was way beyond me, and then I saw it, a little black smudge on a brown plastic-coated wire. I poked it with a small screwdriver and bingo it came apart. The two ends of the brown wire were soldered to two of those things I mentioned earlier, so I re-soldered a new piece of wire to the same things and reassembled it all; bingo again, it worked.

I have told that story to many people and none seemed as impressed as me, yet I count it as one of my outstanding achievements, definitely on a par with programming a video recorder.

Sapientza Island is 4 miles long with a maximum width of a mile and separated from the mainland by the Methoni channel, approximately a mile wide. We'd anchored in the little bay at the south-eastern end of the island and were there for six days and the only life we saw were birds; the island was, indeed, uninhabited.

With the westerly wind still blowing a force six I dare not leave the boat to explore ashore, as *Blue Skye C* had dragged her anchor three times; twice in daylight and once at night. The bay gave us reasonable shelter, but the seabed was mainly pebble and the wind kept winning the battle against our anchor's efforts to hold us securely.

Generally, we were in good shape, well rested, no problems from officialdom and plenty of books to read; we just had the one niggle, we were hungry. Our food stocks taken on board at Rhodes had been based on a three-day, non-stop passage, with a times two safety factor. Then, as a belt and braces exercise, we had doubled it to cover us for twelve days. We had added a bit in Crete, but clearly not enough; my excuse is that we were distracted by our port authority problems. No matter, the bottom line was that sixteen days after leaving Rhodes, our big meal of the day was sardines and cream crackers.

By 8 November the wind was back up to force seven, threatening the alarming prospect of having to choose between starvation and officially re-entering Greece to buy food. The following day's 6.00 a.m. weather forecast promised light winds for two days – we were on our way by 6.15 a.m.

There was still a big swell, with deep troughs cutting down our speed, but the wind had dropped to force three, the automatic pilot was doing its job well and the crew's morale was sky high. We had just finished a nourishing breakfast of cream crackers and water biscuits, when the automatic pilot packed in – the crew's morale dropped down to sea level.

Blue Skye C's 08:00 log reads: big swell, steering difficult. Helming very hard for Jean, but she can manage half-hour stints.

Decision time, we had ascertained that in the present conditions Jean couldn't manage more than half an hour's helming. We had only covered 15 miles and at our present speed, it would take another forty-six hours to reach Malta: a daunting prospect. The alternatives were no more attractive, if we used Greece and Italy to achieve a series of shorter passages we would double the overall distance to be covered. If we returned to Greece for repairs to the automatic pilot we would have no guarantee of success this side of Christmas.

The wind was still down at force three and I reasoned that the big seas created by the previous prolonged high winds must soon reduce. I made my decision, we would continue; the wind strengthened to force four.

Midnight log: I think sea improving, steering easier, very tired. Log 03:15: calm at last, steering easy, staying awake difficult.

The sun poked its top above the horizon behind us and bathed *Blue Skye C* in a warm, cosy glow as she powered her way at nearly 12 knots over a flat, glassy, millpond sea. As the song says: what a difference a day makes.

A somewhat bleary-eyed Jean took over the helm, whilst I had a walk on deck. Why are there so few moments like this at sea: the sky a stunning blue from horizon to horizon, the sun a large golden ball floating on glass. Leaning on the handrail, I watched our bow cut through the flawless surface of the sea; like walking through un-trodden snow.

In our flat and featureless world there was nothing to point the boat at and Jean, who has never managed to get her mind at one with steering by compass, was leaving a wake that was far removed from arrow straight; our varied course would take us through the area of floating rubbish about a half mile ahead.

It was aggravating to see floating rubbish thrown overboard by seagoing litterlouts. The litter we were approaching must have been from a big ship and covered an area the size of two football pitches. I went back to the wheelhouse and slowed our engines, I didn't want plastic bags and the like blocking our engines' cooling water intakes.

I swore, for it wasn't ship's rubbish, it was globules of black oil, obviously from an oil tanker washing out its storage tanks. Hundreds and hundreds of floating lumps like little bowler hats. It was too late now to steer around it, for we were in amongst it; it would stick to the hull at waterline level and would take days to clean off.

I swore again and went out on deck to have a closer look at the foul stuff. There wasn't a mark on our hull; the small bowler hats were turtles, hundreds and hundreds of baby turtles, their little legs pumping away ten to the dozen.

With four hours' sleep, a shave and a hot shower – hunger pangs apart – the world was a lovely place. I took over the helm from Jean and in no time at all, she had produced coffee and a plate brimming with cream crackers. We didn't mind now, Malta was only four hours away.

Malta is low lying and it took a while for us to sight land, but once seen our approach didn't take long. I spoke to the coastguard on the radio and he gave me mooring instructions and confirmed that customs and immigration officers would meet us on arrival. GA had arranged for an agent to assist us in Malta, so by the time we entered Lazzeretto Creek in Marsamxett, north of Valletta's harbours, there was a welcoming committee waiting for us.

They must have wondered about us, for the normally immaculate, gleaming white *Blue Skye C* was streaked in broad bands of rust stains. The pounding seas had forced out most of the sealing compound between deck and hull topsides, giving the boat an overall rust wash that gave us the appearance of an old tramp steamer.

As I manoeuvred our stern towards the quayside, my late friend Roy Poulter's words came to mind yet again: the best part of sailing is coming into harbour.

I asked the customs officers to let us know immediately if, during their search of the ship, they happened upon anything to eat, but they never left the aft deck dining table. They asked a few standard questions, I signed a form, they drank a cup of coffee and then they bid us goodbye.

We showered and changed and I found that I could get into a pair of trousers that had been too tight to wear for months. Weight Watchers would die for a slimming system half as effective as an unplanned sea passage extension, mixed with a large dollop of apprehension. The agent told us that a nearby Indian restaurant opened at 6.00 p.m.; we were leaning on the door at five minutes to.

There was much to do before we flew back to the UK for Christmas. Measuring, planning and ordering everything required for fitting a new electric windlass that could be operated from the wheelhouse and full ship's air conditioning was a considerable task. On our return my first job would be to remove the windlass with all its hydraulic system before I could commence the two main projects. I would have fourteen weeks in which to complete the work before the first guests were due to arrive. Said quickly, it sounds plenty of time, but in the same period I had to fit in a fortnight in the boatyard to paint the hull. If that doesn't impress you, please take into account that all the equipment, fixtures and fittings had to be shipped in, some from the UK, and this bothered me, some from Italy; those trousers wouldn't be too tight again for some time.

Again we had a super Christmas holiday, starting and finishing with a visit to Worlingworth Hall. The middle bit was more hectic than normal, because the planning for Lynne and Roy's wedding had begun. Although it was to be an October wedding, the arrangements had to be well advanced whilst we were in the UK. Those of you with experience of a daughter getting married will be no strangers to the anxiety factor, an inherent ingredient for those arranging a wedding. The anxiety factor can thrive readily in normal circumstances, but the additional 1,300-mile communication problem wouldn't help.

The wedding invitations were carefully chosen and the delivery date agreed; all well in advance of our planned return to Malta. No surprise then that they did not arrive on the due date. After several phone calls and heated altercations they arrived, just two days before our return flight to Malta. We were hugely relieved to receive the package and opened it eagerly; the quality of the printing was excellent, marred only by the fact that the information it conveyed was incorrect. It was just a little reminder of how easily a small detail can derail a big plan.

Hot sunshine awaited us in Malta when our plane lifted off from a snow covered England in mid January. We liked the friendly Maltese but the really big plus was the fact that they all spoke English. After nearly three years of struggling with French, Greek and the odd skirmish with Italian and Turkish, Malta offered a welcome respite. Maltese English was easier to understand than many of those dialects found outside of Yorkshire's boundaries.

Malta, like many Mediterranean countries, has a history of being occupied by a variety of nations. The Carthaginians were the first to occupy Malta in the ninth century BC, followed by the Romans, then the Arabs and the Normans. The Turks had a go, but were beaten off by the Knights of St John, who later capitulated to the French in 1798. They didn't hold it for very long, for Malta was, in naval terms, very strategically situated, so Britain took it from them in 1814; it no doubt miffed the French big time.

Many of you will have seen those Second World War film clips, showing that incredible allied relief convoy in 1942 – decimated by days of submarine and aeroplane attacks – breaking the Italian and German blockade and finally limping into Malta's Grand Harbour. The island had been relentlessly bombed for about a year and the Maltese were collectively awarded the George Cross for bravery. Malta became independent in 1964.

I well remember Dom Mintoff becoming prime minister in 1971 but it seemed that he had little love for Britain. By the time we first arrived in Malta, Dom Mintoff and the Labour Party had been in power for fifteen years.

We arrived back in from the UK in January to find Malta's general election campaign in full swing. By comparison, Britain's general elections are tame stuff. The main thrusts of the political campaigns weren't via television and newspaper; they were by rallies, processions and fleets of horn-blowing cars bulging with flag-flying passengers. When the blue flag carriers' passed the red flag carriers' – which was often, for Malta is not all that big – mutual hate was displayed by word and gesture. Several people were injured and one killed during a shooting confrontation; incredible when considering that Malta's total population was below 400,000.

Those of us living aboard boats moored in Marsamxett were advised to keep our gangplanks raised and maintain a low profile, despite the general carnival atmosphere with flags, posters and stickers attached to everything that didn't move.

I have to say that freedom of choice didn't seem to be high on the list of government priorities – for government, read Mintoff – and parents weren't very happy that the government had made the teaching of Libyan a compulsory school language, without so much as a by your leave.

Our own plans to spend some of the summer cruising around Malta were scrapped when we became aware of the Maltese Government Berthing Regulations 1975.

Extract from Maltese Government Berthing regulations 1975:

> *In terms of the Berthing Regulations, 1975, the Director of Ports directs that no yachts shall ply or berth within any part of the territorial waters of Malta between ten minutes before sunset and ten minutes after sunrise unless such yachts are on passage to Grand Harbour from beyond territorial waters or proceeding from any local harbour to sea beyond the territorial waters.*

The regulation simply stops all islanders and visitors alike from staying the night in bays or anchorages around the islands of Malta, Gozo and Comino. Once the sun has gone down you must be tucked up in your designated harbour – you have a choice of three in Malta and one in Gozo – and there you stay until ten minutes after sunrise.

A consequence of this regulation is that many Maltese boat owners spend their holidays cruising around Sicily, whilst foreign boats simply dismiss Malta from any cruising plan whatsoever. One has to wonder why the Maltese government would wish to inflict such restrictive and draconian regulations on their citizens. No prizes for guessing that the politicians would claim that it was in the best interests of the country and what the voters wanted; security is always a good excuse at such times. Just how beneficial to the nation the regulation was must be debatable, certainly the boating industry must have suffered; it was an industry destined for further pain when the British Navy vacated their base in Malta in 1979.

(Twenty-two years ago when we sailed from Malta the boating industry was in decline. I understand that it is now in good shape and that the boat charter business is strengthening; I wonder if the *Berthing Regulations 1975* have been scrapped.)

After fifteen years the Labour Party was voted out in favour of the Conservatives and with election fever over, life assumed normality; only the fading stickers on trees and lampposts reminded us of the political campaign madness.

Spring must have been in the air; for we had a sudden spate of newly-weds arriving in their wedding cars, requesting to come on board *Blue Skye C* for photographs. I agreed to let newly married couples, bridesmaids and the best man to come aboard for their photo shoots, but I vetoed full family groups with parents, grandparents, aunts, uncles, best friends and drunks.

I couldn't quite understand the relevance of a nautical-themed white wedding, but it appeared that *Blue Skye C* wedding photographs were becoming a cult thing. Indeed, after just four weeks, we'd had six wedding photograph sessions, all happy events but they were playing havoc with my work schedule. I realised that saying yes to the first couple had been a mistake. I took the easy way out and started varnish work on the aft deck handrails; wet paint signs became the weekend norm until the end of the spring wedding season.

To add to the wedding theme, we received notification from the post office that there was a parcel addressed to us awaiting collection. We were expecting the parcel, as Lynne had already told us that the reprinted wedding invitations were on the way. I waited in a long queue for about forty minutes until it was my turn to hand over my little form that the post office had sent to me.

The system was that two rather disinterested characters checked the collector's little form against their own paperwork and then placed a docket in a tray already half full of similar dockets. A considerable number of massively disinterested gofers selected – not I might add in any discernible order – a docket from the tray and disappeared through a door, presumably in search of a parcel with a matching docket. Sometimes, a gofer would actually return with a parcel and the expectant throng fell silent, as if waiting for the announcement of a winning raffle ticket number. The lucky named person rushed to collect his or her prize whilst the rest started talking again.

There was no way of knowing whether or not your docket had been selected or if it still languished amidst the others and so it came as a pleasant surprise some twenty minutes later when my name was called out. There was some dissatisfied mumbling from those who had been waiting longer than me, so I made my way to the counter intent on keeping a low profile.

No matter where you go in the world, if you have to deal with someone who doesn't like their job, it's odds-on that they will get up your nose. What I had here was a post office worker who not only didn't like his job, but also clearly believed that the customer was the root of all his troubles. No good morning, no smile and certainly no eye contact. Head down, he pushed a form at me to sign and head down, he collected it.

'Twelve pounds,' he mumbled whilst making a note on a form.

'Sorry?' Why do we English say sorry when what we really mean is "could you repeat that, please"?

Without raising his eyes, he scribbled on a scrap of paper and pushed it across the counter. I turned the paper around, so I could more clearly see the scrawled figure, £M12.70.

'What's this for?' I asked, genuinely perplexed.

'Import duty.' Head still down, shuffling papers, the tone of his mumble suggested that I was wasting his time with such a query.

As £M12.70 was over £20.00 sterling, I thought that it was about time that I had Mr Charm's full attention. I slammed the palm of my hand on the part of the counter I estimated was within his vision and raised my voice a decibel or two.

'Import duty, you want import duty for wedding invitations?'

I had his full attention, along with everyone else in the room; the silence could be described as pregnant. I sensed that those on my side of the counter were on my team and those on the other side were divided into he who had an awkward customer and the rest of them that didn't.

'You can buy wedding invitations in Malta, imported goods damage our economy.' He looked around for signs of approval from the keenly interested spectators; all eyes turned to me.

'I'm not selling the damn things, I'm going to write on them and post them back to England; complete with Maltese stamps, incidentally.' My team nodded their heads, for they could see my point.

'You could have bought them here, better for our economy.' He saw a few nods from my supporters and sensed he had me on the ropes.

'With no duty to pay, it would have been cheaper for you.'

'What about the economy of my country, the country where my children live, the country where my daughter will be married, the country where the wedding invitations will be delivered; where does Malta come into it?' We were level on points, but I sensed that I had the sympathy vote from my team.

'You are living in our country, if you live in a country you should contribute.' He adopted a smug and righteous countenance. All eyes swung back to me. I half turned, to ensure that everyone in the room could hear clearly.

'I am the captain of a British registered motor yacht moored in Marsamxett; the owner of the boat paid for six months' mooring and harbour dues upfront. We have two Maltese engineers working right now on our engines and generators and there will be no change out of £1,500.00 sterling. Soon, the boat will go into the Manoel boatyard, where the bill will not be less than £2,500.00 sterling. We pay a monthly fee to a Maltese yacht agent. We buy provisions, we eat at your restaurants and we pay for a telephone service that hardly ever works, along with an electricity supply that breaks down on a regular basis. We pay for all this without complaint, and you,' I stabbed a finger at Mr Self-righteous, 'you have the effrontery to lecture me on contribution.'

My team were fully behind me now and there was some light sporadic clapping; being that there was no immediate comeback, I pressed on.

'In my opinion these cards, which are not staying in Malta, should not be subject to import duty at all, never mind an iniquitous 30 per cent on the total value. So I'm not going to pay your duty, I'd rather leave them here than be subjected to such robbery. If you can find a couple called Jean and Alwyne with a daughter called Lynne getting married to Roy, you're quids in.'

Mr Self-righteous appeared to be looking for assistance and it duly arrived in the form of a small, chubby and altogether far more pleasant-looking man, who had listened to our verbal exchange from the far end of the counter.

'Good morning, captain,' he smiled sympathetically.

'Good morning,' I replied and offered my best smile, with not a trace of aggression or animosity.

'I hope you will understand that we do have regulations to follow but at times, regulations don't suit a particular set of circumstances. However, there has to be some charge, would you be prepared to consider £M3.00?'

His words were spoken quietly and I was pressed from behind as my followers leaned forwards to hear what was being said.

'Yes, of course.' I quickly produced the money. 'I hope my comments didn't cause offence, I was a little upset,' I apologised.

He held his hands in the air. 'My own daughter is married. The wedding is a happy day, but,' he waggled a hand, 'the lead-up can be stressful.'

We shook hands in a parental bond. I looked at Mr Self-righteous, prepared to forgive and forget, but his eyes never lifted. The office was back to normal and clutching my parcel I left; on my way out I received a few congratulatory slaps on my back.

Coincidence is a phenomenon that everyone experiences from time to time – just how remarkable the coincidence is generally measured on a personal yardstick. Some would deem it a remarkable coincidence to meet an old school acquaintance in the local supermarket for the first time in forty years; others would claim it more remarkable that the coincidence had taken forty years to occur. If the same two people had met following a car crash in the Australian outback, that would be truly remarkable, if not to say careless. In between those two extremes, most people have experience of a coincidence that required the joining of several unrelated elements to bring it about.

You may remember that when Jean and I left Cannes bound for Greece, we also left *Spindrift* behind. It had been a sad moment for us to part with the boat that we had worked so hard to build and which had, in return, looked after us well in some very scary conditions.

Prior to leaving Rhodes we had received a letter offering £6,000 for *Spindrift*. Considering that she had cost over £9,000 in materials alone, the offer was derisory. On the other hand, it was costing nearly £1,500 a year in mooring fees and insurance charges, a fact well known by the prospective purchaser. Boats, unlike cars, appreciate in value, but not at £1,500 per year for an 8·5m yacht, so with much reluctance I accepted the offer.

It seemed coincidental that at the same time that I sold *Spindrift*, several Mirage 28 production models, similar to *Spindrift* only in that they shared the same hull moulding, were being sold off by a Greek charter-fleet company at the bargain price of £9,000. I tried not to think about it.

Alex, our agent in Malta, had taken to dropping in from time to time for a coffee, at which time we would put the world to rights. We discussed many topics, but the world of boating generally figured highest on the list. Naturally, I touched upon the story of *Spindrift's* recent sale, although Jean maintains that the phrase "dwelt upon" would have been more appropriate.

'That's a coincidence, I'm just selling a boat named *Spindrift*,' Alex murmured as he selected another biscuit.

'Yes, the name turned out to be more commonly used than we had anticipated when we chose it.' I selected a biscuit before Alex ate all the best ones.

'What colour was yours?' He sprayed a few bits of his HobNob about as he spoke.

'Aquamarine, one of the best hull colours I've seen.' There were only two HobNobs left and Alex was taking one of them – I chewed frantically.

'Actually, I like the colour of this one I'm selling; it's a sort of bluey green.' He bit into his biscuit.

'That is aquamarine; it's a bluey green.'

My eyes met Jean's. No, we shook our heads, it surely couldn't be. Alex noticed our silent exchange and recognised what our combined thoughts had been.

'No,' he said, 'this boat's not a home-built one, it's professionally built: carpentry, electrics, engine, rigging and everything; it's perfect.'

He took the last HobNob.

'Mirage 28 with black anodised mast, boom and toe rail, three cylinder 10hp Bukh diesel engine. There are no internal fibreglass mouldings, everything is built in teak, it has a stainless steel gimballed oven and oatmeal-coloured tweed upholstery. And it is, of course, the only Mirage 28 with the sail number seventy-six.' I paused for breath.

Alex was still holding the unbitten HobNob. 'Bloody hell!' Absent-mindedly, he replaced the biscuit. 'I don't believe it,' he said. Then he suddenly perked up, 'I'm selling it to the local doctor and he's asking all sorts of questions that we can't answer; you could answer them all. Would you mind meeting him?'

Jean and I walked through the boatyard looking for *Spindrift* and for some reason we found ourselves holding hands. *Spindrift* looked perfect and as I patted her hull, I felt strangely guilty. I had left her in France and had sold her without going back to see her, and now she was in another foreign country – a coincidental meeting if ever there was one.

I spoke to the doctor, who was extremely enthusiastic at the prospect of owning *Spindrift*; it was clear that he had fallen in love with her and would have bought her no matter what answers I had given to his questions.

Whilst my original story of *Spindrift* to Alex had revealed the fact that I had sold her for £6,000, he didn't reciprocate with details of the deal he was striking with the doctor. He just confirmed that the vendor had arranged to sail *Spindrift* from Cannes to Malta to get a better price and had delivered her the week before we'd arrived on the island. I wasn't sure that I wanted to know how much the doctor was paying but I asked him anyway.

'I have to confess,' he told me ashamedly, 'that I used the fact that the owner had to go back to France to force the price down. He wanted £14,000, but I said that my highest offer was £12,500.' He paused sheepishly, 'It was a long way for him to bring the boat and he had to pay the agent's commission and his own return air fare.'

'I wouldn't worry too much, I feel sure he will have recovered his costs,' I comforted.

All in all, we enjoyed our stay in Malta. The Maltese were friendly people and we became good friends with our next-door neighbours Juana and Chris. Juana was a very petite and pretty Menorcian and her quietly spoken English had a masking effect on her wicked sense of humour. She was an architect, but had put her career on hold to join Chris on his extended cruise to South America. Chris was handsome and at 1·9m tall he appeared huge when Juana was by his side. He had sold a successful business for several million and had left the rat race to those who thought that the marathon was a good competition to be in.

Chris was a divorcee and a target for women seeking a rich and available man. Juana had inherited half of her family's estate, which included a considerable portion of the island of Menorca that had been in the family for a few hundred years. Juana, oblivious to her beauty, presumed that most suitors were after her money; they were made for each other.

After some time they admitted that both they and their crew had had misgivings when they saw the rust-streaked *Blue Skye C* taking up the berth next door, crewed by a couple who shot off to a restaurant without washing down their salt-encrusted vessel. They feared the marine equivalent of today's "neighbours from hell", who can be the equal in all aspects to their land-based counterparts. The only plus point for an unfortunate neighbour is having the ability to move house and home should the situation become untenable.

It didn't become necessary for them to move and Jean, who excels in the skills of homemaking and is a naturally good listener, was looked upon by them and was affectionately referred to as Aunty Jean.

GA arrived for a break from the English weather and as always, he knew the area and all the best restaurants. There seemed to be few places in the world he hadn't visited, the majority of them well before being targeted by travel companies. Once again, it didn't surprise me when he knew of and could describe many of the obscure places that Chris and Juana had visited in South America and as always, GA's memory and wit became sharper in the presence of an attractive female.

By the beginning of May all work on *Blue Skye C* had been completed, including the annual boatyard visit. The only jobs left were those common to all boats: the ever-present washing and polishing, thankless tasks carried out in the knowledge that one trip out to sea will render it necessary to do it all again.

After six months in Malta we were ready to leave and I can look back on only the one little skirmish with authority when collecting the wedding invitations; that speaks volumes for Malta from someone who has difficulty in controlling a knee-jerk reaction to almost every form of officiousness. The bottom line is that the island of Malta is populated by friendly people, enjoys a hot Mediterranean climate and is surrounded by warm clear blue sea; what's not to like?

Mary and Ian joined us for a week in Malta and would also make the short passage with us to Sicily. They planned to take the ferry back to Malta from Catania on the east coast of Sicily, where GA had arranged to join us for the onward passage to Mallorca.

Over the course of two days we said our goodbyes to the friends that we had made during our stay in Malta. We had a leaving party with Chris, Juana and their crew the night before we left and we all got a bit emotional, as you do.

We left our mooring at 5.00 a.m. on Saturday 23 May 1987 bound for Sicily. Juana and Chris looked quite saddened as they waved us off; mind you, I don't laugh a lot at five o'clock in the morning, either.

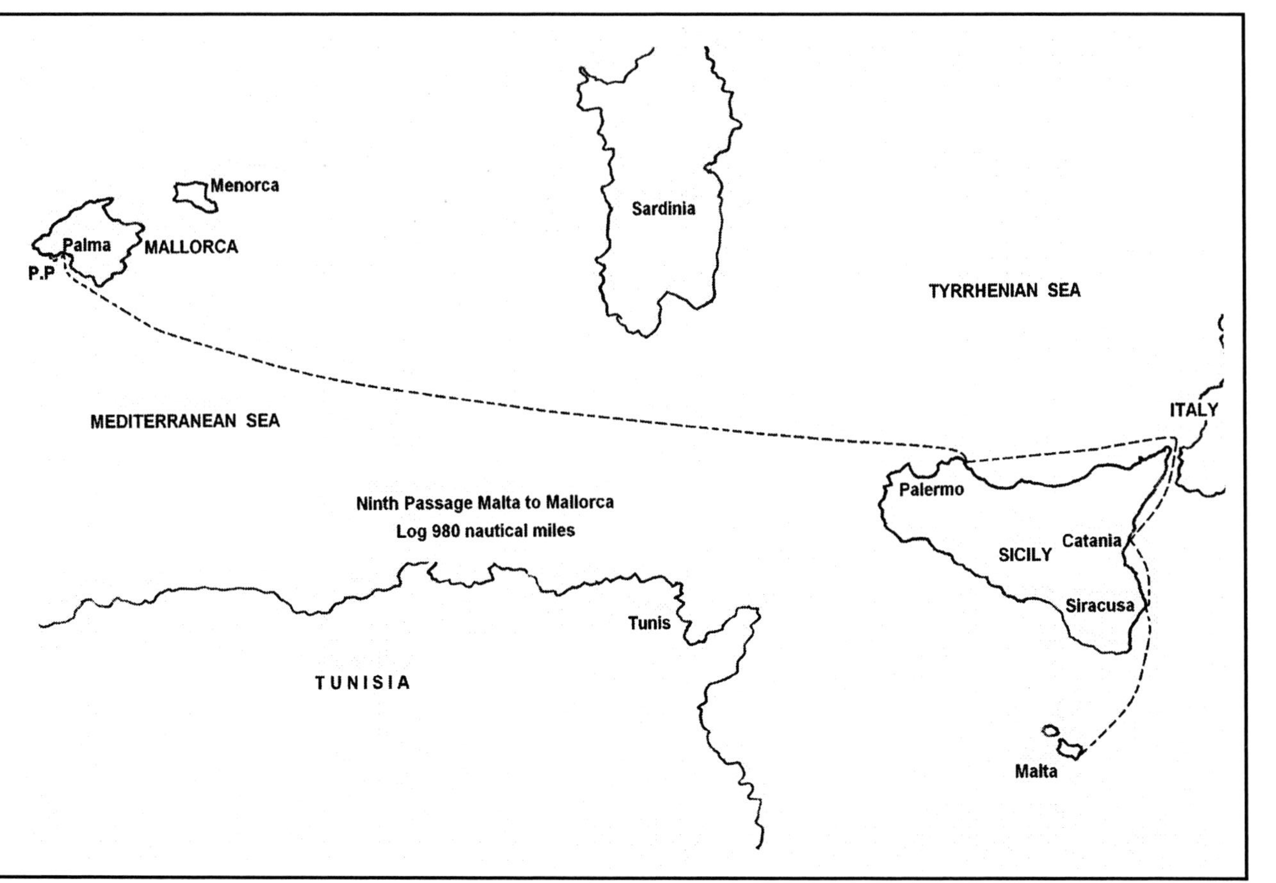
Menorca
Palma
MALLORCA
P.P
Sardinia
TYRRHENIAN SEA
MEDITERRANEAN SEA
ITALY
Palermo
Ninth Passage Malta to Mallorca
Log 980 nautical miles
Catania
SICILY
Siracusa
Tunis
TUNISIA
Malta

Chapter Seventeen

Was the fuel man Mafia? Through the walls of death to Mallorca.

In the days of yore, making war and attacking your neighbour seemed to be the thing to do. Most Mediterranean countries have a history of being attacked, none more so than Sicily. It all started, as often was the case, by the Greeks, just over 700 years BC. Since then, Sicily has been colonised, occupied or ruled by the Phoenicians, Romans, Barbarians, Arabs, Normans and the Spaniards.

Not surprisingly, the locals formed a protection group, which became known as the Mafia. Their original brief was to look after the weak and the poor during the Arab conquest; they achieved this by using blackmail and much not very niceness. The fact that each reigning authority was never able to glean information to uncover the Mafia organisation was in the main down to the protection afforded by the *Omerta*: the code of silence.

However, like many such protectionist organisations, be they guerrillas, secret societies or political pressure groups, they generally start off for the right reasons, but once the original objective has been achieved, the leaders display a reluctance to disband; the management structure continues, but self-serving agendas tend to take precedence.

I suppose that it's logical that your chosen mode of travel when visiting a new town, city or country will have a strong influence on your first impressions. One airport seems to look like most others, to the point that even Third World airports can suggest a level of development way beyond the actual. The taxi route from airport to hotel can induce a feel-good factor, provided that it avoids a short cut taken through a city's slum area. As often as not, a train will deposit you into the centre of things and the sense of a city's atmosphere can be almost immediate.

However, when you approach a country by sea, it's still possible to feel that mixture of excitement and uncertainty which mariners have experienced throughout the ages. Today's navigators, unlike Columbus, no longer expect to be welcomed by spear-carrying natives, but characters that don't require spears to create a threatening ambience frequent some dockland areas.

When we entered the Port of Siracusa, situated at the southern end of Sicily's east coast, our reception was neither hostile nor welcoming. We tied up alongside the quay, but passers-by in dock areas are unlike marina grockles; their scrutiny of your vessel seems to lack the grockle-type curiosity factor. A few stared truculently through our windows and others lobbed their cigarette butts onto our teak deck. It seemed prudent to moor stern-to – we felt more comfortable putting a stretch of water between the quay and *Blue Skye C.*

I took Mary with me to the customs and port captain's offices, where her language skills underlined how such knowledge can smooth your path. Another plus was that being with a pretty and attractive young woman ensured a level of assistance I hadn't experienced before during our Mediterranean cruising.

I can't say that I found Siracusa to be a particularly endearing place, maybe it was half-day closing or perhaps it was because I wasn't in the right frame of mind. It may well have been, and I'm ashamed to admit this, that I was viewing every stranger as a potential member of the local Mafia. Perhaps I'm more susceptible to the influence of films and television than I care to admit.

Next stop was Catania, where Mary and Ian would leave us and GA would join us. Depressingly dirty and grimy buildings surround Catania's harbour. However, we did receive a very warm welcome from the mooring manager as we tied up to a floating pontoon in the inner Porto Vecchio Harbour.

The manager seemed to take a shine to Mary and Ian and the next day he took them in his car on a sightseeing tour of the area, finishing with a trip up Mount Etna. He was voluble about the fact that the volcano had virtually wiped out Catania just over 300 years ago and he seemed quite excited about the possibility of it happening again.

The following day our friendly Sicilian, now known to us as Paulo, brought fresh fish on board and took over the galley; he prepared a local fish and rice dish and also provided the wine. Apparently, the local dish couldn't be fully appreciated unless accompanied by this specific local wine. He had a wealth of Mafia-related stories and kept us entertained until the early hours.

On the last day Mary and Ian had just a short walk to the next quay to board the ferry for their return trip to Malta. Meanwhile Paulo, who wouldn't hear of me hiring a taxi, was driving me to the airport to collect GA.

I have to say that GA didn't take to the man who was providing the transport from the airport to *Blue Skye C.* The day was hot and the stifling heat in the car was in stark contrast to the coolness of GA's attitude towards Paulo.

'What's he after?' GA sucked in his cheeks as he watched Paulo walk back to his little quayside office.

'Well, he's been very pleasant and helpful since our arrival, he's probably hoping for a good tip.'

However, GA was clearly sceptical of Paulo's motives for offering such generosity. I was used to GA assessing people on gut reaction and once they had been pigeonholed, that was it. He left little room for reassessment; they would have to turn water into wine before he would acknowledge that they might have a passing talent. I was also used to the fact that his assessments usually proved to be incredibly accurate.

'I've spent some time in Sicily and the Sicilians I've met didn't strike me as being over generous. I'd watch him if I were you.' He sucked in his cheeks again and nodded. 'They all need watching.' The whole race was condemned out of hand.

Having waved goodbye to Mary and Ian from the ferry quay, we made our way back to *Blue Skye C.*

'When do you want to be off?' I asked GA.

'As soon as we can, I don't rate this place.' He wasn't happy.

His demeanour wasn't improved when he saw the bill. His misgivings had been entirely justified. The bill didn't itemise the trip to Etna, the dinner, the wine or the taxi service, but it was all allowed for in spades.

I am, of course, fully aware that few things are free in this modern world and I already had a provisional figure in mind for Paulo's tip, as a thank you for his kindness and his generosity. I needn't have given it a thought, for clearly there was no way that Paulo intended to be out of pocket.

Any bill with a total displayed in lira is going to be a shock, but Paulo's was traumatising.

A bit late in the day, I discovered that the Ormeggiatori Cooperative is a group of boat attendants who lease an area of water and a quay in a harbour and offer a mooring service. There is no recommended price structure, but as the official tax for staying in an Italian or Sicilian harbour is cheap, the Ormeggiatori charges seemed to be based on whatever they could get away with.

I'm not sure if Paulo was a member of a cooperative, was employed by one or was simply a bit of an entrepreneur, but whatever he was, he had the authority to reduce the bill considerably after an hour of haggling: down from enormous, to massive. Naturally, I revised the figure I had planned as his tip down to a more reasonable zero. I maintained eye contact with him as I handed over the cash.

'You are aware, of course, that this agreed total includes your tip.'

He lowered his eyes and made no comment. It didn't make me feel any better for knowing that he knew that I knew we had been ripped off.

The Sicilian element of our journey was proving to be disappointing. Our first sight of Palermo Harbour warned that a change for the better wasn't on the cards.

Blue Skye C's beautiful, shiny white hull cut through the black oily sludge of Palermo Harbour as we manoeuvred into a mooring at the fuel quay. Beer cans and bottles, twice their normal size with the added coating of thick black oil, lay rather than floated on the slimy mess. Part of the harbour had the appearance of a giant scrap-metal yard, where brown rusting vessels wallowed uselessly in the thick harbour liquid; a graveyard for vessels that no one could afford to do anything with. And neither would they for a year or two more until the EU grants arrived, making those who know the ropes an extra few billion lira.

The immediate surroundings of Palermo Harbour offered no improvement. The walk to a restaurant took us between high-rise flats and an obstacle course of burst refuse bags thrown from the upper levels; the walk wasn't an appetite builder.

It was Saturday night and the restaurant was packed, so we eased down a few gin and tonics before a table became free. Things were looking up and unlike the port, the restaurant had a telephone in working order; we would be able to make the return journey by taxi.

'I'm not impressed with this place, Alwyne.'

GA, was sitting at the breakfast table drinking coffee and staring dolefully at the harbour surroundings. 'How soon could we take the fuel on board and get away?' he added.

The sun shone out of a cloudless blue sky – there aren't many places that can look as depressing as Palermo Harbour on a sunny Sunday morning. God knows what it's like when it's raining. The place is without doubt the worst I have visited anywhere in the Mediterranean.

'Well, I'm not sure how long it'll take to get the permit for the duty-free fuel, but hopefully we can get it in time to have fuel on board by tomorrow evening.' I was as keen as GA to be away, but knew that acquiring the necessary documentation would be a long-winded affair.

'Do we have to have duty-free fuel? We could never get it in Greece.' He really did want to leave as quickly as possible. Then, as an afterthought, he added, 'How much cheaper will it be to get duty-free fuel?'

'About eleven, maybe twelve hundred pounds,' I answered.

'We don't need to be off today, do we?' He looked cheerfully at the rapidly improving surroundings. 'Another day won't make much difference, will it?' It wasn't really a question.

I was first in the queue when the maritime offices were opened for business. The large building appeared to be manned entirely by uniformed naval personnel. Young ratings clutched sheets of paper in the time-honoured way as they walked along corridors. National servicemen have to find some way of passing the time. It was some three hours later that I emerged into the sunlight victoriously clutching my own piece of paper; a good morning's work at about £400 an hour.

The fuel quay manager was a scrawny individual, who could have been any age between fifty and seventy. His face was deeply tanned and was etched with scowl lines, which, like his clothes, would have benefited from a wash. He fitted well into his surroundings: he looked just as dirty and depressing and smelled no better; customers didn't dally in his poorly ventilated office.

I don't think he liked me and I knew that I didn't like him, for despite the fact that *Blue Sky C's* filler pipe was inset into the topsides about a foot below the deck level, he managed to douse our teak deck with diesel and smear black rubber marks from the diesel delivery pipe on every varnished and painted surface he could reach. Why just be careful, when with a little more effort you can really spoil things?

I was in the engine room monitoring the fuel tank levels, when the drumming sound of the incoming fuel suddenly stopped. I feared that the delivery pipe nozzle had freed itself from the inlet pipe; the image of diesel oil spewing over the boat encouraged me to break the engine-room-to-deck speed record. GA met me on the aft deck.

'He's shut off the fuel, says he won't take payment by credit card or Euro cheques.'

I looked at my watch; we had twenty minutes to get to a bank before they closed. We made it with seven minutes to spare, but our hopes were immediately dashed when an assistant, far more interested in tidying his till than serving us, informed us that we could have no more than £200 cash on a Euro cheque. What is the point of a common market, when each country in it makes up its own rules and then allows them to be further altered by local interpretation?

We took the £200 and went back to the boat to pool all our cash. We managed a total of just over £700, not even halfway there.

Meanwhile, Jean had been plying the unclean one with coffee and sandwiches, to prevent him from carrying out his threat to leave the quay for a meal, with no guarantee of returning on the same day.

GA went down to the master cabin to look in the safe, even though I had assured him that I had used the entire ship's float in Rhodes, which was why I had paid the fine in Crete out of my own pocket. I'm sure that like me, many of you have looked in the same drawer several times when searching for your misplaced wallet, purse or car key and then, with huge relief, found the lost item in the first drawer you had previously searched.

GA's shout alarmed me and I rushed down to his cabin. I knew that the aggravation on the fuel quay and at the bank was getting to him and I was worried at what I might find. His grin was ear to ear.

'Two thousand pounds and three thousand dollars – all in this envelope.' He held the envelope triumphantly aloft. 'I think this calls for a drink, dear boy.'

Stinky insisted on seeing the cash before he would start pumping fuel again and once refuelling was completed, I was invited into his inner sanctum to pass it over. I didn't waste too much time with pleasantries, for the office was hot and the gagometer reading was reaching the nausea level.

The cash was in £50 denominations and I told him to keep the change, which would give him about a £15 tip – far more than he deserved in my book, but the change would have been in lira and I preferred to let him have the money than await the change. I think that in our dealings with the fuel attendant to date, we had seen his best side. His meaner disposition was rising rapidly to the surface, the dark, grubby brown complexion was deepening in hue and his lips were almost black. I hoped he wasn't going to pass out, for mouth-to-mouth resuscitation was simply not an option.

He was shouting as I backed away to avoid the flecks of spittle. I was having difficulty understanding the cause of his rage. I only caught his drift when he spoke slowly, for in agitated mode he was incoherent. I'd had enough of his ranting and turned to leave. He grabbed my arm but let go quickly when I gripped his wrist.

'Much pounds you no pay,' he blurted, but slowly enough for me to understand. I felt bad; I'd not given him the correct money, it was no wonder he was angry.

'I'm sorry, I thought I had counted it out correctly,' I apologised.

I scrutinised the bill again, then recounted the bundle of £50 notes that Mr Charm had thrown contemptuously onto his desk.

'You must have miscounted,' I said, happy that I hadn't made a mistake. 'There's the full amount plus a £15 tip,' I added.

I hadn't intended to give him such a big tip, but now I was pleased – he would be embarrassed to have made such a fuss.

'Fifteen pounds,' he spat on the floor, 'much pounds you no pay,' he prodded himself in the chest, 'you pay more,' he shouted.

Yes, I have no doubt that you grasped what his problem was in less time than it took me.

'You cheeky sod!' My shout was louder than his. 'You have the gall to demand a bigger tip because we saved money buying duty-free fuel. What the hell has the cost of the fuel got to do with your tip?'

I gave him two, maybe three seconds to answer and started again.

'First of all, I did all the work getting the paperwork processed with no help whatsoever from you. Secondly, you've been a pain in the arse since we arrived and you don't deserve the tip I've already given to you and thirdly, I've not charged you for the sandwiches and coffee that my wife made for you.' He flinched as I touched his nose with my pointed index finger. 'And you didn't give her a tip at all.'

I doubt that he understood much of what I said, but he knew that a tip increase wasn't on the cards. He was mouthing what I presumed to be Sicilian profanities as I made my way back to *Blue Skye C.* Jean said that I looked white and agitated when I arrived back on deck. I wasn't surprised; the man was the nastiest piece of work I had ever come across. I remembered that Paulo had confirmed that Palermo was the seat of the Mafia organisation; perhaps not a good place to make enemies.

'You look as if you need a drink, dear boy.' GA handed me a whisky; I coughed, he'd not bothered to add water.

Apparently, our shouting match in the office had been easily heard on board and by anyone within a 50m radius.

'I think it may be a good idea not to hang around for too long, he's working his dislike for me into real hatred.'

I nodded towards the glowering manager, who was standing in his office doorway and mouthing what I presumed to be further abuse at me.

After another half-hour spent casting malevolent glares in my direction, he locked up and drove off at speed. It was his normal finishing time for the day, but my imagination had him speeding off to attend a hastily convened Mafia meeting. How would they view the deliberate slight of under-tipping one of their members? Could it be that a percentage of the duty-free saving on fuel was deemed to be a Mafia protection payment?

No, I took a grip of my overactive imagination. Even the Mafia wouldn't expect a cut from a visiting yacht's duty-free saving on fuel and if they did, I felt sure that they would have provided detailed payment instructions in advance.

I put the whole thing out of my head. Nonetheless, I was up before four the next morning and *Blue Skye C* was heading out of Palermo Harbour by quarter past.

Mallorca was our destination and our estimated passage time was about 40 hours; unfortunately, tuna fishing nets were delaying our progress. We encountered them between Sardinia and Sicily, the row of floating oil lamps stretching as far as the eye could see to the north and south of our westerly course. I steered a northerly course, parallel to the net, for well over a mile before rounding the end and resuming a westerly course. Then, twenty minutes later, we came upon another and again we had to alter course by 90 degrees to clear the net. When my watch came to an end, I had carried out the same manoeuvre seven times.

I handed over the watch to GA and went below for a sleep. When I was due on watch again, Jean related GA's approach to tuna net avoidance; he simply sailed straight through them. His theory was that the nets were below our keel level and that the float line would skid off our hull and pop up again. He carried out this manoeuvre four times; each time the floating lights followed us for about 500m before breaking away. Greenpeace would no doubt have approved of GA's approach to the fine filament nets, which they refer to as walls of death, creating pain and misery to the dolphins that become trapped in them.

GA's aggravation was directed at fishermen who felt that they had the right to make huge areas of open sea into a potentially dangerous obstacle course for seagoing vessels; particularly when the use of such nets was illegal for EU fishing fleets.

I have to confess that my decision to go around the nets was made because of my fear that our stern gear may become fouled; concern for the nets wasn't my prime motive. I felt that lying dead in the water with a few hundred yards of net and line wrapped around our propellers and rudders would cause considerable inconvenience. Neither did I believe that being found in such a plight by Sardinian and Sicilian fishermen as they sought to haul in their catch would be in our best interest.

I look back on that night as a big let-off as later inspection in Mallorca highlighted just how close we had been to calamity. The leading edges of our forward glass-fibre stabilisers bore deep gouges, cut by the ultra strong float lines before they eventually snapped; both propellers were tangled mop heads of nylon net and resembled giant purple cauliflowers. They had done well to drive us on to Mallorca; surely one more net would have done for us.

Chapter Eighteen

Mallorca, a sailor's paradise. Not all jockeys diet.

We arrived in Puerto de Palma, Mallorca, just before lunchtime, 4 June 1987. The sun shone from a cloudless sky as we moored stern-to the quay of the Paseo Maritimo, the long palm-tree-lined road and promenade that borders Palma's large harbour.

Mallorca, what can I tell you about an island that most of you will know well. It's a magnet to all who love sailing and there can be very few sunshine holiday lovers who haven't made at least one visit to the island.

It seems to me that nearly every Mediterranean country seeks to fit a tourist industry in amongst its every day life, whilst Mallorca fits its everyday life in amongst its tourist industry. Sunshine, clear blue sea, sand, food and drink, sightseeing, rock-climbing, walking, cycling, golfing, sailing and every other water sport known to man – with the exception of surf boarding: a sport that the virtual tide-less Mediterranean sea will never cater for – is all provided by an island approximately 90km long x 80kmwide. My first impression was that the island had an overall holiday ambience and I felt that I could live with that.

Since leaving Cannes, I had found that a considerable element of a skipper's job was to insulate guests from the inconvenience and considerable aggravation spawned by pompous officialdom, in which respect Greece was still a bad memory. Here in Mallorca, the Q flag was still flying from our yardarm after three days. I took it down, as no one was the least bit interested.

Yet again, it was no surprise that GA knew someone in Palma and he lost no time in contacting Megan Ellis. Very few UK citizens take the gamble to change their lives completely and chance their arm in a foreign country with no pension or benefits umbrella. By and large, any such move should be preceded by some degree of preparation; just walking away with a clean pair of socks in a rucksack could, unless you're extremely resourceful, end in tears.

Megan was and indeed still is extremely resourceful. That's not to say that she didn't make plans before taking her gamble to leave the UK, but circumstances created a situation that would have persuaded all but the most determined to abort the whole project. Trained in France as cordon-bleu cook, Megan and her husband had owned a successful restaurant for many years but, unfortunately, their marriage broke up and with it their business venture.

It had been a traumatic period in her life, but ever a fighter, she bounced back and became the manager of a distinctive restaurant in Woodbridge, a job in which she was very happy and successful. But years of being an employer ill prepare one for the role of employee. In addition, memories of what now looked like wasted years were still fresh and showing no signs of receding.

Megan decided to start her life again outside the UK, along with her daughter Amanda; they planned to open a restaurant in Mallorca. Amanda's last-minute decision to withdraw from the enterprise in favour of marriage to a man just recently met, left Megan somewhat out on a limb. Undaunted, she decided to go it alone.

By the time we arrived in Mallorca she had been there for a year, working as a sales representative for the same estate agent that she had commissioned to find her a suitable restaurant property; very resourceful woman is our Megan.

GA knew Megan because a friend of his owned the restaurant that she had managed in Woodbridge, and he met with her to find out the best place to moor *Blue Skye C.* Megan gave him the guided tour, during which he booked a mooring. A couple of hours later we sailed into the marina that was to be our home for the next three years or more: Puerto Portals.

Puerto Portals had only been open for nine months when we arrived and at that time there were fewer than 100 boats in a marina which was built to accommodate 650. We were met by two *marineros* – even I knew what the name meant – in a hard-hull inflatable and having guided us towards our mooring, one went ashore to receive our stern warps whilst the other passed us our permanent bowline; boat mooring couldn't get much easier than this. All heady stuff when compared to the warlike manoeuvres one had to adopt to procure a mooring in Rhodes.

Everything in the marina was designed to make life afloat the pleasure it should be. Quaint and picturesque harbours are fine for a season, but the joy of having a permanent base with your own designated water, electricity and telephone connections knew no bounds. It should be said that many Mediterranean ports and marinas do have such connections available, but here in Puerto Portals there was one distinctive advantage: they all worked.

I know that I keep banging on about officialdom, but throughout the world there are too many individuals of an arrogant and stupid disposition – whose wages are paid in the most by the very people whose lives they make a misery – occupying jobs which give them an authority that they are incapable of applying with any degree of intelligence or common sense. One has to suffer this scourge of the modern world in every walk of life, but once out at sea there is a refreshing lack of it; back on land, however, it's alive and healthy.

Bud Abbott, a friend that I have referred to earlier, was the skipper of a beautiful timber-built motor yacht named *Moon Maiden.* Bud and his wife ran the boat for a wealthy lady owner, who liked to take her guests cruising each year in Greek and Turkish waters. *Moon Maiden* was a large and instantly recognisable vessel that had sailed in Turkish waters for several seasons and so it came as some surprise when Bud was arrested for smuggling. I'd had problems myself with pompous port officials, but never managed to get arrested.

Bud had originally entered Turkish waters with *Moon Maiden* at the Port of Datça – Datça, you may remember, was where I found the port officials in their beds, so you won't be surprised to learn that they had run out of the required documentation issued at all entry ports; foreign vessels had to make these available for inspection at all times. Bud was told that he could carry on to Bodrum and collect the documentation from there. The port captain wrote a note in Bud's passport should they be questioned before reaching Bodrum.

There were no problems at Bodrum, where the necessary documentation was issued and after a six-week cruise in Turkish waters, *Moon Maiden* returned to France. *Moon Maiden* continued to visit Turkey every year thereafter and never had a problem.

The owner eventually sold *Moon Maiden* and bought a larger steel-hulled ship, which was based in Turkey. Bud, with his engineer and a couple of crew, went to collect the vessel – now renamed *Moon Maiden II* – from the port of Istanbul. He sailed the vessel across the Sea of Marmara and down the Dardanelles, to the exit port of Canakkale.

Here it was that the customs official – possessor of a PhD in stupidity – noticed a small entry in Bud's passport, the very one written in Datça some years earlier. The note was of course written in Turkish and Bud, with a passport full of foreign notes, had never given it a thought; it specified that *Moon Maiden* had a television.

'Ǽ … Ψ?' the Canakkale customs official demanded. Which the linguists amongst you will have immediately translated into 'Where is your television?'

Bud, however, had to struggle a little to fully understand just where the official was actually coming from, until he eventually grasped the point and was able to explain that the entry in his passport – inserted some years earlier – actually referred to the vessel *Moon Maiden*, not *Moon Maiden II*.

The customs man was having none of it and arrested Bud on a charge of smuggling televisions. Apparently, there was no love lost between the police and customs officers at Canakkale and the police officer sympathetically locked him in an empty ground-floor office. He explained that whilst the concrete floor may not be comfortable, it would be preferable to the smelly basement cells, which apparently weren't much improved since the Dark Ages.

By now, the media had learned of the English captain arrested for smuggling. Surrounded by photographers and reporters, Bud was taken to court and indicted. In the eyes of the media, Bud's situation had become untenable, for whilst they may have deemed his crime heinous, far worse was the fact that the England football team had recently beaten the Turkish national side by eight goals to one.

As Bud was led upstairs to the courtroom, he reacted to the overzealous media photographers by grabbing a fire axe from the wall and threatening to do terrible things with it; he was now charged with smuggling and assault with a deadly weapon. He spent a second uncomfortable night on the concrete floor, made far worse by the interpreter's small error of omitting the word "if" from the statement: you are found guilty of assault; you will serve a seven-year jail sentence.

It was the owner of *Moon Maiden II* who came to Bud's rescue. The very determined lady had tracked down the Turkish Ambassador, in spite of the fact that the Turkish Embassy in London had declared that the Ambassador was away and couldn't be contacted. She lost no time in acquainting him with all the relevant facts in a concise and forceful manner. On receipt of their Ambassador's message, Turkish higher authority brought an end to Bud's four-day internment.

Perhaps the authorities recognised the flakiness of the prosecution's case, but I favour a more basic political fiscal expedient; many extra tourists would be required to make good the loss of foreign currency should the likes of *Moon Maiden II* cease to visit their country. So much trouble caused by just one useless, stupid official; regrettably, every nation has too many of similar ilk – the cost to the world must be incalculable. I would stress in Turkey's defence that during our few visits to that country, the authorities always treated us with helpful courtesy.

Mallorca is like a giant superstore whose clientele are tourists. Tourism is the main provider of Mallorca's wealth and everyone from the island's top administrators down to its refuse collectors appear to be fully aware of it. The result of this general awareness is that visitors arriving by plane or boat are made welcome. Everyone, no matter who or what they are, likes to be made welcome. The achievement of such a fundamental criterion is ridiculously easy and cost effective to achieve and yet so many in the leisure industry fail to do so.

Puerto Portals was built to make boat owners welcome and it was built to make boat owners feel good and the boat owners that the management wanted to welcome and make feel good were those with plenty of money. Puerto Portals is an upmarket marina where moorings and services aren't cheap and our monthly bill was around £2,500. Rundown, grubby vessels rarely entered the port and if they did, they read the price list and departed in haste. The marina had everything: boatyard, shops, restaurants, discos and bars. You could buy anything if your wallet could stand it.

You and your chequebook could dine at Tristans and eat nouvelle cuisine, provided that you weren't hungry; or you could have a three-course lunch and a carafe of wine in the nearby village of Portals Nous for the equivalent of £3.50. There were also shops displaying the latest male and female fashions – a service for those who buy clothes without asking the price.

As you might expect, there were several yacht brokers' offices run by superior beings who wore designer sunglasses and talked on mobile phones whilst the office phones rang unanswered. They had a few boats you could buy for under £200,000, but most ran into the millions. All prices included the agents' ten per cent commission; yacht brokers appeared to be quite relaxed.

Equally relaxed were the sales staff in plush, spotlighted estate agents' offices. Young women with long blonde hair and young men with even longer blonde hair ever ready to show the latest million-pound holiday villa. For those spending a few million on a holiday home, an extra service was close at hand. Designer furniture and 2m x 2m designer paintings with matching curtain materials were displayed under powerful spotlights. Experts were on hand to explain what the artist had in mind when he or she spilled their paint on the canvas.

Fortunately for ships' crews and the more circumspect millionaires, the port did have other restaurant, bar and shop choices, all set in beautiful palm tree and flowered surroundings.

We settled into life in Portals without problems; it was certainly easier to run a boat from such a base. Food supplies, drink, spares and services were all on hand and preparing for the arrival of guests wasn't the nail biter that had often been the case in Greece.

GA and Mother came for a holiday and mini cruise, during which we checked out various anchorages. Unfortunately, Mrs Hubbard didn't take to Puerto Portals as readily as most; she still preferred Rhodes. For starters, Portals was large and spacious and the shops weren't bunched together and selling the same souvenirs. Mother wasn't exactly short of a bob or two, for over the years she had acquired enough shares in GA's group of companies to put herself in the Millionaire's club, but she still liked a bargain and bargains were thin on the ground at Portals.

Mother was from the old school – she remembered the early days when she served behind the counter of the small electrical goods and repair shop that she and GA had started following his army demobilisation. She always spoke about the early days with fondness. There's no doubt that she enjoyed being rich and the perks that came with it, but it was when she talked about the old days, the days when she and GA had started their first business, that the sparkle came back to her eyes. Some might argue that years of running a house and raising a family had robbed her of the chance to exploit her potential. GA would argue that her insistence on driving to the next village to purchase the dog food because it was a few pence per tin cheaper, underlined her lack of business acumen. However, regardless of other viewpoints, Mother was adamant that Puerto Portals was designed and built with the sole purpose of extracting the maximum amount of money from anyone stupid enough to fall for it.

It was a valid point, but the truth is that anyone with a passion for a particular sport or pastime will always spend more on it than is rational. Boat owners, golfers, football supporters, no one is exempt and everyone can recognise the other person's fallibility when the other person's passion isn't shared.

My only worry was that like water dripping on a stone, Mother's derogation of Portals would wear GA down and land us all back in Greece.

Whenever GA informed me that he had offered a *Blue Skye C* holiday to anyone, he always followed it up with a commercial.

'Lovely people, they'll be no trouble, you'll enjoy their company.'

I think that he genuinely considered our well-being, for during our time on board *Blue Skye C,* he never sent anyone who gave us even the slightest problem. It has to be said that had there ever been any opposition to my basic rules, a mere suggestion that GA wouldn't like it would have been sufficient to quell any mutinous thought. However, we did wonder what we had in store when GA informed us that our next guest was a lady jockey.

The holiday had been offered as a thank-you gesture for her having taken quite a few of his horses first past the winning post in the previous season. I had never met, or seen for that matter, a lady jockey, but I was aware what a tough and dangerous job it was to be a National Hunt jockey, so I had a pretty good mental picture of what our next guest would look like.

My mental picture proved to be way off the mark, for Gee Armytage turned out to be a petite and incredibly attractive blonde the only big thing about her was her personality. By the time I had met her at Palma Airport, her party of two had swollen to six. There were three National Hunt jockeys, Gee Armytage, her brother Marcus and Martin Boseley. There aren't too many successful lady National Hunt Jockeys but Gee was one of the few, having ridden two winners at the 1988 Cheltenham Festival. Her brother Marcus was to become even more successful in 1990 when he rode Mr Frisk to victory in the Grand National. Whilst the other three guests were not jockeys, Sarah Whitaker, Michael Caulfield and Richard Philips, were all steeped in the – what to me can only be decribed as the very dangerous – world of horse racing.

GA once told me that Lester Piggott's only form of sustenance on race meeting days was water sipped from a screw-topped tonic water bottle that he carried with him; when he wasn't racing he dieted. The group we had on board ate as if each meal was going to be their last and water played no great part in the quenching of thirst. Like all healthy and active young people, prodigious quantities of food and drink had no obvious detrimental effect on them whatsoever.

They were all of a similar age to our own children and we couldn't help but treat them as we would our own family; even the telling off I had to deliver one night came out like a parent's reprimand rather than a captain's dressing-down.

Following grumbles from our bleary-eyed guests at breakfast about their lack of sleep, I complained to the skipper and guests of a neighbouring boat who, having arrived back from a night of onshore revelry, continued their celebrations on their aft deck until three in the morning.

The following night I awoke in the early hours to hear the sound of similar revelry and wasn't best pleased to find that the noise was coming from the aft deck of *Blue Skye C*. I arrived on deck in time to hear Gee laughing and giggling in the water between boat and quay, inviting the investigating port security guard to join her for a swim. My main source of annoyance was the fact that having given our neighbours an ear bashing on the subject of consideration to others, I had now been hoist with my own petard.

Once Gee had climbed back on board and I had them all together, I conveyed in no subtle manner just how pissed off with them I was and left them all staring at their feet and looking quite embarrassed. Apparently Gee had been feeling tired and had left the main group drinking in a bar at around midnight and on boarding *Blue Skye C* she had hoisted the gangplank up on its davits so that the latecomers couldn't get on board.

Eventually having had her fun, she let them embark with the exception of her brother, who arrived a few minutes later to find the gangplank back in its raised position. Unfazed, Marcus, to loud applause, tightrope walked across the gap on the stern shoreline, which was a feat demanding some considerable skill.

Gee, ever the competitor, failed in her attempt to emulate her brother's high-wire act; she gained high points for entertainment value, but her water entry apparently needed work. Noise in the form of laughter and loud applause would have been difficult to suppress. The following morning on the top galley step there was a letter of apology signed by them all. I felt a reet grump. (Yorkshire-ism for a man lacking in humour.)

Each to his own, for horse riding seems to me to be a pastime sufficiently dangerous in itself, without compounding it further by jumping huge fences deliberately built in front of life-threatening ditches. Life is made more dangerous for a jockey who is generally surrounded by a crowd of other jockeys mounted on steaming animals, each capable of snapping your bones by merely leaning on you; just falling off a stationary one can be a plaster-cast job. This group of young people were happy, polite and fun to be with, but the happy-go-lucky exterior clearly hid inner strength and bravery; I mean, some of these horses are 2.5m high with muscles.

Most of us, however, have an Achilles heel. It's snakes for some and spiders for others, but for our intrepid horse riders it turned out to be big seas. Our return journey from the island of Cabrera found us in a strong beam wind with big seas to match. We'd spent the night at anchor in Cabrera Bay and through the gap to open sea I could see the large rollers. I explained that the journey back to Puerto Portals would be very uncomfortable and it would be prudent to remain at anchor until the following day.

But they wouldn't hear of it, for it was Marcus' birthday and a table had been booked at a restaurant for a celebratory party that evening. Besides, it didn't look all that bad from the anchorage. Their skipper was perhaps being a little overprotective – a killjoy even – because I wouldn't allow them to play spray dodging on the foredeck as we progressed towards the open sea.

The first big roll had them all crowding from the aft deck shelter into the wheelhouse, the first signs of apprehension flitting across studied, casual countenances. A little while later, all except for Gee Armytage were now lying on the wheelhouse floor, two of them holding rigidly onto the feet of my pilot's chair.

After two hours they wondered if we should return to Cabrera. I explained that we were past the point of no return. It was an unfortunate phrase, for whilst it's a skipper's normal reference to a position beyond the halfway point of a passage, I could see that such terminology hadn't evoked the calming influence that I had intended.

'Get us back safely, Alwyne, and we'll do whatever you want.' The plaintive cry came from below my chair.

'Does that go for you all?' I enquired.

'Yes.' The answer wasn't as compact as written, more a disparate amalgam of piteous affirmation.

I entered into a rambling dissertation in an effort to take their minds off the perceived danger they were in; my light-hearted effort to persuade them otherwise wasn't convincing them. I dwelt awhile on the adverse effects of the seawater currently spraying all surfaces of *Blue Skye C* and easily gained unanimous agreement that they would hose and wash down the superstructure from stem to stern upon their safe return to Puerto Portals.

With Cap Blanc on our beam, we were able to alter course, resulting in a distinctly easier motion, which effectively convinced them all that they now had a slim chance of survival.

My street credibility hit an all time high with neighbouring skippers, when they witnessed me supervising our six guests as they eagerly and with great industry washed and scrubbed the salt off *Blue Skye C.*

Our equestrian group treated Jean and me to dinner that night, celebrating Marcus' birthday, and Master Philips, possessor of the gift of impersonation, had everyone in stitches with his take-off of me and my Yorkshire accent. Jean insists that he got it absolutely spot-on, but to me it seemed extremely over exaggerated.

We had enjoyed their company and it had been a good trial run for holidays based in Puerto Portals.

'Did they all have a good time?' GA enquired.

'Oh yes, they all enjoyed themselves very much,' I assured.

'Did they eat and drink much? Was it expensive?' he queried.

'Don't ask,' I suggested.

'Right, best leave it, dear boy.'

Chapter Nineteen

Princess Diana in Puerto Portals. The Rescarca in Ciudadela is best avoided.

Over the next three years we had many enjoyable cruises from Portals, which had soon become a very popular port. GA's friends Pat and Judy Betts bought an apartment overlooking the marina and a Sunseeker speed boat which was a sleek, high-speed job in which Pat steamed everywhere at 30 knots.

Blue Skye C operated as the mother ship for the August cruise. Pat and his friend Barry Emerson, his son Ben and a school friend slept aboard the Sunseeker; GA, Mother and the remaining wives, friends and daughters all crowded onto *Blue Skye C.*

We would cruise at a steady 10 knots whilst Pat and Barry zoomed ahead to a check out the less crowded anchorages and zoomed back to report. Then off they sped, before meeting as arranged for lunch.

For three years running we cruised in August on flat-calm waters, which helped when setting out buffets for about fourteen people. It was hard work but enjoyable, they were a super crowd and were always ready to pitch in and help. They never failed to show appreciation to Jean for the time she spent preparing countless meals.

GA complained that it was all too noisy, but really he enjoyed it; if he hadn't, it wouldn't have happened for three years on the trot. The downside for me was the increased volume of washing-up; it was not, in my view, a fit pastime for a ship's captain, but everything in life can't be perfect. Much, however, can be perfect and when I'd finished my nightly chore, I often stood on the foredeck holding the rail with crinkly washing-up fingers and watched the sun go down.

Sunset is a magical time on board ship in settled weather and at such times, as often as not, GA would join me with a whisky glass in each hand; in deference to the tranquillity of the moment, his question would be murmured, 'Drink, dear boy?' He liked sunsets as much as I did and we always watched them in silence; the sun dipping below the horizon was the signal to drain our glasses and return to the aft deck for a refill.

Puerto Portals was now home to us and was similar to living in a village in that there was a community of boat owners and skippers who lived and worked there. Much like living in a village, the gossip played a major role in our daily lives: the usual who was sleeping with whom and when. There were cliques and there were former friends who no longer spoke to each other. There were neighbourly arguments between the crew varnishing handrails and next door's crew hosing down their decks. Shouts of alarm would be heard from those breakfasting on their aft deck, when the boat next door fired up its malfunctioning 2,000hp engines and enveloped them in thick black oily smoke.

The Portals community actually centred on piers one and two, because these piers provided moorings for boats large enough for permanent living. There were fifty-five moorings between these piers, for vessels from 25m to 38m. The marina had berthing facilities for over 600 boats ranging down to 7.5m craft. Owners of the smaller boats used them at weekends and summer holidays and were rarely seen for seven or eight months of the year. There were a couple of moorings on the outer mole for 60m vessels, but they were never occupied for longer than two months by the same ship.

So piers one and two became the epicentre of the marina and had the BBC made their soap opera about community life on Puerto Portals piers one and two, rather than the ill-fated *Eldorado*, they would have had a big hit on their hands. The scriptwriters would have had an ample supply of ready-made storylines; Portals was teeming with characters from every walk of life.

Typically, no one was fazed when Geoffrey, joint owner of the popular Wellies Bar, was arrested and jailed for money laundering. The recipient of this service was a suspected international drugs dealer named Marks; the ex-English public schoolboy was sought out and eventually arrested by the United States authorities. He frequented Wellies Bar, but I have to say he never looked like any of those international drug dealers you see on TV.

When Geoffrey had served his time – courtesy of the Mallorcian prison service – he was welcomed back into the Portals community as if he were an errant pop star. Who knows how many boat owners or skippers from piers one and two could add a little more detail to this anecdote.

Portals had a glamorous setting: Spanish architecture, palm trees and shiny megabuck boats. A simple stroll to the shops often required a detour around a long-legged beauty, surrounded by an entourage of dress arrangers, hat adjusters and make-up repairers. Several more arty types ponced around addressing everyone as darling and the fashion magazine photographer ignored everyone as his camera clicked like a machine gun; the model conscious only of the camera as she puckered and pouted.

Film shooting attracted more interest, particularly if a well-known celebrity was involved. The take generally required the star to board a large, floating gin palace and assume a statuesque stance on the aft deck; a thirty-second cameo that took two hours to shoot. Yet, no matter how famous the models or film stars were, it was royalty who drew the crowds.

When King Juan Carlos of Spain and his boat *Fortuna* were in Portals, the shops and restaurants did a roaring trade. When the number of visiting tourists increased even further, we knew that a visit from Princess Diana was imminent.

At such times access to our pier was restricted, whilst grockles and media photographers got no further than the barrier of mean-looking men with their meaner looking dogs. The clear water in the port couldn't hide the divers as they glided beneath the surface, in search of anything that might explode. Above, the binocular-toting crew of a helicopter constantly patrolled the port and its approaches. It must be a strange life indeed, to have to live within such an obsessive security cocoon. In one way I never felt safer, yet I found myself checking unfamiliar faces for anyone bearing a passing resemblance to the Jackal.

Many years ago, when I was about 9 years old, I was on my way home from choir practice at Leeds Parish Church. Heading for the bus station I had to stop at the roadside, whilst three large black cars drove slowly by. As they passed, I stared directly into the eyes of one of the passengers and received the slightest but nonetheless perceptible nod of acknowledgement. The man on some special visit to Leeds was none other than Winston Churchill. From the day I became aware enough to recognise the danger of being at war, this man had been a God; his speeches to the nation on the wireless banished my fears that German soldiers could come knocking on our door. It was a wartime child's nightmare and a bad dream for many adults; Churchill's words gave me, along with the nation, hope and reassurance.

It was one of the most extraordinary moments in my life and the fact that this incredible man had actually acknowledged me made such an impact that I can remember it to this day. Whenever I question the sanity of those who throng to catch sight of a pop, sport or film star, I try to temper my scorn for such idolatry, by recalling how I felt on that special day so many years ago. Having said that, I find it hard to establish even the remotest similarity between the achievements of any pop, sport or film star and those of Sir Winston Churchill. With that memorable day in mind, I was able to fully appreciate the feelings of the three septuagenarian ladies when they met Princess Diana on the end of pier two.

We knew one of these grandmas, as she was a regular visitor with her son and family to his boat moored on the opposite side of the quay to *Blue Skye C.* This time, however, she had come with two of her friends, a sort of grandmas' convention. Their stay coincided with Princess Diana's visit to a superb timber sailing ship, *The Virginian,* moored at the end of our pier. One evening, the three grandmas could contain themselves no longer and assembled a discreet 40 or 50 metres away from the aft deck of *The Virginian,* where Princess Diana was sitting and chatting. A car was waiting for her and as she walked down the gangway towards the car, she spotted the little group and promptly walked over to them.

She said hello and asked where they were from and were they enjoying their holiday. She hoped that the good weather would continue for them and that they would all enjoy the remainder of their stay. Then she wished them goodbye and slid into the waiting limousine, which whispered silently away. The three grandmas walked approximately 50mm above the ground for the remainder of their holiday and couldn't have got wet if they'd fallen overboard.

All this happened before Princess Diana's marriage break-up. Reporters and cameramen weren't allowed on the quay and neither were the general public: there was just Princess Diana and three grandmas.

Certainly at that time she could gain no public accolades for her brief acknowledgement of the three ladies, but I hope that she got a good feeling from doing what she did. Her action was as natural as Winston Churchill's totally non-advantageous acknowledgement of a nine-year-old schoolboy.

When we left Cannes, we left the millionaires' playground; Greece and Turkey attract the more serious sailors, but the Riviera has the more serious millionaires. Mallorca is unlikely to ever match the Riviera in that respect, but Puerto Portals was making every effort to climb up the league table.

Way back when the man broke the Bank of Monte Carlo, having one million pounds in your bank account meant that you could buy just about anything you wanted without the worry of falling on hard times. Such a bank balance ensured that you could truly live that exclusive millionaire lifestyle.

Today, however, there are millionaires in abundance; the problem is that one million pounds is no longer enough to enable one to be a fully paid-up member of the financially elite club. To join such a club now, the word millionaire must be preceded by the combining form multi, perhaps even multi-multi; it must be difficult for them now that billionaires are in such plentiful supply.

The millionaires in the Portals community were seriously quite well off; they definitely fitted into the multi category. Strangely, I don't think that many of them had recognised that living aboard a multimillion-pound yacht in a row of very similar yachts on the same quay is much like living in a row of less expensive terrace houses. Furthermore, they lack the privacy enjoyed by those less expensive land-based dwellings.

I'm asked on occasions what it was like to live amongst such a concentrated number of multimillionaires. Well, not surprisingly, apart from the fact that they don't wince as readily as the rest of us when they see the restaurant bill, it was no different from living in any other normal community. They have amongst their ranks, in equal proportions to the rest of society: nice ones, quiet ones, loud ones and prats.

One thing I found very difficult to understand is why a man clever enough to make a fortune could, after three very expensive divorces, stroll along the quay – swimming briefs hidden below his overhanging belly – proudly holding hands with the blonde and petite next nubile wife to be. How could he be so incredibly stupid as to believe that she was madly in love with him and craved only his body?

So, would I like to be a millionaire? You can bet your life on it. You wouldn't be wrong if you espoused the theory that being rich is no guarantee for happiness and good health; however, that same principle applies whatever your financial status. Would I like to be a millionaire to the power of ten? The temptation is to say that I'd settle for one million, but on the basis that I never heard anyone in Portals suggest that they would prefer less than they had, I have to conclude that more is better. Whilst Jean and I lived in an environment that attracted those with multi-bucks, our friends John and Nora Ayling lived in an environment that attracted those with megabucks. John was the captain of the ship *Leander* and Nora was the housekeeper, a position that carried more clout than the name might suggest.

Leander is 75m long, has five decks and requires a crew of twenty-four to run it. The ship is elegant, opulent, palatial and state of the art. None of the ferry or cruise-ship vibrations on *Leander* when her massive engines push her along at 15 knots cruising speed, for the whole interior floats on anti-vibration mountings. In addition to the standard stabilisers that reduce roll when a ship is moving through the water, *Leander* has a system that moves 50 tons of water between strategically placed ballast tanks, to ensure that she doesn't rock when at anchor.

The master state room and a further ten en-suite staterooms enable those chartering Leander to take a few friends with them. The entrance hall, saloons and furnishings are sumptuous and anyone can charter the whole ship for just $50,000 per day. (Circa 1990s.) *Leander* can be chartered for any length of time, but John tells me that the average charter period is ten days. So for ten days she's yours for half a million dollars; of course, if you want to eat and drink, there's a separate charge. If you prefer, like many do, you can include amongst your entourage of bodyguards, maids, fitness instructor, telephone operator, pet minder and guests, your own chef and kitchen staff.

If you wish the ship to leave port, then naturally you will have to purchase fuel and provided that duty-free fuel is available, you could fill her up for about £80,000. If you were to think that only a few had the wherewithal to charter such a vessel you'd be wrong; there is never a shortage of clientele.

Leander's captain and wife team demanded extra skills to those required on *Blue Skye C.* Their guests were truly international and considering the tariffs involved, more than a degree of flexibility was essential. When two Arabian sheikhs dispatched their Chippendale bodyguards to recruit as many girls as possible from the local disco, Nora was left with the job of getting rid of them all in the early hours of the morning; apparently, they were reluctant to leave. The sheikhs weren't specifically charmers, but they were very generous tippers.

Meanwhile, life on *Blue Skye C* remained much the same, no Arabs and no ladies of the night, but I wouldn't like you to think that I'm just a dull old fart; which was clearly how I was viewed by the girls who accompanied GA's grandson John and friend Paul on holiday.

John, in his late teens, took the blow of his mum and dad's decision to join him on holiday very well, for we had been originally informed that only John, Paul and their girlfriends Sue and Sally were coming on the trip. When I saw Sue and Sally, I had a fair idea as to what may have contributed to Janet and Robert's decision to join them.

Sue and Sally were twins with centre-page looks and attributes. Front page as well for that matter. Lest you think that I'm some kind of voyeur, I hasten to add that I was alarmed to conclude that my detailed knowledge of Sue and Sally's vital statistics was entirely owing to my total lack of personality and presence. Whilst we were in port, both girls sunbathed in topless bikinis, and, quite properly in my opinion, they always sought the shelter of the foredeck away from the lust-filled eyes of grockles, neighbouring crews and some of their employers. The saloon roof, however, provided an ideal area whilst we were cruising for sunbathing mattresses and pillows; these were lined up against the wheelhouse windscreens and when I was seated on the helmsman's chair, the saloon roof adjoined the wheelhouse at about my chest level.

John and Paul always occupied the outer mattresses, whilst Sue and Sally lay on the two inners. This arrangement ensured that whilst seated at the wheel, four naked breasts constantly obstructed my view. Jean's observation when she saw me squinting around the line-of-sight obstructions did nothing for my self-esteem.

'I don't think they view you as being sexually active, pet.' The observation was followed by a sympathetic pat on the knee.

Whilst my ego may well have been dented, I realised that few males would consider it a violation of their human rights if forced stare around or between naked breasts on a daily basis.

By the time we made the trip from Pollensa on Mallorca's north-east coast, to Ciudadela on the west coast of Menorca, I was quite used to peering around whatever parts of Sue and Sally's anatomy happened to be obstructing my view at the time; the views on the return trip differed in every way.

Menorca is a good cruising area, there are many bays offering safe, attractive anchorages and for those of you who prefer less commercialisation, it is the place to be. Jean and I particularly like Ciudadela: it is a very picturesque harbour, where you can moor stern-to the quay within a few metres of numerous bars and restaurants.

On our first visit we had enjoyed meeting Chris and Juana, whom we hadn't seen since leaving Malta. They were busy altering part of Juana's huge family house prior to their forthcoming marriage. Once again, the advantage of knowing the right people was emphasised, for one word from Juana and we had a prime mooring on the quay, whilst newcomers were being turned away.

On this our latest trip, being turned away on our arrival would have been an advantage, for had we not obtained a mooring, we would have moved on to find a safe anchorage, returning to Ciudadela at the end of our Menorcian cruise. However, we moored in the centre of the crowded quay and the day was spent meandering around the town and then people-watching whilst having a beer at a strategic outside bar. In the evening after drinks, we all ambled to a nearby restaurant and had dinner at a quayside table; by eleven thirty, with the heat of the day only marginally cooled, we sat chatting and drinking coffee.

The strange thing about being a skipper is that part of your mind never stops working on any information that may have relevance to the safety of your vessel. It's totally automatic but doesn't seem to apply in such depth if you're on someone else's vessel.

I was in mid sentence when my antenna picked up the warning signal: out of the corner of my eye I had seen a floating coke can travel past at about 5 or 6 knots, yet there wasn't a breath of wind.

'We've got trouble.' My remark was made to no one in particular, as I left my seat at a run.

By the time I reached *Blue Skye C*, the gangplank was half a metre above the quay and rising. I jumped onto the gangplank and raced along the aft deck, whilst searching my pockets for the wheelhouse door key. I had read about this particular phenomenon in the pilot when we'd first visited Ciudadela, but two years later it had passed to the back of my mind.

The phenomenon is known locally as the *Rescarca* and it occurs under certain Mediterranean meteorological conditions, a high pressure in one area and a deep depression in another. When these specific conditions come together, the most likely time being a late summer evening, the outcome is that a sudden rise in the sea level forces an influx of water to shoot along the narrow three-quarter-mile entrance to the harbour, raising the sea level in the inner harbour by several inches or several feet. The date, time or severity of the *Rescarca* cannot be predicted. The water maintains its increased level for about two minutes and then the whole lot rushes out again.

Reassuringly, the pilot informs that local fishermen often give warning of this phenomenon; it doesn't, however, specify whom they give the warning to. Another slightly misleading statement made in the pilot is that during this phenomenon, the water level can rise and fall by 1·5m which I surmised meant that having risen by 1·5m the water level will drop back to its original level; not so.

I knew that the safest place to aim for would be the centre of the harbour, away from all the other vessels and I desperately hoped that *Blue Skye C*'s engines would, as usual, fire first time; they did at the first push of her starter buttons.

When I rushed back onto the aft deck to untie our stern lines, I was surprised to see Paul on deck and John pulling Jean on board from the dingy into which Jean had jumped; the gangplank was now too high above the quay to be reached. The yacht on the next mooring was already scraping its rudder on top of the quay, where waiters were rushing to save their floating tables and chairs.

I gunned the engines and *Blue Skye C* accelerated away from the chaos of the crowded moorings. The speeding current pushed us rapidly towards the end of the harbour, but our anchor held good and we lay perfectly centralised at the end of a bar-tight chain.

There was a lull whilst we waited and wondered what would happen next. Then we began moving at a rapidly increasing speed, swooping in an arc, like a swinging watch on the end of its chain. I held the anchor windlass switch down, desperately trying to shorten the anchor chain before our stern wiped out the half-dozen fibreglass yachts lying directly in our path. Our dinghy, hanging from the stern davits, bounced off a couple yacht pulpits before we cleared danger.

Having swung through 180 degrees back into the middle of the harbour, we were held once again by a bar-tight anchor chain; we stared in astonishment as the water level carried on falling. An 18m yacht moored at the ferry quay suddenly keeled over, lying on its side on the harbour floor, its mast and rigging tangled with a similarly beached vessel; it was as though someone had pulled the plug out of the seabed.

All around us boats were grounded, jumbled and damaged, whilst *Blue Skye C* floated in the centre of the harbour on a tiny lake; the only stretch of water left that was deep enough to float on without touching the bottom.

Waiting for the inevitable return of water was nerve-racking, but only for a minute. Then back it came, noiseless and waveless; speeding water like a fast-flowing river. This time I was ready for it and by juggling the power between the port and starboard engines I was able to exercise some degree of control as we were once again swung through 180 degrees.

Finally, everything calmed down and when the water appeared to have settled back to its normal level, I lined up to go astern into our mooring.

Janet, Robert, Sue and Sally were waiting on the quay for our return, along with two harbour officials, whose gesticulations were clearly not part of a welcome ritual. They wouldn't accept our stern lines and insisted that we were too big to moor there in such conditions.

The night was as black as the ace of spades and outside the harbour, big seas were running. Seeking a safe anchorage along an unfamiliar coastline in the dark and in such conditions wasn't a safe option. So John collected the shore party in the dinghy and we prepared to spend the night at anchor in the middle of the harbour.

International law decrees that ships can seek shelter in any port from the danger of storm-swept seas. I explained this point of law to the port captain, who had just instructed me from an official looking craft, to leave port immediately.

'If Rescarca come back, your ship cause damage, you leave.' It wasn't a request.

'No, I've just explained, you can't send me out into dangerous conditions. I'm staying here and that's final.' I glowered stubbornly down at him.

'Seas not too big for your boat, you go now.' He was sounding impatient.

'Look, I'm not going to argue any more. I'm not taking this vessel out of the harbour tonight.' If I refused to move, what could he do?

'You not move I call gunboat from Mahon, we pull you out of Ciudadela.'

Oh yes, I thought, that would do it; I decided to leave.

John operated *Blue Skye C*'s powerful searchlight, swinging it from side to side as I gingerly navigated the narrow channel from the harbour to the open sea. With the sea running east to west, I chose to return to Mallorca and set a course for Pollensa. Janet enjoyed the passage back, as surfing down the waves of a following sea was a *Blue Skye C* speciality.

Surfing wasn't to everyone's liking; Paul in particular who, having chosen to sit in the aft deck dining area rather than go below to his cabin, uneasily entered the wheelhouse, wondering what was causing the white flashes in the sky behind us.

I attempted to calm him by explaining that it wasn't some dangerous meteorological phenomenon lighting the night sky, it was merely the beam of our stern light reflected from the white crests of the waves that were above us when we were in the bottom of a trough. They say everyone is happier when they have all the facts, but Paul didn't seem overjoyed to me.

As mentioned previously, the Puerto Portals Marina had only recently opened when we chose it as our base and there were no details of it listed in our Islas Baleares East Spain pilot. All the shops and restaurants had been offered a year free of rents, to enable the marina to be up and running as quickly as possible. Consequently, the end of the first year saw several shops and restaurants closing down, but these were quickly reopened by new and more competent businesses.

Meanwhile, all the larger moorings had been taken and there was an ever-growing waiting list of owners keen to base their ships in Mallorca's prime in-vogue marina. Of course, there was always a berth available for the King of Spain's ship *Fortuna*; with such clientele, port charges could be increased yearly without the fear of a mass exodus.

Blue Sky C was probably the oldest boat – and in my opinion the most beautiful – berthed in the prime mooring area of jetties one and two, and when all boats were in their allotted berths, the manoeuvring space between appeared alarmingly short of elbow room. *Blue Skye C* was easier to manoeuvre than some of the lighter semi-displacement vessels and handling her was now second nature to me. I could gauge to the foot when leaving or returning to our mooring, whatever the wind conditions. It was therefore satisfying to note that neighbouring skippers didn't pay much attention when we left or re-entered port, whilst the mere suggestion that some vessels were about to enter or leave was the catalyst for the decks of neighbouring boats to be crammed with fender-bearing crew and guests.

I had never forgotten the adage "slowly, slowly catch a monkey". Neither did I ever attempt to make a bad line-up into a good one; if I got my line-up wrong then I aborted and started all over again. I could live with a small error, but not with the nightmare of being responsible for the type of almighty cock-ups that some skippers regularly created for themselves.

Every boat reacts slightly differently to instructions, such as the delay factor between the changes from ahead to astern, the level of engine revs required to get the vessel in motion and how fast the bow will move in a beam wind; never a problem if there's room to spare, but critical in restricted situations.

Displacement vessels – which means that their hulls displace the vessel's total dead weight of seawater – such as *Blue Skye C*, which moves through the water at a maximum of 12 knots, aren't pushed around by the wind as easily as her semi-displacement fibreglass neighbours. A semi-displacement vessel will rise slightly out of the water when approaching cruising speed and will then plane at high speed, but in harbour, under slow revs with a lively wind, it may handle like a pig; albeit a very light plastic one.

Being the skipper of a very large and expensive motor yacht with a dozen crew or more must be heady stuff, particularly so if the skipper lacks in years. Older skippers are aware of the dangers that await those who believe they have all the answers, particularly if they haven't yet been asked enough questions.

Consequently, much entertainment was provided by some of the more arrogant skippers. It's true that arrogant captains aren't the only ones prone to making mistakes; it's just that everyone enjoys it more when they do. Some foul-ups weren't so funny at all, dangerous in fact, but others could be either embarrassing or funny, depending on whether or not you were personally involved. You would think that being lampooned for an amateurish cock-up would ensure that the error would never be repeated, but some skippers never learned.

The captain and crew of a large 26m semi-displacement gin palace had started preparations on Saturday for their Sunday day trip; the owner sparing no expense as crates of champagne and food for thirty guests was taken on board. The sun shone from the usual cloudless sky as the champagne breakfast was served on the top deck, following which the guests lounged on recliners or stood around in groups chatting and drinking more champagne. The noisy revelry, combined with the state-of-the-art built-in sound system on maximum volume, ensured that they had the attention of all the neighbours. By the mid-morning departure time, grockles and boat owners from other quays had swelled the numbers of interested spectators.

The young skipper, now on the fly bridge deck, was the centre of attention; ladies young and old were greatly impressed by his clean-cut handsome profile as he issued orders into the microphone of his headset communications system. His similarly equipped crew were poised to leap into action on receipt of any instruction.

The aft lines were thrown ashore, bowlines were dropped and the monster eased away from the quay out into the manoeuvring area. The ship began turning, port prop full ahead and starboard prop full astern, confused water foamed and the guests applauded, laughed and cheered in equal measure.

'Don't go back any further,' I involuntarily urged, seconds before the awful screeching sound announced that one of the props was well and truly snarled by the bowline of the ship two berths away from *Blue Skye C.*

'Don't try to break free,' I further urged as the skipper gunned the engines in an effort to get free – oh dear.

The skipper, his headset now discarded, was shouting orders at his crew; this was no time for quietly spoken instruction, but further communication was pointless, they were going nowhere. They would be tethered until the port divers had finished cutting them free.

The guests took it well, the champagne kept coming and those who had been slightly apprehensive of going out to sea were positively bubbling; for they were probably much happier being held by the stern in port, than they would have been if anchored by the bow in a bay. They were of course in a minority; being surrounded by smirking spectators wasn't to everyone's liking.

They were set free at about 3.00 p.m. and gamely set forth out of port with the skipper helming from the inner wheelhouse; the open bridge deck had lost its appeal.

Once again neighbouring skippers and some owners had tagged Jean as Aunty Jean; they often called in for coffee and at times to offload their problems. I'm not sure why they thought that telling us would ease their problems, maybe they thought that as we had worked for the same owner for so many years – twelve months is gold watch time in this business – that we were exceptionally wise and knowledgeable.

Quite often their problems turned out to be dissatisfaction with their captains and crew or the live-aboard girlfriend was creating more problems than they needed. Somehow, it didn't seem right; if we were smart enough to offer advice to multimillionaires, how come we were washing decks?

Chapter Twenty

Blue Skye C is sold. Should we build a villa? Just six months on another boat.

Mrs Hubbard wasn't enjoying the best of health, which meant that GA was not arranging as many sailing breaks. During this period he appeared to be quite unsettled and he began looking at Mallorcian estates; he fancied converting one into a hotel. He told us that Megan could manage the restaurant and Jean and I could run the hotel; he never actually enquired what we all thought about the idea.

However, the most alarming proposition he considered was the one I dreaded; namely that we should return to Greece.

'You see, Mother liked it best when we were sailing in Greece.' He said it almost apologetically, as if he'd been unkind to her by leaving.

The fact was that she did indeed prefer to be in Greece, or more specifically Rhodes, in preference to Puerto Portals; but as a place to stay rather than a base to sail from. To GA, Mandraki Harbour was a springboard to island cruising, to Mother it was a gangplank to trinket shops, bazaars and market stalls. GA was of course fully aware of the reasons for Mother's preferences, but I liked his loyalty in keeping such information to himself.

GA's unsettled demeanour had a knock-on effect on Jean and me and suddenly we were considering our future, a subject that hadn't been uppermost in our minds for several years. Back in the UK "recession" was the buzzword; it was not the right time for a move back home.

Why not, thought I, buy a house in Mallorca that would give us somewhere to live if and when GA decided to sell *Blue Skye C.* I went one step further: why not, thought I, buy a piece of land and have a villa built – that way we would get a better house for less money. I've said it before: sometimes I can be a complete plonker.

Jean wasn't quite as sure as I was on the latest idea, but she agreed to it on the proviso that we could find the right piece of land. I had really warmed to the idea; the fact that £1.00 was now only worth 185 pesetas did nothing to dampen my enthusiasm. I asked Megan to find us a piece of land and Megan, being Megan, wasted no time in finding one: I think I was pleased.

GA offered to let me buy *Blue Skye C* with a view to running it as a charter boat. At that time, skippers were being encouraged to take charters in the periods that their owners weren't using their boats. This suited the agents because firstly it increased the range of charter options and secondly they could make more profit on vessels that weren't charter registered. This was a practice equivalent to paying back pocket cash to non-tax-paying builders.

I asked some of the skippers doing such charter work how they got away with not paying the relevant tax to the Spanish authorities. They assured me that the authorities could never prove that they were chartering. I considered this approach to be somewhat simplistic, for in my experience the authorities in Mediterranean countries didn't put proof of innocence high on their list of priorities. Plenty of time for you to prove your innocence after the fine has been paid.

I really didn't want to become a Spanish taxpayer and I was too much of a pessimist to risk illegal chartering, and whilst the prospect of owning *Blue Skye C* appealed, I chickened out. Although I had gone through the process of considering all the alternatives, the "hope to get away with it" option was never on the cards. With my record of success with officialdom, I stood a better chance of receiving a Spanish early retirement pension.

About nine months later, virtually every marina in Mallorca had two or three non-registered charter boats chained to the quayside. Proof or no proof, such boats were going nowhere. Hopefully, the owners had already received sufficient charter fees to cover the cost of paying their fines; guilty or innocent, each vessel would remain chained to its bollards until its fine was paid. Most owners would no doubt be rich enough not to have to worry about such little inconveniences; I on the other hand would have been a very unhappy bunny. Being a pessimist can sometimes work in one's favour.

It was a sad day for us when *Blue Skye C* was sold, for it had been home to us for six very happy years. We had enjoyed a good relationship with GA, his family and all his guests, and some of the friendships made during that period have proved to be long-standing.

Our children and their spouses had good memories of times spent on board *Blue Skye C*. Stuart and Amanda even elected to spend their honeymoon on the boat and would have done so, had Pat and Judy Betts not offered their apartment overlooking Puerto Portals Marina as a honeymoon suite. On reflection, Stuart admitted that he might have appeared a tad sad, had he spent his honeymoon with his mum and dad. The rhyme was unintentional.

We continued to meet with GA from time to time and we spent a few days with him at Worlingworth Hall several months after the death of Mrs Hubbard. His general demeanour appeared to be as buoyant as ever and his passion for horse racing was undiminished, but there was a difference. GA was always the dominant one, Mother was the follower, but I'm sure that her influence on him was greater than many would recognise; like an anchor, never seen but holding firm when required.

For Jean and me it was the end of a memorable era, but as the saying goes: "as one door closes another one slams." We agreed to carry on looking after *Blue Skye C*, ensuring that she looked her best for prospective purchasers. There was the usual mixture of genuinely interested viewers and the pain-in-the-butt tyre-kickers. However, a genuinely interested viewer was one Tony Rush, who clearly had the money, but he was no Geoff Hubbard: few boat owners were.

Eventually, he decided against buying *Blue Skye C* in favour of a much newer boat moored on quay one. I was quite pleased, because he clearly didn't recognise the deep pleasure and heart-warming satisfaction that the ownership of such a classic craft as *Blue Skye C* would engender. Surprising really, for he lived in a listed building in Buckinghamshire, which suggested an appreciation of bygone classic design; the reality seemed to suggest otherwise.

The whole point of listed buildings is that the owner must ensure that all its historical features are preserved; however, Tony viewed things differently. His beautiful home had the original Queen post roof trusses in its structure; though, not as prevalent as the better known King post roof truss. To some historians, Queen post roof trusses bordered on the orgasmic.

Tony decided that the uneven roof, normally described by estate agents as quaint or rich in character, should be straight and level; so he had the roof rebuilt before the local council became aware of it. The story was related in a "the council can't tell me what I can and can't do with my own property" tone of voice: nuff said.

Missouri Star, the ship he subsequently bought, was originally designed as a 40m survey vessel but was eventually built as a private pleasure yacht, with an overall length of 23m. Inspection of the original drawings showed that basically 17m had been cut out of the middle. However, the specification remained virtually the same and much of the equipment designed for the original vessel must have been purchased before building commenced, for it had an enormous anchor winch, way and beyond the requirements of the much shorter vessel.

At the stern was an equally impressive hydraulic crane, designed to raise or lower buoys and survey equipment between deck and sea. Its main job now was to handle the two large fibreglass speed crafts, complete with huge outboard engines, and the small car stored on the top deck. Situated at the forward end of the top deck was a 3m curved funnel; as a 40m vessel it would probably have had presence, on a 23m vessel it was not a thing of beauty.

How anyone could choose such a boat in preference to *Blue Skye C* was beyond me, particularly as this top-heavy-looking craft was nearly a million pounds more expensive. Thank goodness I wouldn't be its skipper.

'Tony Rush has asked if you would skipper his boat,' the sales agent Derek Fowler announced as he walked up the gangway.

I admit to experiencing some surprise, for on the few meetings we'd had, I'd felt no affinity for him and Jean tells me that on such occasions my facial expressions can be read like an open book.

'Well, it's nice to be asked and please thank him for the offer, but I'm not looking for another job; I've got stacks of work to do on our new house in Arta.' The matter was closed.

Tony, however, wasn't the type of man who accepts a no for an answer when he wants a yes and he began dropping in to *Blue Skye C* at regular intervals, offering Jean and me the job of running his new boat. He never revealed his reason for wanting us to run his boat, but there was no doubt in my mind that his persistence was fuelled by our refusal of his offer; unacceptable for a man who seemed to put getting his own way at the top of his must-have list.

The news that our villa's completion date was going to be delayed prompted a change of heart with regard to Tony's job offer. After some discussion we agreed on a six-month contract. I felt sure that working for Tony Rush wouldn't be as fulfilling as working for Geoff Hubbard and in that respect I was spot on the mark.

I spent the first four months on refurbishment jobs, like pulling out all the hand pump toilets and replacing them with electric-driven models and altering cabin layouts, etc. However, it was the nasty smell in the owner's cabin, or rather getting rid of it, which proved to be the hardest job of all. Nasty boat smells invariably emanate from the bilges and this smell didn't buck the trend.

The propeller shafts ran through two bilge bulkheads below the master cabin and the compartments between were three quarters full of stinking seawater. I also found, to my alarm, several tons of lead ballast submerged below the black liquid. Proof, if any were needed, that this top-heavy vessel in adverse sea conditions would roll like a pig.

It took me three weeks of twelve-hour days to pump out the water, take out the lead billets and encapsulate them in resin before replacing them. The previous crew, all four of them, had lived on the boat for several years, presumably happy with the smell, so why couldn't I do the same for six months? I must be mad.

By the time we had returned from Calpe boatyard on mainland Spain and a mini cruise with Tony, his wife and friends, we only had six weeks left of our six-month contract. During the months of refurbishment work, Tony was a constant visitor, along with his wife Marsha – a very pretty and attractive woman and a very pleasant and considerate one. She clearly loved her husband and pamdered to his every whim, whilst Tony seemed to accept all such treatment as his right; I think that she had much to put up with.

On our return trip to Mallorca, I reminded Tony that we had only six weeks of our contract left and he appeared totally taken aback. He pointed out that I had agreed to skipper two fortnight cruises for his two sons and families. I agreed that I had, but had presumed that he would organise for his sons to take their holidays within our six-month contract. Both his sons worked for him, so timing wasn't a problem. There was never any doubt that I would honour my agreement, I just didn't want the six months to stretch into seven or eight, which seemed to be his goal.

I wasn't worried that he wouldn't pay for any extra time, for he had paid our six-month salary in full the moment we had started working for him. I have to say that I found him to be a man of his word and whilst at times he displayed a generous side to his nature, his oft sarcastic and derisory treatment of many – his friends and wife included – wasn't an endearing feature. I cannot claim to have been treated in such a manner, but to be in his company when he applied it to others never sat well with me.

The cruises we did with his sons proved to be very different. The eldest son Garry and his wife Sally and baby daughter Daisy were an absolute delight; it was as if we were on holiday with our own family. It was the most relaxing period we'd had since moving onto the boat. However, the youngest son Mark had much growing up to do. He and his wife Mandy arrived a day before their guests, another young couple whose names I feel shouldn't be recorded. They were employees who worked in one of the garage and car sales companies that Mark managed for his dad. They appeared to be an ill-matched group.

Whatever your holiday choice happens to be, the behaviour of other people can mar your enjoyment. In the boating world, that idyllic anchorage that you dreamt of all winter can change from a dream to a nightmare by the simple addition of a few water toys; particularly when those who drive the toys are bereft of any respect or consideration for the well-being of others. We had such water toys on board, along with two young men to drive them who were definitely lacking in respect or consideration for others. We had a jet bike – a sort of water motorbike – and a two-seated high-speed sports boat for towing skiers. No matter how many times I warned that they should keep clear of anchored boats and swimmers, the message never seemed to sink in.

On our journey from Soller to Pollensa, we anchored in the spectacular and beautiful bay of Cala de la Calobra. There was a collective sigh of relief from the crew and guests of other anchored boats, when we finally stowed the water sports toys and left them all in peace.

We had the same situation in Pollensa Bay, but telling Mark and his guest to keep away from moored boats and swimmers was a pointless exercise. Thankfully, there were no accidents, except the one when I forgot that the ski boat was still tied behind us whilst I manoeuvred the boat astern. Unfortunately, the damage was such that it couldn't be used again on that trip: Oh dear.

At long last the cruise was nearly over, just one day and night to go. I planned to go straight from Pollensa to Puerto Portals, but our two water sports enthusiasts wanted to call in to Calobra to do some more jet-skiing. I suggested that as they were flying home the next day, it may be better to get back to Portals, where their wives could go ashore should they wish, whilst they did their jet biking thing in Portals Bay. It was a busy area where boats rarely anchored, an ideal spot for them to buzz around and be a danger to no one except each other. Mark wasn't impressed with the plan, for he wanted to anchor in Calobra.

There was quite a strong swell coming from the north-west as we made our way along the northern coast at about 8 knots. The ship's stabilisers were just managing to keep us steady as I angled the bow diagonally across the deep troughs. The vessel, with its top-heavy sunbathing deck, also home for the new water sports toys, a motorbike and the crane, could really roll in such conditions if the helmsman didn't take precautions.

I asked Jean to ensure everything in the galley was stowed safely and then join me in the wheelhouse. Jean securely wedged herself into her seat and settled down with her book. We were 2 miles off Calobra, when I altered course slightly and put the boat broadside on to the swell; I reduced our speed a little and switched off the stabilisers.

The first roll was a big one, followed by another that was quite alarming. The screams from the top deck were masked a little by the sound of recliners sliding from port to starboard; Mark's trip from the sun deck down to the wheelhouse can't have been an easy one. Action Man looked a little pale as he fell through the door.

'What's happening?' There was an edge of concern in his voice.

I had adopted a casual position, one foot resting on the steering console, the other locked solidly around the base of the helmsman's chair. Jean looked up from her book as I half turned in surprise.

'Sorry?' I said enquiringly.

'The boat, what's happening to the boat?' Our low-key reaction was causing some uncertainty.

'Oh, you mean the rocking.' My ankle was nearly breaking with the pressure as the boat struggled to raise itself from a particularly severe roll.

'Beam sea,' I confirmed, 'often happens around this area.'

'Will it be like this in Calobra?' His grip on the handholds had turned his knuckles white; he was getting the hang of it.

'Well,' I said thoughtfully, 'the swell will run straight in there, of course,' then added reassuringly, 'but I don't think it'll be dangerous.'

'Well, what do you think? Should we go straight on to Portals?' A first. It almost sounded like a request for advice.

'I thought you wanted to do some jet biking in Calobra?' I asked in a concerned tone.

'Well I thought you said that we could do that in the bay at Portals; it would give the girls chance to go ashore.'

At last, he was learning. He went up several notches in my estimation.

'That seems a good idea,' I enthused. 'The other good point is that the swell often eases beyond Calobra; we'll keep our fingers crossed, shall we?'

After ten minutes I began easing the boat onto a more comfortable heading and finally I switched the stabilisers back on.

Mark and his entourage left bound for the UK. I can't say that I was sorry to see them leave, but I have to say that on that last evening and following morning, Mark displayed a more likeable disposition. I hoped that the improvement would continue. They went with our full blessing.

Chapter Twenty-one

Building a villa in Mallorca, how hard can that be? The signs that a builder is going bust are much the same in any country.

I was quite excited when Megan arrived to drive us over to view the piece of land that she had found for us. Jean's demeanour, however, leant more towards the apprehensive, for she wasn't fully convinced that building a home in Mallorca was the right move; it suggested too much permanency for her liking. She preferred the idea of an apartment somewhere, a dwelling that could be bought complete and sold quickly should the urge to return to the UK come upon us.

'What do you think?' I asked Jean as we took in the view.

'I love it,' she answered.

'We'll have it, Megan,' I confirmed.

We had been on site for all of ten minutes. Well, it's often said that your first impression is usually right.

To get there we had to thread our way through the narrow streets of Arta, a little town about 6 miles inland from the east coast resort of Cala Ratjada. Once through the maze of streets, there was a narrow, winding road that finished at a remote sanctuary known as L'Hermitage, home for a few brown-robed monks.

We had driven just over half a mile from Arta, along a narrow, winding road, before turning onto an unmade stony track. A couple of hundred yards further on, we turned left through a gap in a dry stone wall that was the boundary of a *finca* that went by the name of Na Cuberta, a Mallorcian phrase meaning the shelter.

At the top end of the L-shaped 1.4-acre field was a tumbledown stone ruin, which had once been a two-roomed peasant family home; likely shared, I am told, by a couple of sheep and a goat. Adjacent was a stone built Mallorcian oven, which had also fallen into disrepair.

We stood in front of the ruin and gazed down the field at the mass of almond trees covered in pink blossom; thick as the blossom was, we had apparently missed the best of it by three weeks. Over the tops of the almond trees we could see across the little valley to where the land rose steeply and sharply, towering above the town and showing off – like a scene from a Walt Disney film – the centuries-old yet well-preserved Arta Castle. Stunning was the only fitting description; we never had a visitor who wasn't captivated by the view.

Our decision to buy the land and build a villa on it was the start of a six-year period of joy, with a sprinkling of heartache thrown in for good measure. There is no doubt that we approached the whole venture with a degree of naivety which, considering the fact that I had spent nearly forty years in the building industry, suggests that I had been in the wrong job. If you were to ask me now what precautions should be taken when purchasing property abroad, my first response would be to ask how long have you got? Probably the best advice would be to buy several books on the subject and let scepticism be your watchword.

Actually, when embarking on house purchase or building project, most do's and don'ts apply whether you are abroad or at home, it's just that abroad they do things differently, you don't speak their language fluently and their workmen think you're thick.

I mentioned scepticism and large doses of it would probably prove to be a major weapon in your armoury. For instance, don't assume that just because there's a light fitting and a switch in a room, there must be an electricity-bearing cable between the two. If your dream house has taps, turn them on. Should you be lucky and witness water flowing into the basin, pull out the plug and check to see if your feet are getting wet. Treat anything you are told by your agent, notary, solicitor or builder with extreme caution and always insist that whatever you are told is confirmed in writing. Oh yes, I almost forgot, it's best if you are lucky.

We were delighted to read in the details that Na Cuberta had mains water and electricity. It could be argued that the description was a bit misleading in that the mains water supply was courtesy of a black plastic pipe draped along walls and field boundaries between the village and Na Cuberta. I tested it at eight in the morning and other than the low water pressure it seemed fine; I was to learn that by midday the pressure hadn't improved, but the water temperature was very close to boiling point.

I was pleased, however, to note that the pylons bearing the mains power line ran along our boundary and terminated at the entrance to our land. The new supply had been organised by our neighbour, whose villa was on the next field; after we bought the land we learned that we could be connected for just £15,000.

The opportunity to buy the land arose when Megan was doing business in an estate agent's office in Cala Ratjada. Whilst there, she overheard one of the agents talking about an exceptionally beautiful piece of land that they had just received instructions to sell on behalf of a young schoolteacher, Magdelena Bakaikoa Eskala. Magdelena and her boyfriend Jaime, an out of work trainee solicitor, had commenced building their own house and were surprised to learn that the completion of the foundation work more or less coincided with their realisation that they had run out of money. Or at least that was the official story, though I suspected after meeting Jaime that he found that he was no more suited to the building industry than he was to the legal profession.

Magdalena was born and bred in Arta and unlike many of her age group she could speak Mallorcian. It was her ties to the old guard of Arta that had enabled her to acquire this prime building plot, along with the advantage of what later proved to be a somewhat questionable mains water supply.

I'm not sure how all the locals viewed Magdalena's decision to sell up and move to the Canaries, but I can say that the owner of the surrounding land, who sold the plot to Magdelina, wasn't best pleased.

I touched earlier on the subject of tourism, which is a massive financial success in Mallorca, and the Mallorcians have embraced it in such a way that visitors to the island are made to feel welcome by all, traders and officials alike. But – there is of course always a "but".

Mallorca has a population of about 300,000, which is massively outnumbered by tourists week by week throughout the majority of the year. With the prime aim of increasing the number of visitors each year, the authorities allowed more and more, bigger and bigger hotels to be built; along with more marinas and golf courses. Naturally, a proportion of the increasing number of tourists fell in love with the place, so much so that they didn't want to be tourists any more: they wanted to be residents, they wanted to own a piece of the island. Not a trend that the average Mallorcian particularly wished to encourage.

The Mallorcians, being like any other nationals – I use the word advisedly, for many see themselves as Mallorcians rather than Spaniards – want the best of both worlds; rather like most of us really. So I found the agent, the architect, builder, solicitor, notary, bread-shop lady and anyone else who benefited financially from our presence, very helpful and friendly. All others were guarded but willing to wait and see how we turned out. The exception was the farmer who had sold the land to Magdalena, who oozed resentment. He appeared to be related to about 10 per cent of the locals and could call in to most of the town hall departments for a cup of coffee; an unfair advantage that he utilised to the full.

I had presumed that by buying a piece of land on which development had already commenced, all the formalities would have been completed. Not so, for curiously Magdalena must have been exempt from the abundance of documentation that the town hall now demanded from us.

Demands for the sight of a host of certificates and permits were received on a near weekly basis from the Ajuntament D'Arta, a town hall with attitude; my resentful neighbour was pulling a few strings. Acquiring these extra permits and certificates wasn't easy, for they turned out to be outdated requirements pertaining to old local laws, which generally no longer applied. The demand that I submit each permit or certificate for scrutiny required me to visit obscure departments in numerous office buildings situated in Manacor and Palma. Having located the relevant office, the officials rarely gave the newly acquired document more than a perfunctory glance.

I wasn't happy to learn that the now departed Magdalena and Jaime had neither paid the architect nor their last two mortgage repayments and now that we owned the land, we apparently owned the debts. Back in the UK, I would have laughed at such a claim; here in Mallorca the joke was not belly-laugh material.

The Spanish have a house-purchasing system passed down through the ages, which seems to require a degree of eye closing by the authorities. The practice was devised to minimise the annual property tax assessment, the calculation being based on the overall property value. The procedure was simple: the Spaniards had two property values. The first was the original value on which the annual property tax was based. The second was the sales value, which included property improvements and the year on year inflation price rise. The vendor and purchaser would meet in the solicitor's office and would complete the sale officially at the lower value and then the solicitor would vacate the office and the purchaser would hand over the cash difference unrecorded. The exchange was always in cash, for the transaction had to be non-traceable.

Throughout the years of low inflation and stagnant property prices prior to the influx of foreign purchasers, such a system wouldn't have unduly alarmed the tax authority on the small island of Mallorca, for the majority of the locals rarely bought and sold property. Dwellings tended to be passed down through the family and more often than not grandparents plus their children and their grandchildren lived in the same house; probably one of the main reasons that the strong family unit is still prevalent in Mallorca. It would be a brave administration that sought to alter this age-old practice.

However, when the British, Germans and the Danes began buying older properties from the Mallorcians and refurbishing them, it became a multimillion-pound market and the taxman felt that it was time that he got his share of the spoils. There followed a period of confusion, during which time a variety of initiatives were introduced, aimed at securing a capital gains tax from foreigners when selling their properties.

I learned that the financially acute circumvented the tax by purchasing property through an offshore company. The property then became an asset of the company and the purchaser was the beneficiary. The company, registered in say Gibraltar or the Channel Islands, could be sold as often as required without attracting a tax on capital gains, because the recorded owner, to wit the company, never altered. That seemed a good idea to me, so I sold Na Cuberta to Dovetail Properties Ltd – an offshore company I had purchased in Gibraltar for £900.

Clearly, my astute financial manoeuvring shocked the Spanish authorities into action and they introduced a new law. They decreed that any offshore company holding Spanish property assets had to declare the identity of the beneficial owner, who would be liable to pay Spanish capital gains tax and any other taxes on the property held by the company.

I received a letter from Gibraltar confirming that talks were being held with Spanish government representatives, as it was felt that their new law took scant account of international law. They held high hopes that the matter could be resolved in time, so they were prepared to reduce my annual charges until the matter was settled. This was all too tenuous for me, so I bought Na Cuberta back again, I paid taxes and solicitors' fees for the third time, plus the Dovetail Properties Ltd. liquidation costs; I never claimed to be a financial genius.

In the meantime, building was progressing, but was not without its problems I might add. The agent had chosen the builder because he had provided a professional quotation backed by an impressive-looking bill of quantities. I'd expressed concern that the bill of quantities didn't include foundation materials and was assured that they weren't required, as the existing foundations were perfectly adequate. I requested written confirmation that the architect's engineer was in full agreement.

We had our first site meeting attended by the architect, engineer, builder, agent and me; there were two others whose identity was never revealed – they weren't introduced and they didn't enlighten us in any way. I sensed that everyone thought that the extra two were with someone else; indeed, they could well have been a couple of stray hiking tourists. Having marked out the exact swimming pool location I gathered the group together.

'It's important that you all understand that I don't want any of these almond trees to be removed or damaged.' I pointed towards the three trees nearest to where the pool excavation would be.

They all looked blank except the builder – a short, stocky man whose permanent ear-to-ear grin never slipped; his name was Rafael.

The agency that I was using had two partners: one who spoke Spanish, English and German and the one at the site meeting who spoke only Spanish and Mallorcian.

'*Es muy importante el arbol es no* ... er.' I pointed towards the trees and made tree-chopping gestures. Everyone nodded vigorously.

'*No problema, no problema,*' Rafael confirmed delightedly. He repeated the phrase several more times to the gathering, as if not chopping trees down was one of his specialities.

We all moved to the stone ruin, which I intended to restore myself. The walls formed a backing to what would be the rear courtyard. The ancient grapevine overgrowing the ruin was laden with the sweetest and juiciest grapes I have ever tasted. It was to be the centrepiece of the courtyard.

I spoke to the group. '*Es muy importante el vine es no* ...' I repeated the tree-chopping bit, to more nodding.

'*No problema, no problema.*' Rafael was getting quite exited; so far, he felt that he could achieve everything that the Englishman requested.

We moved to the side of a large pile of dressed building stone, which Magdalena had acquired from somewhere. I didn't want the builder using it and charging me for my own stone, best that everyone was aware that it belonged to me.

'La piedra es mio.' I pointed towards the stone and then prodded my chest. 'You understand ... er ... *usted entender*?'

'Ahh, si, si ,señor, no problema, no problema.' Nothing was further from the Rafael's mind; clearly, he would never dream of using my stone.

I repeated the process with four stacks of concrete walling blocks, four steel cages of roofing tiles, eight 5m lengths of 225mm x 50mm timber and a concrete mixer. All would be required when I set about the restoration of the old ruin.

There was much shrugging with heads held to one side, hurt almost that I should even suspect that such an honourable gathering could be anything less than scrupulous in ensuring that my materials remained safely mine.

There was another hour of pidgin Spanish and inventive sign language before I left the site quite cheered by the enthusiasm displayed by all involved with the project. Even the two suspected tourists seemed to be quite upbeat about the way things had gone.

Work on site was due to start in two days' time, but I resisted the urge to be there when it started and resolved to let a week go by before my next visit.

We could see tyre marks as we turned through the entrance to the site. I grinned at Jean as we got out of the car; there were a dozen workmen and a dog scurrying about, things were really happening.

There was so much going on that it took a while for us to assess the overall progress, but our attention was drawn to certain particulars. Huge trenches were being filled with concrete, where the concrete block foundations had been the previous week; one week into the project and extras claims would already be in the pipeline.

By the swimming pool excavation works, lay three almond trees, bulldozed out of the way, so that the digger driver wouldn't be too inconvenienced. We rushed over to the ruin, which had been converted into a cement store, the ancient vine removed to make way for the 5m lengths of 225mm x 50mm timbers that had been built into a concrete block wall extension to support a temporary roof. I looked in bewilderment at Jean, who was near to tears. She'd had great plans for displaying the vine.

'Buenos dias, señor y señora.' Rafael greeted us effusively as he climbed out of his car, his wide smile slipping when he sensed that all was not well.

'What the hell is all this?' I shouted with arms held out sideways at shoulder level. 'You're supposed to be a builder, not a bloody demolition expert.'

My Spanish was OK for shopping and passing the time of day, but it was totally inadequate in such a situation; you can never gain the ascendancy in a dispute with anything short of total fluency in the appropriate language.

Every man on site had grasped the fact that I was fed up and was concentrating very hard on his work, including the two youths who, with particular diligence, were backfilling a large hole with my dressed stone.

'Put that bloody stone back!' I yelled.

The youth preparing to throw a large stone into a hole nearly gave himself a hernia in his effort to hold it back at the last moment.

Rafael gave a superb performance as he stormed around the site berating everyone in turn. He kept the tirade going until he adjudged that I had grasped that he was in no way to blame for any of the things that had gone wrong. He came back shrugging and shaking his head. He spoke too rapidly for me to recognise more than the odd word, but the general drift was that unlike the old days, today's workmen could no longer be trusted.

We drove into Cala Ratjada and pointed out to our agent a few of his shortcomings. The commission that we had agreed to pay him for managing the building project on our behalf was renegotiated. His embarrassment was such that he agreed to terms that in normal circumstances he wouldn't have even considered.

Looking back it was probably my only victory, for in my dealings with Rafael, even when my will prevailed, I always suspected that I had been outmanoeuvred. Sign language is no substitute for dialogue.

My father had been extremely hard of hearing and by the time I was six or seven, he'd had to wear a hearing aid. It was a very sad day for me when I realised that deaf people were often viewed as not being too bright. The worst were the genuinely dim, who having amazingly grasped a very simple element of a group conversation, suddenly saw himself or herself as a deaf person's intellectual superior; there was never a realisation that they had access to much higher levels of information input. It therefore came as no great surprise when I recognised that many of the scruffy and grubby-looking peasant labourers witnessing my struggle to understand a point that the builder was making, viewed me as a much lower form of intelligence.

Good progress was made over the first two months – there were certainly no rain hold-ups and I was becoming quite upbeat about the prospect of an early completion. Though, my euphoria began to diminish in equal proportion to that of the diminishing workforce, for it didn't take long for the average of twelve operatives on site to be reduced to three men and the dog. A couple of weeks later I drove on site to find only one man; at least he had the decency to look embarrassed, for clearly neither of us could identify just what task he was supposed to be accomplishing.

Even more alarming was the fact that the decrease in manpower and progress wasn't matched by an appropriate reduction of the monthly invoice. After an icy conversation with the agent, he was persuaded to get the builder into his office for a hastily convened meeting.

'Why is the work stopping?' I asked Rafael via Lance.

The builder spoke avidly for several minutes.

'He says he's not sure what you mean,' Lance explained.

'No manpower,' I pointed out. 'Four months ago there were twelve men and a dog on site, today there's only one man and no dog, what's happened to the dog?' I was trying to keep things light.

I grasped my forehead as I recognised the word perro in the builder's explanation.

'He says the dog belongs to one of his labourers and is only on site when he is there,' Lance explained.

'Oh my God! Forget about the damn dog; that was meant as a joke. I want more men on site. There'd better be some progress next week or I won't be paying last month's bill. Tell him that,' I prompted.

It was the first thing I had said so far that Rafael had recognised as a possible *problema.*

'He says that there will be more men on site tomorrow and he hadn't realised that you were in such a hurry to move in,' Lance explained, then added, 'he says that there's no problem.'

It was now December and the villa was beginning to look impressive. All the almond trees were leafless and without the intervening foliage it was just possible to see part of the villa roof about three quarters of a mile distant from a bend in the L'Hermitage road.

Easier to spot was the tower, which you either liked or disliked; it wasn't small enough to ignore. We were never sure if the tower had been Magdelena and Jaime's idea or the architect's, but we were told that the tower had both aesthetic and practical attributes. It could be argued that our acceptance of it was down to the fear that resubmitting the planning application to omit the tower might jeopardise the whole project. It was a risk we weren't prepared to take, so we decided that the tower was actually impressive and gave the building presence.

The practical aspect of the tower was that not only would it provide a perfectly useless little room, but also, by housing a water tank in the top of it, the water pressure could now be constant and improved.

There are often stories in the press describing how people have been misled by builders and tradesmen carrying out construction work and just as often I have marvelled at the naivety displayed by many of the victims. So how could I, after all those years in the building industry, fail to acknowledge that the laws of physics don't alter from country to country; simple, I wanted it to be so.

I'd glimpsed the tower from the bend in the road as I'd left Arta. Excitedly, I'd turned into the drive and there it was: a 2·4m by 2·4 square tower, double the villa's height of floor to eaves, with three vertical 2·4m by 30cm windows to two elevations. It had a battlement touch about it and seemed to be guarding the arched entrance to the courtyard, very impressive if you like towers. So impressed was I that it was some time before I noticed the large square hole that had been excavated in what was to be the courtyard area – twenty minutes later I was in the agent's office.

'I'm glad you've called in.' Lance was all smiles. 'I have the complete set of working drawings that require your signature.'

'Do they show a large hole in the courtyard?' I asked with exaggerated politeness.

Lance was getting to know me by now and he slipped quickly into defensive mode. He took a pack of drawings from a glossy white folder and began opening each one.

'I'm not exactly sure,' he answered guardedly, 'what size hole are we talking about?'

'Well, didn't you see it on your last visit?' I asked with exaggerated concern.

'They must have excavated it yesterday.' Suggesting, yet not confirming, that he had been on site the day before. 'Ah, here it is.' He spread out one of the drawings triumphantly. 'It's for the *cisterna*.'

I studied drawing number eight entitled "*Cimentacion y Saneamiento Detalles*", which as some of you will know, translates into foundation and drainage details. I noted that the *cisterna* was an underground collection tank for all rainwater draining from the roof and would have a storage capacity of 17,000 litres, around 3,750 gallons; that's no small downpour.

'Look, Lance, I'm aware that as the water storage tank is on the drawing, it's been included in the builder's price, but it's a big, reinforced concrete tank set into a hole excavated in rock; we are not talking cheap here. Why didn't someone ask if I wanted it? Most of the villas I've seen don't even have gutters, let alone a drainage collection system.'

'It will save you a lot of money in the future,' Lance assured. 'Water is very expensive in Mallorca; incidentally, you'll find that rainwater is very soft and super for drinking.'

'I'm not sure I'd want to drink it after it's run down the roof and along the gutters and drains,' I answered dubiously.

'Oh, it's perfectly safe.' He was warming to the subject now for, unlike most of our meetings, he was pleased not to be on the back foot. 'All the houses on this side of the island collect rainwater; it's too precious to waste.' He clearly felt that he really had looked after my interests here.

'OK, OK, I see the point of not wasting water, but I ought to have been asked. It strikes me that it'll take many a year before we recoup the costs involved,' I grumbled. Then, as an afterthought, I asked, 'Incidentally, how do they get the water from the underground tank into the domestic system?' Alarm bells were beginning to ring in the back of my mind.

'Oh, it's a simple system: a small electric pump and a pressure cylinder. Turn on the tap and the water comes out under pressure. When the pressure in the cylinder drops the –'

'Electric pump boosts the pressure back up,' I interrupted. 'I understand all about water pressure systems, I repair one on board on a regular basis. What I don't understand is why, if we're going to have a water pressure system, do we need the bloody tower?' The silence was definitely pregnant.

It was of course my own fault. I knew when I tested the supply pipe that the water pressure wasn't strong enough to push water higher than about 1metre but when I was told that the pressure varied, it was nice to believe that they had it all under control. I blamed myself for not fully controlling the project, even though I wasn't supposed to; that's why I paid an agency, or at least would have paid had they performed. In the end, their fee was much reduced.

Lance, who was an American, was a charming man and really did try to be of assistance. He understood the northern European psyche and could sympathise when the ways of the Mallorcan building industry got to me. But Lance was the administrator and he ran the business element of the estate agency with a team of saleswomen.

Sergie was supposed to be the building expert; he was the Spanish director that all businesses in Spain at that time were legally obliged to have. There's many a useless Spaniard made a good living on the back of foreign businessmen, all owing to that little piece of Spanish legalistic protectionism. Sergie was such a one.

With 95 per cent of the agency's business coming from the Germans and the English, his ability to speak only Spanish and Mallorcian wasn't a massive business advantage. But then neither was his building expertise and his acting as the agent in charge of our project highlighted either his lack of ability or his lack of interest; though, I suspect a large dollop of both.

The end came, however, when, having berated the unfortunate builder for taking the four steel cages of roof tiles, he managed to convey to me that he wasn't the culprit and that Sergie was the guilty one. Sergie apparently had a little business that he ran in addition to his agency involvement; he bought and refurbished old properties. He clearly felt that as we were having new roof tiles, he somehow had a right to use our stock of old ones on his latest project.

Fortunately, Sergie wasn't in the office when I called and neither was Lance, so I left a fairly succinct message with the receptionist and fumed my way back to Puerto Portals. The tiles had been returned when I next visited Na Cuberta; I correctly assumed that Sergie wouldn't be seen on site again.

It was good to see all the plasterwork finished, for this was where the Mallorcian tradesmen excelled. Their stonework was a dream, but their brickwork and block-laying failed to impress; mercifully, irregular walls with undulating courses of bricks and blocks were transformed by plasterers, who achieved machine-like finishes with incredible speed.

However, it wasn't good to see water stains on the completed plasterwork in the main bedroom and bathroom, situated below the flat-roofed area that provided the access to the tower room.

'*Mass lluvia,*' Rafael explained, '*mass lluvia,*' he repeated, raising his hands and shaking his head sadly. I looked enquiringly at Julie.

Since the parting of the ways with Sergie, Lance had felt obliged to assist us at site meetings, by sending one of his staff to act as our interpreter. Julie was a stunner, with black hair and large dark eyes. Our relationship with the architect and the builder had improved noticeably since she began attending site meetings, for she had a tendency to wear the type of figure-revealing clothes not often seen on a building site.

'He says that there has been lots of rain,' Julie explained.

I was taken a little by surprise. I was, of course, aware that there had been some spectacular thunderstorms tracking over Mallorca the previous day, but I couldn't quite grasp the thrust of his reasoning.

'Is he seriously suggesting that we should expect the roof to leak whenever we have heavy rain?' I asked incredulously.

In answer to Julie's interpretation of my question, Rafael became quite animated and I identified the phrase *mass lluvia* on several occasions but little else.

'He says that flat roofs often leak in heavy rains and that his own office roof is leaking in many places. He's offered to take you and show you how much more his roof is leaking than yours.' Julie's facial expression registered her embarrassment as she repeated the builder's illogical argument.

'Tell him,' I fumed, 'that I don't give a tinker's damn how wet his office is, there's just no way that I can accept that my roof will always leak in heavy rain.' I couldn't believe that the builder could seriously proffer such an argument.

Julie stopped talking mid sentence when the architect interrupted. I was surprised to note that he looked decidedly agitated, an emotion he had never before displayed, but clearly something was upsetting him. Rafael was looking uncomfortable to the point that I could only assume that the architect was actually arguing on my side, which, considering the size of his interim bill, wasn't before time.

One of the few advantages in employing a Mallorcian architect – which I presume also applies in mainland Spain – is that payment to the architect is made via the College of Architects, who take a percentage of the architect's fee. Having already paid 50 per cent of the total fee to the Collegi Oficial D'Arquitectes De Balears, I was automatically protected by this august body should any of part of the building designed by the architect fail to correctly carry out its intended function.

Clearly, the architect had recognised flaws in the builder's argument that flat roofs are intended to leak in heavy rain conditions and I presumed that attempting to support such a theory before a committee of his peers wasn't on the cards. It took only a few testily spoken words from the architect to silence Rafael's rhetoric, which he followed with an affirmation to Julie that the flat roof would be made watertight without delay.

It was following this site meeting that we had to leave Mallorca for Calpe on mainland Spain. I wasn't happy with the way the building project was going and I couldn't wait to get back to check on everything. To say that on our return I was disappointed by the lack of progress was an understatement.

We wanted to move into Na Cuberta as soon as our six-month contract with Tony was completed and I began to apply more pressure on the builder, who on good days was Rafael and on bad days was Señor Corraliza; he was beginning to be addressed as señor on a regular basis.

Had we been in the UK, there is no way that we would have moved into a new house as incomplete as Na Cuberta was in June 1990, but I felt that unless we were on site permanently, the work would never be completed.

This belief was strengthened by the fact that Rafael was becoming increasingly more difficult to contact and I had noticed on the last two visits to his office in Arta that the usual staff of three had been reduced to one. When a British building company's normal procedures or a long-term employee is no longer in evidence, it's a fair bet that it's having cash-flow problems and I had no reason to suppose that it would be any different in Mallorca. I was unnerved when I recognised the familiar signs. The nightmare possibility that Rafael's company would go bust and his creditors would seize Na Cuberta filled me with alarm. The fact that we had paid for all the work completed to date would cut no ice; it would be like the young couple's mortgage payments, the debt would be sought from the easiest target: us. Rafael and I had another meeting.

Those of you with experience in the UK building industry will know of companies that have limped along for many years, staving off insolvency by juggling payments to suppliers; two months' credit taken here and three months' credit there. The whisper that "No Bricks Builders Ltd" is about to go belly up doesn't have to be true to persuade an edgy supplier to pull the plug and thus start the stampede by all suppliers. End of "NBB Ltd".

With this in mind, I made no reference about my fears to Lance or our solicitor Javiar De La Rossa; I just gave instructions to the both of them that we wanted to complete the contract and move into Na Cuberta. Both strongly advised against such a move. They argued that to do so would make it impossible to force the builder to complete any unfinished work.

To the amazement of both our agent and the solicitor, the builder acceded to a completion of contract agreement at a reduced contract price, reflecting the value of the work not completed. I didn't tell Lance or Javiar De La Rossa that Rafael and I had come to an agreement; he would complete all unfinished work for cash and there would be no invoices and no receipts.

We moved in and Rafael nearly finished everything before his company went bust four weeks later; it had been a close call.

Chapter Twenty-two

It's a dream house, pity about the electricity and don't mention the kitchen.

With a protective arm draped around Jean's shoulders, I surveyed the view from our terrace. A few hundred years ago monks had laboured in the sun to build Arta Castle. Since then, nature had taken its time to provide a setting for it that no artist could have bettered. This view was ours, the peace and tranquillity was ours and the unfinished villa was all ours.

My dream to leave Yorkshire to sail around the Mediterranean was over; done that now. Na Cuberta was the next project and our new dream: a dream house in dream surroundings, all set in sunny Mallorca.

The basic requirements for male dream-chasers are a supportive wife, an inability to recognise inherent dangers, a supportive wife, a blithe belief that should things go wrong it will all work out right in the end, and of course, a supportive wife. Unfortunately, my dreams always seem to take an incredible degree of hard work to achieve: basically because my dreams never fall within an affordable budget. I reiterate my theory that the belief that you can only truly enjoy something if you've had to work hard to get it, is complete tosh. When I was a teenager, a pal of mine was deliriously happy pulling the birds, courtesy of the MG sports car his dad had bought for him. The knowledge that his car had been easily come by, didn't appear in any way to reduce his state of euphoria.

Back to the view from the terrace: it was perfect, with the exception of the immediate foreground. The house and swimming pool looked, not surprisingly, as if a bankrupt builder had left them on an unfinished building site.

We had purchased what would eventually be a superb property. All that was required was a few more finishing touches, such as fitting out the kitchen, installing an electricity supply, moving about 100 or more tons of rubble, rock and clay, and laying approximately 250 square metres of stone paving; the latter would enable us to reach the pool for a swim without the aid of strong boots. I dare not even think about the ancillary list of jobs, such as repairing boundary walls, fitting gates, landscaping/gardening, surfacing the drive and renovating the old *finca*.

A couple of sheets of A4 paper were required to list – in small script – the jobs required to turn the empty building into a home; a list that didn't include the estimated cost of furnishing Na Cuberta. Reading the various lists appeared to induce in me a form of breathing difficulty of a nature usually allied to panic attacks. The question I used to agonise over was popping up again: have we done the right thing?

Had we been in the UK, the situation would have appeared grim, but with the sun never failing to arrive first thing in the morning and refusing to leave until late evening, our plight wasn't unbearable.

The large room that was to be our kitchen was beautifully tiled and that was it, so we had to barbecue every evening as the sun went down. The midday heat persuaded us to take leisurely lunches; I'm rather partial to those huge, misshapen Mediterranean tomatoes smothered in Jean's French dressing and accompanied with fresh crusty bread. Not all was perfect, however, for without a refrigerator, chilling the Chardonnay was a problem.

Wonderful as it all was, it really wasn't as it should have been. I knew that it was going to take years rather than months to attain the Na Cuberta we envisaged, but during that period we wanted to enjoy, as near as possible, those amenities that we all take so much for granted in the UK.

When we ordered the kitchen, the showroom salesman assured us that there would be no problem delivering and fitting everything in mid June; why did it come as no surprise when they didn't arrive on the agreed starting date.

There were times when I viewed the Mallorcian laid-back, simplistic *mañana* approach as quaint; it smacked of bygone days before the time-costs-money era, computers and programmed deadlines. Stepping down from a hot pavement into the dark coolness of a little backstreet greengrocer's shop and having to wait while the shopkeeper enquires about the health of a customer's grandmother isn't a problem. Being left waiting whilst several customers and the shopkeeper discuss whatever happens to be the main community topic at the time isn't aggravating. You probably only want a bag of those large, misshapen but delicious tomatoes and a melon, but no rush, if you don't start lunch at 1.00 p.m., it's *no problema*.

I'm not sure why this should be, for when someone in front of me in a UK supermarket queue engages the checkout girl in conversation, it drives my blood pressure up to near boiling point. However, the Mallorcian environment is different and one can slip easily into their ways, an approach that I'm sure can extend one's life expectancy. Nonetheless, the appeal of this Mallorcian approach to life was all well and good when shopping for vegetables, but the pursuance of the bygone-day lifestyle is usually tempered with a strong dose of selectivity.

One was tempted to wonder if the failure of the Mallorcian service and commercial sectors to provide anything by or on a mutually agreed date applied only to foreigners; did the locals also suffer the same cavalier treatment? It wasn't as if times and dates didn't mean anything to the islanders; they have dozens of Saints' days to celebrate and never miss one of them. What's more, I find it hard to believe that even a peasant would arrive in town to sell his pig the day after market day.

I called the kitchen supplier – a misnomer if ever there was one – from our local telephone box.

'My name is Chappell, Na Cuberta, Arta.' Said slowly and naturally, of course, and loudly but very carefully and clearly enunciated. 'Your men didn't arrive yesterday to fit my kitchen as agreed, is there a problem?' It's extremely hot inside the telephone box, but I'm calm and relaxed.

'Que?'

'Oh shit.' I take a deep breath, 'Do you speak English?' Said perhaps a tad tetchily, but calm for all that.

'*No entiendo.*'

'Is there anyone there who does speak English?' I'm still calm.

I hasten to add, lest you think that it's unreasonable to expect kitchen suppliers in Mallorca to speak English, that the main thrust of this particular kitchen supplier's sales pitch was that their English-speaking staff made dealing with them a pleasurable experience for all English-speaking customers.

'No entiendo.'

'Cualquier habla Ingles alla?' This was my last shot; another "*no entiendo*" would put me out of the game.

The fifty peseta coins I had lined up in the chute exasperatingly punctuated the silence as they dropped eagerly into the hungry machine, whilst outside the box an unsympathetic queue was forming.

Countless hours spent in phone booths throughout the Mediterranean, whilst seeking connections to the UK, rendered me immune to all forms of body language utilised by those outside wanting to get in.

'I help you, yes?'

I breathed a sigh of relief. 'Ah, yes, my name is Chappell of Na Cuberta Art –'

'I not hear you very well, you want the kitchens or the bathrooms?'

I have to say that whilst I thought that I was bearing up well, I wasn't as calm as I had been.

'I want the kitchen department.' I may have been a tad curt there.

'Yes, we can build for you the kitchen. You come to see, is better for you to come to see.'

A deep breath, Alwyne, take a deep breath. The deep breath didn't appear to offer any significant relief.

'I have seen your kitchen displays. I have placed an order for kitchen units and equipment; your men should be here now fitting things. Where are they?' I was speaking loudly but not shouting.

'You ordered a kitchen?' He sounded incredulous. Clearly, ordering a kitchen from this supplier was no mean feat. 'When did you order, what is your name?'

'April, I ordered at the end of April, my name is Chappell.' At last we're getting somewhere.

'I have to know your name.'

'Oh, for god's sake ... my name is Chappell C.H.A.P.P.E.L.L.'

I was losing my cool and the sun was poaching me through the phone-booth glass. Sweat was dripping off my nose and my spectacles were trying to follow suit; my shirt and trousers were sticking to me, but I wasn't shouting.

'Don't shout at them,' Jean had warned.

I presumed the silence meant that the order book was being perused.

Palma was only 60 miles away, but the rate at which the coins were being devoured suggested that it was further. The last coin slid noisily yet effortlessly into the black box – my sweat-soaked hand tightened in exasperation, launching the handset like a squeezed cherry stone against the glass-sided booth. With one hand clutching my copy order form and one foot jamming the booth door open to improve ventilation, my balance was impaired to the point that only after the third lunge did I bring the wildly gyrating handset under some semblance of control. With the mouthpiece to my ear, hearing what was being said was not easy, I reversed the handset.

'... order book and with no order is no possible to 'elp you. Is best you order 'ere, you come 'ere to order, *si*?'

'What do you mean you have no order? I've paid a bloody deposit.' Now I was shouting.

The kitchen man could no longer hear me, the money had run out. Perhaps some of the Arta locals had heard me; the two gum-chewing youths at the head of the waiting queue certainly had. They no longer leant with faces pressed against the glass the booth; when I made my somewhat bad tempered exit, their body language lacked some of the earlier aggression.

The fresh-bread aroma permeating from the baker's wood-fired oven guided me to his shop, where his wife and daughter served hot, crusty bread wrapped in flimsy paper held by a clever twist. The wrapping looked good but rarely completed the journey home intact.

The baker's daughter was in her mid twenties and she seemed be totally unaware of the effect that she had upon all male bread purchasers. Certainly, my sons Ian and Stuart never saw the bread collecting detail as a tiresome task. However, following my fruitless telephone call to the kitchen supplier, Arta's many attractions were lost on me that day. My mood wasn't improved by the Mallorcian partiality for the siesta, which meant that the kitchen supplier couldn't be contacted again until late afternoon. Frustration had been no stranger to me during the building of Na Cuberta and over the next few years we were to become bosom pals.

Our original introduction to the kitchen supplier had been through Ann and Paddy, two of our friends who lived in Palma. Ann was fluent in Spanish and I felt that a call from her would be far more productive than anything I could achieve from a meeting, which would no doubt have degenerated into an ill-tempered confrontation.

Paddy described the scene in the kitchen showrooms when Ann laid into the manager; it seems he would have had an easier time with me. Paddy felt sympathy for the man whose welcoming smile had quickly turned into the expression of a hunted animal. She concluded her verbal attack on the unfortunate sales manager by confirming that the level of their future orders would fall considerably, were the details of their performance to become general knowledge amongst the ex-patriot community. Certainly, anything short of maximum effort to make good their woeful performance would warrant an airing in the island's English readers' newspaper *The Daily Bulletin.*

The kitchen units and equipment arrived in mid July. It was an unusual experience, for whilst the delivery was three weeks later than originally planned, the supply vehicle arrived exactly on the newly arranged date and time; not only that, but the fitters arrived as well. The two young clean-cut tradesmen worked non-stop throughout a siesta-less day. At around 6.00 p.m., they pronounced that they had finished and my inspection revealed that they had done an excellent job. Everything fitted perfectly, with the exception of the work surface; there wasn't one.

I drew their attention to this apparent oversight and made the point that the let-in sink unit and cooker top had nothing to be let into; furthermore, the lack of a work surface would almost certainly lead to the cutlery drawer becoming full of crumbs.

There can be no stronger argument against our politicians' quest to tie us ever closer to Europe than the fact that we don't, nor ever will, share with our European neighbours a similar sense of humour. It's not anything to do with a language problem, for both of the fitters could speak English very well. Indeed, one of the fitters spoke with fluency and I couldn't help thinking that his language skill was being wasted in his present job. It was he who had been told to explain to us that the marble worktop was to be ordered from a company in Arta and it was thought that it would be better for us to place our order directly with the supplier. The suggestion was proffered as an unselfish concession from the kitchen supplier and whilst I doubted the inferred benefit, I happily embraced the new arrangement, for it negated the possibility of having to make further phone calls to the company; a thought too painful to contemplate.

So we now had a kitchen of sorts: we had a refrigerator, an oven, a washing machine, an extractor fan and a kettle but no electricity. We had some beautiful kitchen units but no worktop; the sink unit and gas hob remained in their packaging. Other than having somewhere to store a packet of corn flakes, not a lot had changed. I would still need the blowtorch to make our morning coffee.

I'm not sure why two of Mallorca's largest suppliers of polished marble and granite were situated in Arta but it was certainly convenient.

We contacted the company recommended by the kitchen supplier and their representative arrived thee days later to take measurements.

His English was on a par with our Spanish; however, he was able to convey to us that the last thing we really wanted was a marble work surface and as for white marble, that was a definite no-no. Apparently, white marble sucks in stains like blotting paper; leave a cut tomato on white marble and you'll know exactly where you left it for evermore. Marble-quarry owners may well dispute such a claim and I have to say that I never noticed any stains on the white marble in our bath and shower rooms, but then again, we never left any cut tomatoes in there. I did wonder why the marble supplier didn't pass on this information to the kitchen supplier, who'd shown us the marble worktop samples in the first place.

Granite was the thing. Impervious to stains and hard wearing, it apparently looks as good in twenty years time as the day it's fitted.

'Right,' we said, 'granite it is; we'll have white, *granito blanco por favor*.'

He shook his head. 'No posibal *granito blanco*.'

He said he would show us some samples to choose from. He didn't return that day or the next. Why couldn't these people do what they said they'd do? It was five days later before a man arrived to remind us that we hadn't been to select the granite yet and did we know that they closed in four days time for the whole of August; we were in the showroom within ten minutes.

We chose our granite from a selection of beautiful samples, thanked the salesman for his good advice and requested confirmation of the fitting date.

'Setiembre quinto.'

For one awful moment I thought he'd said September the fifth, but I knew that I had misinterpreted. I turned to Jean.

'What's that in English?'

'September the fifth,' Jean gasped.

'*Si*, September five, no before.'

All our entreaties requesting a pre-August fitting were met with protruding bottom lip, upheld hands and shoulders shrugged to the ears, the classic Mediterranean body language used in circumstances that apparently can only be controlled by the Gods.

I told the salesman to forget the order, though not in those exact words, haughtily confirming that I would place our order elsewhere. He pointed out that I couldn't go elsewhere, because everyone in the building industry would be closed for August. I pointed out that as they had told us that the work could be carried out four days after the order and then waited five before telling us that they would be closed in three, I'd rather give the order to anyone else regardless of delay.

The second granite and marble supplier, which was nearer the centre of Arta, had a different feel to it; there was no shiny showroom with spotlights and glittering tiles, in fact, no showroom at all. I wandered into the workshop and spoke to a man who was attending to a very large machine which was dwarfed by the block of granite it was sawing through. He turned out to be the owner, the type who would rather be on the shop floor than in his office. He called one of the men working on a nearby workbench to attend to the big granite cutter whilst he spoke to me.

Yes, he had the type of granite we wanted and yes, they would be able to supply and fit the worktop we wanted and yes, it could be done in August, even though they were closing for a period. Apparently, everything was '*No problema.*' I'd heard such promises before, but it was the only one we had and even if we didn't see him again before September, it ensured that I wouldn't have to go back cap in hand to the supplier we felt had let us down.

The owner came himself to measure our kitchen a week later, but he wouldn't specify a fitting date. Surprisingly, it made me feel better, for it suggested that he didn't want to make a promise he couldn't keep. Lo and behold, he did what he said he would do; the worktop was fitted in August, albeit with only a few days to spare. The icing on the cake was that it was considerably cheaper than the other company's quotation. You may not be impressed, but it figures as one of my major victories.

Frustrations can be experienced on many levels and not having electricity weighs in at about eleven on a scale of one to ten. It's quite frustrating when the average temperature is 30°C and there is no electricity to make your gleaming new refrigerator go cold. There's nothing to stop you from storing your drink and perishables in there, but somehow it's not the same.

Lying back on your terrace recliner with a warm can of beer, surveying your new swimming pool full of water that is rich in dark green algae, doesn't quite do it. A supply of electricity to the pool's filtration system for several hours a day would keep the water sparklingly clear and inviting; we are talking big frustration here, huge even.

Another frustration was that our mains water supply pipe, the black plastic one that was draped along the top of drystone walls for most of its journey from the village, didn't really fulfil its intended function. The supply wasn't continuous, in that at times there wasn't a supply at all. In fact, the only feature that could be guaranteed was that when water did actually flow, the pressure would be weak and the water temperature would be extremely hot.

It would have taken most of the year to fill the swimming pool and underground storage tank with our mains water supply, so we had to have spring water delivered by tankers. Underneath our courtyard we had just short of 4,000 gallons of cool, crystal-clear water, but without electricity it wouldn't reach our taps and showerheads. The Chinese don't hold the patent on water torture.

I can assure those of you who think that we had been lax in our efforts to acquire an electricity supply, that more time and effort had been expended on this particular need than any other throughout the construction project.

The original sales details for the building plot had specified the availability of a mains electricity supply and we had fallen in love with the location before we were informed that the service came with a £15,000 price tag. Our neighbour had organised the initial supply two years earlier at a cost of £45,000. The arrangement was that he would receive reimbursement if and when other property owners wanted to connect in. We would be the third, so our share was £15,000, plus the cable costs on our land.

In addition to the connection charges, the cost of electricity on the island was well above UK rates, made worse by the falling exchange rate now at 180 pesetas to £1.00. I was beginning to view the service as the locals did, a luxury rather than a necessity, but it was different for the locals, for it's always easier to do without that which you have never had. For us, it was never an option; we had to have an electricity supply. Well, we were used to living with generators on board *Blue Skye C*, so why not carry on doing so.

My youngest son Stuart is an electronics engineer, so who better to check out the alternatives available for home-generated electricity. If you wish to succeed, you must learn the art of delegation.

Stuart came up with a Lincolnshire company called Matchpower, who were working on a project to provide complete electricity supply systems for farms or dwellings where mains services were only available at very high cost. I made contact. Several companies could supply the basic components for such systems, namely a generator, a battery bank and an inverter. The generator charges the batteries when it is supplying the high power demands of equipment such as cookers, heaters and washing machines. The batteries provide electricity for lighting, television and other low power equipment via the inverter; that is a device which changes battery DC current to mains AC current.

I presume that you are now bored with batteries and inverters but I know you will be impressed with Matchpower's microchip control unit, a clever device which manages the whole system and automatically switches from generator to inverter as demand requires. Provided that the generator could be sited or insulated so that it couldn't be heard, it would be just like mains power but cheaper.

I got on well with Graham Chapman, the company's owner, who, recognising a possible future market, made me an offer I couldn't refuse. He would purchase a large generator capable of providing more than the average household power requirements and he would then build up the system at the factory and test-run it. He would supply everything, with the exception of the generator, free of charge, including transport, shipping and installation.

My role was to pay for the generator and when the system was installed and running, I was to provide regular reports on its performance under day-to-day working conditions. Once the equipment was operating as a viable alternative power supply, I would be granted the sole agency rights for supplying the equipment to Mallorca and mainland Spain.

Architects and builders had their eyes on hundreds and hundreds of remote sites in Mallorca, on which exclusive villas could be constructed. They had the labour, they had the materials and best of all, they had large numbers of German and more than a few British prospective purchasers, who were all jostling each other to acquire a dream home in the sun. However, unlike the local Mallorcians, the one thing that all the newcomers would have in common was that they would never have experienced life without electricity and would certainly have no intention of trying it out.

The Spanish electricity supplier GESA didn't appear to be overly concerned that the power that they supplied fell well short of demand.

From time to time they increased their generating capacity, but it was never enough. It was a sort of self-regulating system, rather like a baker who views his empty shelves at the end of each day as proof that he has baked exactly the right number of loaves. GESA would probably make an effort for a new hotel complex or holiday village, but supplies to fancy villas off the beaten track? Well, maybe in a couple of years, but it'll cost.

Within two months of returning to Mallorca with photographs and specifications of Matchpower's system, several architects and agents were enthusiastically requesting further information. I was excited about the future possibilities, particularly when Lance suggested that his company was ideally suited for a partnership role in the venture.

All I needed was the prototype system installed and running. Hopefully, it wouldn't be long in coming, for Matchpower had been working on my project for some time now. On my latest visit to Graham's factory I had seen the system running under test conditions and we had discussed the delivery and installation programme; there seemed little doubt that everything would be ready on time.

Had someone asked my advice on planning a similar project, I would have pointed out, with the knowledgeable air of one who has seen it all before, that the very nature of design and development work puts timetable planning firmly into the imprecise science category. Hence, I was still sitting on my terrace with a warm beer, looking at my bright green swimming pool water. Well I wasn't about to buy a small generator to supply power to the refrigerator and the pool filtration system, was I; not when Graham's system was almost ready for delivery. In spite of our problems, we were enjoying life at Na Cuberta. How could you not enjoy barbecuing every day without ever having to consider alternative inclement weather plans?

Our immediate electricity problem was eased when a friend, fed up with being served warm beer on his visits, arrived with a 4-kilowatt generator in the back of his car and insisted that we borrow it until ours arrived. It took three days to get the pool water crystal clear, but the beer was ice-cold at the end of the first day; things were really looking up.

Ever since leaving the UK there was always a point in each year well before December 31st, when as far as Jean and I were concerned, the old year had ended. It was the time when every thought was funnelled into going home for Christmas. Nothing else was important, for we were going home to be with our family.

When we lived on board *Blue Skye C* my work plan was all about preparing the ship to be left unattended whilst we were in the UK. Whilst the countdown usually started at about the beginning of December, I often noticed that by mid November my favourite shirts had found their way onto Jean's "It's been washed and ironed and can't be used until the holidays" list. This year, however, the malaise hit us early, around about October. The non-arrival of the Matchpower system was of course the root cause. I had taken to ringing Matchpower on a weekly basis, but their estimated delivery period was always in the region of six weeks. Their assurances were giving me all the confidence that a creditor experiences on hearing the phrase "Your cheque's in the post". I pointed out to Graham that whilst his equipment was bound for Mallorca, his delivery estimates should not have a Mallorcian flavour.

I'd had everything prepared for some time now. The generator house, sunk into a rocky hillside about 80m down the drive, was built to roof height and was ready to be completed once the generator was craned into position. A separate housing for the management system, the inverter and battery banks was fully completed and the main cable trench was excavated; yet still no delivery-date confirmation.

November arrived – another six weeks and we'd be back in the UK; too late now for a pre-Christmas delivery. I notified a relieved Graham Chapman that delivery of the power system would have to be delayed until mid January. Now we could look forward positively, knowing that shortly after our return to Mallorca, we would at long last have an electricity supply.

Jean and I love Christmas; for some, Christmas is too commercialised and the whole thing lasts too long, but for us it was always way too short. Slimming and moderation aren't Christmas words; Christmas words are family, decorations, nuts, Thornton's toffee, fudge and chocolates. The size of turkey should be restricted only by oven size and the wine and spirits supply shouldn't be restricted at all.

Lynne, Stuart, Ian and families have carried on the tradition with relish. Having spent a fortnight with each family, all ensuring that the Christmas fare didn't fall below past standards, we journeyed back to the Mediterranean happily contented and considerably overweight. Mallorca's healthier-eating style plus plenty of hard labour would soon bring my belt buckle back into view.

I had of course visited Matchpower whilst I was in the UK. The equipment looked the business and the large, robust and gleaming generator was throbbing away with a steady powerful beat. It was coupled, via an assortment of multicoloured cables, to a white metal box the size of a washing machine. MICRO PROCESSOR was emblazoned in red above an impressive control panel sporting lots of buttons and an information window was flashing the message to anyone who hadn't already noticed: GENERATOR RUNNING.

More large cables were connected to a bank of large batteries set in hardwood boxes and on an adjoining bench a single light bulb was glowing. I admit that I would have preferred to see a more impressive end display; two light bulbs, perhaps.

'I thought it would all be packed and crated, Graham, it's due to be delivered in two weeks' time.' I knew as I spoke that the mid January delivery wasn't going to happen.

'E ... er ... well, we do have a few little problems to iron out yet. It's the software, you see. We're rewriting parts of the programme and then we'll have to test it.' He looked slightly uncomfortable, but only slightly, for the term laid-back was coined for Graham. 'We should be able ship it over towards the end of the month.'

'Come on, Graham, we need electricity. It's over a year ago since you told me it would take six months. Not only is it miserable for us, but the agents and architects I got fired-up months ago are rapidly losing their enthusiasm.'

The problem was that I knew that the delay wasn't caused by lack of effort and getting angry wouldn't speed up the process.

'It's nearly there, Alwyne, but I can't send it until it's working perfectly. I'm sure we'll be able to deliver by the end of January.'

Our plane lifted off from a cold, dark and dismal Manchester; two hours later we were descending the steps from our plane in bright sunshine. Mallorcian January afternoons in the foothills become chilly when the sun drops low in the sky, but the middle hours of most days are hot enough for sunbathing. Thus, the Yuccas had grown 3 inches in our absence, whilst the small weeds we had left were half a metre high and thickening.

Even with the weeds, it was nice to walk around our garden checking the growth of the plants, shrubs and trees we had planted the previous year. I would spend the next few days getting the garden back into shape, but first I would clean the swimming pool and remove the floating, presumed dead hedgehog and the two very lively frogs would have to go as well. The fact that there was only two of them suggested that they were either the same sex or they hadn't been in the pool for very long.

We had lost the November blues and were enjoying the January sunshine, whilst looking forward to having electricity at the touch of a button; not long to go now before the arrival of the generator system. We were still without a telephone, but apparently we had to show more patience, for our order had only been placed a mere twelve months earlier.

Back in the village phone booth I listened to Graham's apologies; the new software wasn't quite right, but they were working flat out and it would be ready any time now. Somehow, the knowledge that they were working flat out failed to lift my spirits; the more I thought about our situation the more depressed I became. It wasn't just that the generator hadn't arrived, it was more the fact that there was no positive information; it's the not knowing which really gets to you.

Optimism is commendable, but at times pragmatism is necessary. The process of arranging shipment couldn't proceed until the system was operating correctly, so how long, we wondered would it take from that point to seeing the delivery wagon arrive at Na Cuberta? It was comforting to hear Graham talk of delivery in four weeks, but logic suggested otherwise. It wasn't too difficult to recognise that there would be no delivery before March.

February started with a rainy and decidedly chilly spell and the nights were still long enough to depress. The assertion that candlelight is romantic had been exposed for the myth that it is and the little generator that I had bought – for we couldn't keep our friend's generator indefinitely – ran out of petrol every ninety minutes, or whenever the rain was at its heaviest.

When the generator was about to run out of petrol, those with keen hearing would recognise the sound of a labouring engine, but if you missed that warning, the dimming lights just prior to total blackout served as a useful guide. We had about five torches strategically placed about the villa, all bought from the local *Ferretaria,* an Aladdin's cave of a hardware store that specialised in fast-fading batteries. The name of the battery manufacturer wasn't a well-known one and was most certainly destined to remain so.

A torch fitted with a new Mallorcian battery could gain some reflected light from the white walls in the villa, it could even manage a pale yellow glow as I crossed the courtyard, but once inside the generator shed it seemed to lose all confidence. The shed interior was dark, even when the sun was at its highest; come the night, it was a black hole that would have sucked the light from a 1,000 watt bulb. Pouring petrol into the small fuel tank – thoughtlessly situated just below the smoking, hot exhaust pipe – was a hazardous undertaking; it was easier all round to go to bed early.

I can categorically confirm that modern-day candles are vastly inferior to the ones used in the pre-electricity era. Jean and I have had as many as six candles each on our bedside tables and found it necessary to be close enough to feel the heat in order to garner sufficient light for reading a book with average-sized print. Yet, I have seen with my own eyes in many a period film or television drama, a huge room suddenly bathed in light by the flickering flame of a single candle.

Envisage Charles Dickens writing away by candlelight – how many more wonderful books would he have written with the aid of an electric light bulb and a word processor? However, whereas Charles Dickens never knew what he was missing, Jean and I could think of nothing else; I have to admit that the whole electricity supply project was adversely affecting our lives.

Na Cuberta, like all Mallorcian houses, was built to keep out the heat and the floors had earthenware tiles to promote a cool feel throughout. It worked a treat in summer but regrettably it was equally successful in winter. However, we did have a large fireplace and a nightly roaring fire raised our flagging spirits. Retiring early to bed became the norm that not only saved fuel but also did wonders for the whites of our eyes.

The night silence was like a blanket and from around 9.00 p.m. to 4.00 a.m., the silence was only broken by the odd squawk from something small having its collar felt by something bigger. Come 4.00 a.m., long before sunrise, a local cockerel who seemed to have lost the plot began its dawn crowing, which kick-started the full-blown dawn chorus. The more vulnerable wildlife joined in enthusiastically, in the hope of persuading any lurking night predators that daylight was imminent.

We had been in bed for some two hours one night, when loud knocking on the door had my body out of bed before my brain confirmed why I was there. During the search for my torch in the inky blackness, I managed to knock it off the bedside table, along with all the candles and my clock.

The tiles were cold to my bare feet as I felt my way to the front door, cursing anyone inconsiderate enough to have come knocking on the door at this time of night. I heard Jean call from the bedroom.

'Don't shout at them.'

I flung open the door. 'Yes?' I said curtly.

'Hello.' The word was spoken from the darkness by one of two indistinguishable forms.

I peered suspiciously into the darkness, wishing I were wearing shoes and trousers rather than being barefooted and pyjama-clad.

'Aren't you going to invite us in after coming all this way to see you?' the voice enquired.

So ready was I to give short shrift for this rude intrusion that I had failed to recognise my own son's voice. Not so his mother; she had recognised it instantly. I have since pointed out that a "hello" heard from the security of a warm bed is not the same as one that comes out of the darkness from a large shape that could well be wielding a baseball bat.

We all kissed and hugged in the darkness. Oh for electricity, but then if we'd had it, Ian and Mary wouldn't have arrived unannounced in an effort to lift us out of our depression, which had been caused by not having it; if you see what I mean. We lit candles and talked; Ian and I had a few whiskeys or more. I was a happy man when I climbed into bed, just as the cockerel got his timing wrong yet again, but Ian and Mary's visit couldn't have been timed better.

A week later, having waved Ian and Mary off, I utilised the airport's modern payphone to contact Matchpower. Graham wasn't there and neither was anyone else who could give me any information on the progress of our power system. I drove into Cala Ratjada the following day and sent a fax to Matchpower cancelling the order; I'd had enough. A bog-standard generator with some muscle and manual ignition system was now top of my shopping list. Anything that would provide us with a half-decent supply of electricity within a foreseeable time span was in the frame.

I went back to the communications office the following day in the vain hope that there would be an acknowledgement of the order cancellation and was extremely surprised to find a two-page fax awaiting me. In short, the fax acknowledged the cancellation, but Graham confirmed that if I would stick with the order, he would have everything delivered within the next four weeks, after which he would come over personally and supervise the installation.

The fact that the generator, for which I had already shelled out £4,500, would have to be sold in the UK at a considerable discount, did have some bearing on my decision to reinstate the order. Of course, I didn't expect the power system to arrive in four weeks and in that respect I wasn't disappointed, but everything had been crated and was ready for shipping. The delay was caused because the bank of batteries that had been used in the power system's development work had been charged with acid and therefore required a totally different set of shipping documentation and insurance. Naturally, this fact wasn't discovered until the last minute and not unexpectedly, the processing of such documentation caused much head shaking and cheek sucking amongst those paid to process such documentation.

Nonetheless, in spite of all such obstacles, the equipment was shipped and it finally arrived in Mallorca, where it was stored in a customs shed, a building from which a burglar would face less difficulty in extracting goods than the rightful owners.

The timing was unfortunate; the talk of border-opening between common-market countries was causing much unrest amongst the Spanish customs personnel. To date, the bureaucrats hadn't confirmed whether or not border-opening would have any adverse effect on the customs services manning levels. Service, however, wasn't a subject that the customs officers were concentrating on at this time.

My heart jumped when I opened our mailbox in the post office and found copies of UK shipping documentation. I had been accustomed to receiving spares and equipment shipped from the UK when we lived on board *Blue Skye C* in Puerto Portals; goods usually arrived between three and five days after receipt of the documentation. The customs officer accompanying the load was only interested in seeing the ship's papers and the captain's passport and usually departed before the shouting started.

The shouting generally occurred because whilst the captain dealt with the customs officer, lorry drivers had a tendency to offload any crate too heavy to lift manually by the simple expedience of levering it straight off the back of their wagon. Rarely did this unloading method prove advantageous and most skippers had experienced the claim-form nightmare that followed such crude unloading practices. My worry that they might similarly damage our generator and equipment was needless, for only foreign yachts enjoying duty-free import concessions were able to benefit from the dubious advantage of a delivery service.

I tried ringing customs and shipping offices, but my limited Spanish invariably fell apart without the aid of sign language. I drove to Palma and spent two hours dodging giant forklift trucks as they sped around the docks shuffling containers. Everyone I spoke to either didn't know where the customs buildings were or didn't understand my questions. For some reason, they kept talking about the airport.

Finally, in a little portable office tucked behind some double-stacked containers, I found a young man who spoke English and he informed me that the customs depot for goods arriving by sea was next to the airport; silly me. A disinterested customs officer, looking mean in his green uniform, glanced at my paperwork and managed to convey that I was woefully short on the documentation front.

'You speak to your agent,' he instructed.

'I don't have one,' I confirmed.

He shrugged with upraised palms and eyebrows.

'You 'ave no agent, then you ave no err ...' He pointed at my paperwork.

'Where's the nearest agent's office? I'll go now.' As I gathered up my inadequate little pile of documents from his desk he glanced at his wristwatch.

'Is closed,' he casually informed me.

The next day I collected some Spanish documents from our post-box and called in to Lance's office with a translation request. Would you believe – a shipping agent had sent them. What's more to the point is that *my* shipping agent had sent them. Don't ask. How I acquired a shipping agent for the whole shipping process is a mystery to me, along with thousands of others.

The inherent safety of any agent's future is in keeping a system complicated, a safeguard designed to deter you from suspecting that you may be able to carry out the process yourself. The system can now be bucked in several industries where agencies now have to offer a real service to attract trade; there's still some way to go in the shipping industry.

When I was a child a decorator was called when a house needed to be painted. A kitchen cupboard required a joiner to fit it and nobody, but nobody, attempted to do their own plumbing or electrical work. Now that the DIY culture is well established, even those who can well afford to pay a tradesman often opt to do it themselves, so that they may experience a sense of achievement.

However whilst it seems unlikely that the professions will ever fall prey to the DIY culture, there are signs of a loosening up of the peripheries. Even the legal profession that has the advantage of being at the forefront of the rule-making system is being nibbled at the edges and many people now make their own will using packs bought off the shelf at newsagents.

When Jean's father died, the bank manager strongly advised me to engage a solicitor to carry out probate; so naturally I decided to do it myself. Perhaps it was the way he used the word engage, for had I required a bricklayer he would undoubtedly have suggested that I employ one. I followed the instructions in the probate booklet and the whole thing was done and dusted inside six weeks, which included the Christmas and New Year period. I even claimed and received payment of overpaid income tax in that same period.

I admit that had Jean's father not left his affairs in such good order the process would have taken longer. Nonetheless, rocket science it isn't and if I had engaged a solicitor, then the high cost would have had much more to do with the eye-watering hourly rate than the complexities of the process.

However, there was no avenue open to bypass the shipping-agency system and back to Palma I went, to meet the agent now representing my interests. It turned out that I was short on documentation and my agent couldn't provide the necessary paperwork without a copy of my passport; he also required a form, completed by my bank manager, confirming that my signature on the form was, indeed, mine. He also required a form from a notary confirming that Jean and I owned Na Cuberta and didn't owe money on it. Just for good measure, he required a copy of the *Escritura* – Spain's equivalent of a UK property deed; one for the villa and another for the land it was built on. All this hassle to collect my own bought and paid- for shipment. I read recently that it was possible to claim a variety of UK social benefits, armed only with a stolen driving licence. Clearly, the bureaucrats of our respective countries work to very different guidelines.

It was Friday and I wouldn't be able to furnish him with everything that he needed before the following Tuesday morning at best. By then, the power system would have been on the island for nearly two weeks; it was mega frustration.

I was back in the agent's office by mid morning Tuesday.

'When can I collect my property?' I emphasised the last two words.

'I'll ring you when the documents are ready for you to collect,' he promised.

'I don't have a phone; I'll ring you. Will they be ready tomorrow?' I asked hopefully.

He shrugged as if to say perhaps and shook his head suggesting no chance.

'I have to make transport arrangements, I need to know when I can collect,' I pleaded.

'I'll do what I can.' Said with a half shrug and lips turned down at the edges. I don't think that the word service is in a shipping agent's vocabulary.

I rang the next day and he thought that there was a chance that he would have all the relevant documents by Saturday morning, but if not, almost definitely on Monday. So at long last I had a definite maybe.

The local builders' merchant had a wagon with a hydraulic crane fitted and as I got on quite well with the owner – and spent a considerable sum on building materials each month – he agreed to let me hire the wagon and his driver for a day to collect the generator and crane it into the generator house.

We set off at 8.00 a.m. on Monday, collected the paperwork from the agent and duly presented them to a cheerless customs officer – the customs service entrance exam didn't award high marks for cheeriness – and it was forty minutes before he instructed us to take the wagon to the main shed doors and wait for the forklift truck.

The huge shed was empty, with the exception of a 2.5m x 1.2m x 1.5m very robust timber crate with a smaller battery-holding crate for company. The frame of the crate was set on 200mm x 50mm runners bolted to 125mm x 125mm bearers and was clad in 175mm x 25mm boards; the timber content alone must have been worth several hundred pounds.

Customs officials had removed six of the cladding boards, presumably to check the contents. I spotted the missing boards stacked neatly against a far wall. On my way to collect the boards I saw several empty offices through the windows of the inner wall and an area where three uniformed officers were chatting by a coffee-dispensing machine.

I heard a door slam as I carried the boards back to the wagon and then a shout and the sound of running feet; I sighed, for I knew what was coming next. The officer stopped in my path, but had to move sharply to avoid being struck by the boards that protruded over a metre from my shoulder. The timbers were heavy and I had no intention of stopping until I reached the lorry; the officer displayed officiousness, whilst my wagon driver shuffled uneasily from one foot to the other. The officer's darkening red face was set off well against the deep green of his uniform; he pointed back towards the wall; a wordless instruction to return the boards.

After months of waiting for electricity, our wait had been increased by what seemed to me to be an exceptionally nit-picking system and now, to add insult to injury, the customs men wanted to steal my timber.

I threw the pack of boards onto the wagon and then selected one of them that had my name clearly stencilled along it. The officer backed off a touch as I swung around with the heavy board in my hands. I jabbed a finger at my name stencilled on the timber and in my best Spanish proclaimed, '*Me llama,*' and jabbed the same finger at my chest.

That was my Spanish for the day; the remainder was delivered in English, cloaked in a Yorkshire accent that most foreigners have difficulty with, but in this instance it was understood clearly.

'This is my name.' My voice was steady but firm. 'This is my address.' I pointed at more stencilled letters; I think I was getting louder. I held the board aloft and shook it. 'This is my timber.' Yes, I was definitely shouting now as I pointed dramatically towards the crates in the centre of the shed. 'And those crates and what's in them also belong to me. Now stop pissing me about.'

A very large forklift truck, driven into the shed by a budding rally driver, broke the ensuing silence; ten minutes later, both crates were loaded onto our wagon and were securely roped down. The wagon driver jumped into the cab, eager to get going; no one bothered to wave us off.

The task of dismantling the crate took longer than the time needed to crane the generator into position. The crane lifted the generator using a four-piece rope sling that I had made up with a series of nautical knots, which impressed the wagon driver. He skilfully craned the generator around an almond tree and into the generator house, which impressed me. It would require the crane to lift and to position the inverter, so we took a break and had a few sandwiches and beers before completing the offloading.

The wagon driver had been a good and a willing worker, one of the best I'd come across in Mallorca, so I gave him a fully deserved big tip, which both embarrassed and delighted him; it had been my most satisfying day since arriving back on the island in January.

I went down to the village phone box to let Graham know that everything was in position and ready for him to come and do the clever bit. A couple of months had passed since I had cancelled the order and whilst we were still without electricity, there was a great sense of optimism in the air.

It was now May and the days were longer and hotter; there were butterflies and an influx of summer birds, to add to the local ones that had stuck out what passes for winter in this area. Spring in Mallorca is probably as good as it gets, for whilst the sun is hot, it isn't uncomfortably so, for it lacks the fierce intensity it attains in July and August; all plant life grows at frenetic speed and yet all is calm and tranquil.

If you visit Mallorca annually at the height of summer, for sun, sea and sand, you could do worse than consider a change to May and June. The sun, sea and sand are all still there, but the vegetation is lush and greener and the sky is bluer; unlike that white glare that often surrounds the height of summer sun.

On this particular day in May I was up and about early; today was the day. Graham and David had arrived on the island the previous day and had called in to say hello on the way to their Cala Ratjada hotel. I would have preferred them to stay at Na Cuberta, on the job as it were, but maybe they weren't too keen to live somewhere that didn't have an electricity supply.

I took up a position on the terrace from where, with the aid of binoculars, I could determine the roof colour of any vehicle passing along the road at the foot of the castle hill. They were due to arrive at about 9.00 a.m. and I was nonchalantly looking for the red roof of their hire car from around 8.30 a.m.; well, as nonchalantly as binoculars will allow. They arrived at 9.30a.m.; which in Mallorcan terms is better than spot-on.

I tried not to be a nuisance but was always on hand should they require any assistance. Which is probably the same as being a nuisance but they were too polite to tell me. A couple of days later I heard the words that I had dreamt of for so long.

'Can you go up to the house and switch a light on.' I was running up the drive before Graham had finished the sentence.

With a slightly trembling finger I clicked on a switch; joy knew no bounds. I ran back down the drive with the news.

'Good,' Graham said, 'can you switch it off now?'

There were tests and checks and more tests and more checks and finally the system was fully operational: well, nearly. The new microchip that was required would be delivered and fitted by an engineer when he came to fine-tune everything in two weeks' time. I just didn't care, for we now had electricity. Electrical appliances could be switched on without having to work out what the power consumption would be; if it had a wire to it, we switched it on.

The young man who came over to do the fine-tuning was a talented electronics engineer, but total success evaded him. It was apparently a software problem and couldn't be solved in-house. So we had a well-manufactured and very sophisticated electrical power system, which, if given the appropriate instructions by a little microchip, would carry out its functions without fault. No doubt today such a chip could be almost bought off the shelf, but back then the shelf was bare.

It wasn't that the system couldn't produce electricity; it's just that it decided not to do so at the most inconvenient times. One of the major problems was the failure of the microchip to recognise when the batteries had dropped below an operational power level, so when the generator was supposed to start up automatically to recharge them, it didn't.

Fortunately, we had a telephone at last and I was able to communicate with Matchpower without having to trek down to the village phone booth. I became adept under instruction at taking intricate gizmos apart and then reporting what I'd found before reassembling them.

After some time the whizz-kids at Matchpower realised that during a period when everything was closed down, the clock on the electric oven was making the 1.5 kilowatt inverter beaver away non-stop and unless we switched on an appliance requiring more than 1.5 kilowatts, the generator wouldn't start; hence, the batteries didn't get charged. We disconnected the electric clock.

Things didn't improve – if we spent a day away from Na Cuberta, we would return to find that the system had shut down and it would be back to candles until the following day. It was Stuart who suggested that I check our radio; apparently, some sets have a small internal diode that continues to take a minute amount of electrical current, regardless of the fact that the radio is switched off; ours proved to be such a one. I pulled out the plug and at last stopped the 1·5 kilowatt inverter from belting away hour after hour, to provide power that wouldn't have outfaced a 1·5 volt torch battery.

The Matchpower system was one of those projects that nearly succeeded. Unfortunately, the timing was wrong, the UK was in recession and businesses were having a difficult time surviving. Matchpower was a company that had always been prepared to spend money on research and development projects but suddenly they were forced to cut back to stay in business.

We'd been within an ace of success; another time, it may well have been one. The project had cost Matchpower much time, effort and money. It had cost Jean and me much heartache, lots of effort and at times outright anguish: oh yes, and money as well.

Some men cherish a beloved old car, a boat engine or some other piece of machinery that they learn how to keep running over the years with a well-placed kick here and a smart tap with a hammer there. Well, over the years, I learnt all about our power unit and could almost diagnose a problem before it became one, but I don't think that I ever came close to cherishing it.

You will have no doubt surmised that owning the sole distribution rights for such units in the Balearics and mainland Spain didn't make me my first million and in the words of Forrest Gump "I got no more to say on that subject".

Chapter Twenty-three

Shangri-La. A neighbour from hell with town hall contacts and Bootsy.

We settled into a comfortable living pattern at Na Cuberta. All our friends and family were besotted with the place and in the summer months we rarely had longer than a two-week stretch on our own. But we loved it, particularly when family arrived for their summer holidays.

Bit by bit the place took shape and with no inclement weather hold-ups, you could plan to do some concreting next Tuesday without checking a weather forecast. The only planning I did was to ensure that jobs requiring much pickaxe-wielding or concrete-mixing coincided with the holiday period of my sons and son-in-law, although I have to say that my daughter could also handle a well-filled wheelbarrow.

I had them convinced, rightly so as it happens, that a much deeper and even tan can be obtained if you keep moving and work hard enough to sweat a lot. None of my family returned home without having acquired a deep, even tan.

After four years of what can be described as a labour of love, Na Cuberta looked a picture. The old Mallorcan oven appeared at first sight to be just a heap of stones piled untidily against the ruins of the original *finca* living quarters. Only when I started to use the stones to build a small wall at the end of the courtyard did I uncover the beehive structure of firebricks that formed the inner lining of the oven; it had been the only means of cooking for the original inhabitants of the *finca*. I restored it to full working order and once we got the hang of it, it provided a superb alternative to a barbecue.

The beehive structure of firebricks was about a metre diameter at the base and the same dimension in height. It was constructed on smooth stone slabs approximately 60cm from ground level. The rectangular wall around the firebricks was built with thick stone and the area around and above the beehive structure was packed with stone and clay and then topped with concrete. The chimney was just a short terracotta pipe and the oven door was 12mm-thick steel plate. There was of course no thermostat; no gas-mark nine. Once the wood fire inside the oven had reduced to red embers, they were pushed to the sides of the oven and the food was placed in the centre.

No gas or electric oven ever roasted or baked anything better than this oven from the past. The only problem was that the oven was rather large and a considerable number of guests had to be invited to warrant the volume of wood required to get the oven up to temperature. But once set up you could cook half-a-dozen chickens or a small pig, with room left over for bread and scones. Whoever owned the original *finca* must have had a large family or an enormous appetite.

No doubt in bygone days the womenfolk would have been in charge of the oven, whilst the menfolk leaned on their sticks watching their sheep and goats. That's all finished with now, for Mallorcian-oven-cooking and barbecuing is man's work. I'm more than happy to let Jean spend most of the day marinating the chicken and preparing the kebabs but when the fire is lit, the tongs are mine.

I put forward my theory at a party in one of my mellow moods, which I slip into quite easily after my fifth glass of wine; the size of the glass appears to be irrelevant. As ever, the following day Jean recounted my party blunders. The fact that Jean doesn't drink ensures that the list of my party blunders is always longer than those of my friends, who have wives that can tipple a bit.

'Joanne's friend was incensed by your remark about barbecues being men's work.' Jean picked up the coffee pot. 'Would you like another cup?'

'Yes please, which one was Joanne's friend?'

'The woman in red.'

'Which woman in red?'

'There was only one woman in red.'

'Nancy and Maureen were in red, weren't they?'

'No, Nancy was in aubergine and Maureen was in pink.'

'Oh, who was the woman in red, then?'

'She was a friend of Joanne's, she's over on holiday; her husband left her last year.'

'Can't say I blame him, I take it she's not trying for another?'

'It was a party, Alwyne, you're not supposed to antagonise people at a party.'

'Well some people are easily antagonised,' I complained. Jean didn't answer.

'OK, OK, if we see her again I'll apologise. I'll tell her that barbecuing is definitely women's work.' Jean didn't deign to reply.

I love standing at a barbecue with a turner-over thing in one hand and a glass of wine or a bottle of beer in the other, flanked by sons and son-in-law. The womenfolk in our family don't really seem to mind at all, particularly in the UK when it begins to rain.

Rain wasn't a barbecue problem at Na Cuberta. Well, not for 90 per cent of the year at least. Our barbecue area was a ring of large flat-topped rocks, some of which were part of a natural outcrop of rock on which the barbecue was built. The central area was paved in stone and was sheltered from the midday sun by a large almond tree.

It had taken my son-in-law Roy and me two days to lever the large rocks into position. That evening, as we all sat on the stones admiring our handiwork and drinking tequila sunrises, Roy named it Tequila Corner. The name stuck; all our visitors to Na Cuberta have fond memories of Tequila Corner.

Our "threshing circle", another relic of bygone days, was a circular drystone wall of approximately 22m in diameter. It was built on a slope, so the wall ran from about ·6m high at one side to 2·5m high on the other. On the top of the circle the ground was level and hard packed. The wheat and corn threshing was carried out on this circle with the aid of a donkey hitched to a wooden arm. The arm kept the donkey walking round the outer perimeter of the circle, whilst the other end turned a stone and wooden thingamajig. I never did find out what the thingamajig looked like, so I couldn't recreate it and in any event, I didn't want a donkey.

So I turned it into a boule area, a sport in which women often make men look inferior and probably accounts for the fact that I have never seen a woman in amongst those groups of Frenchmen who play the game with such concentrated dedication.

The high section of the threshing circle formed the curved boundary to one side of a walled area, referred to by one of our farmer neighbours as *El corral*; it had been a pen for young sheep and goats. I'm not sure that the small glazed drinking bowls set into the drystone walling were as originally built, but I liked to think that they were.

The corral adjoined a much larger walled area of about 1,000 sq metres, where cactus grew to a height of 2·5m with fat and very spiky leaves, which the goats from next door ate with relish. I hadn't realised that a cactus bore fruit that could be eaten and whilst the locals had told me how sweet and juicy the fruit of a cactus was, they hadn't bothered to mention the hundreds of fine hairs that stick into your hands and fingers should you attempt to pick and peel them without wearing industrial-quality working gloves.

The remainder of our land was covered in almond trees, a couple of fig trees and a host of little rocky outcrops. Na Cuberta was built on the top of sloping land and the swimming pool was built about 60cm below the terrace level. The earth and rock from the pool excavation had been formed into a rockery that dropped away from the pool level and joined the natural ground slope 3m below.

As rockeries go, this was a big one; we are talking settee-sized rocks here. Little heather plants would have been lost; it required yuccas, oleanders and palms, anything big without a matching thirst. Stone-paved terracing stepped around almond trees and Tequila Corner; purple bougainvillea climbed the villa's terrace columns.

When the sun was low enough to shoot shafts of sunlight through the almond tree branches, Na Cuberta was breathtakingly magical. It has been known for our grandchildren to speak in whispers at such times, whilst the grown-ups sit in a contented silence, only disturbed by the clink of the ice cubes in the tall tequila-sunrise glasses.

We often sat in Tequila Corner contemplating just how lucky we were to live in such beautiful surroundings. Meanwhile, the farmer who had sold this ruined and decayed *finca*, once the home of peasants eking a living from the rocky land, witnessed it slowly assume an air of luxury; he was to become a thorn in my side, worse even, he was a pain in the backside.

We had fitted comfortably into the small-town life of Arta. The pace was much slower than in the more commercialised holiday and tourist centres and whilst tourists did swell the population on market day, generally everything remained the same. The restaurants and bars catered for the townsfolk and made no attempt to woo visitors with English beer or baked beans and chips.

The *Menu del Dia* at our favourite lunchtime restaurant was a three-course meal, plus half a bottle of wine, all for 700 pesetas per head. The food was whatever was in season at the time: quail, rabbit or partridge in the shooting season. In spring it was lamb, suckling pig and a variety of fish that always tasted better than it looked. Everything was cooked Mallorcan-style, with no effort made to anglicise or Germanise any dish. The clientele was generally a mixture of local workers, either suit or overall clad. If I wanted to meet our bank manager, the mechanic who serviced our car or the men who tiled our villa roof, this was where to find them.

Our grandchildren were a great favourite there in the way that all babies and very young children are in Mallorca. I think it's a Spanish thing; they are natural child-lovers, all children that is, not just their own. Generally, animals come well down the list; the Mallorcian's ride them, work them or eat them; pets don't seem to figure too highly in the scheme of things, either.

We got used to the fuss that the local restaurant owner's wife and daughters always made of our grandchildren, but it was a revelation to see a group of horny-handed plasterers and bricklayers on the next table, billing and cooing over our baby grandchildren; such a sight would be unlikely in the UK. It was even more surprising to witness teenage youths reacting in the same manner, with not a semblance of embarrassment, definitely a sight unlikely to be seen in the UK.

One of the difficulties of living in Arta was that many of the locals, particularly the older generation, spoke Mallorcan rather than Spanish. We had struggles enough with Spanish, but Mallorcan left us dead in the water. Nonetheless, we got by with our very basic Spanish and very proficient sign language.

A brother and sister of indeterminate age farmed the land adjacent to the bottom boundary of our property. They lived in the village in preference to the very basic cottage, where presumably their parents once lived but which now sheltered their little herd of goats.

The charming pair often left us gifts of fruit and vegetables that they were harvesting at the time. Even though we had two fig trees of our own loaded with fruit each year, they would still leave a carrier bag full of ripe figs on our doorstep. Jean tried to reciprocate with jars of homemade lemon cheese and anything specifically English that she had made. We couldn't match their generosity with gifts of homegrown produce, yet they always seemed to be overjoyed with anything that Jean gave them.

The nearest house was set in an orange grove adjacent to the end of our drive. It wasn't lived in, but the Mallorcan owners planned to refurbish the house and spend their retirement years in the peace and tranquillity of the area. They were a friendly couple, but we rarely saw them.

Further along the narrow unmade road were two very large houses, each set in about 10 to 15 acres of tree-filled land. A Swiss couple, Walter and Alice Graffe, who planned to retire there, owned the nearest one. They visited only two or three times a year and we saw little of them. I regret that we couldn't speak their language nor they ours, for we shared a similar sense of humour, but without a common language a dinner party can become hard work.

They were generous people who, during our electricity shortage period, offered to let us run a cable from their property and use their supply. They even offered to finance the installation of mains electricity for us, repayment to be made when we felt we could afford it. We didn't take up on either offer, but the fact that it had been made left us with a good feeling.

Lilo Lusser owned the second villa, a charming Swiss lady who spoke perfect English. She was also fluent in German and she seemed to have no difficulty in speaking Spanish. Those individuals who can converse in several languages and switch from one to the other without effort must have different brains from those of us that can't. I'm sure that the effort put into one's homework has no substantial bearing on the outcome and I remain convinced that no matter how strong my desire to speak a foreign language may be, fluency will evade me. My theory owes some of its credibility to a similar shortcoming, for whilst I enjoy music greatly I can't play a musical instrument, I had piano lessons but never mastered the skill. I cling to the belief that those who have an aptitude in language or musical skills simply have differently formulated brains. How else could Mozart play classical piano pieces at the age of three?

We presumed that we would come and go unnoticed in our little Mallorcian-registered Fiesta. Not so, for as we drove home one evening through the narrow backstreets of Arta, I had to brake suddenly to avoid a football, which rolled across our path from a little side street. A small 8 or 9-year-old boy, who managed to stop himself just short of the car, led the chasing group of children and I waved him across to collect his ball. He glanced at me and shouted 'thank you', before running back jabbering to his friends in Spanish. I revised my presumption; you cannot come and go unnoticed if you stick out like a sore thumb.

Arta had a packed calendar of celebration days fully supported by all the townsfolk. On such occasions it was pedestrians only on Arta's central roads and the cafes, restaurants and bars filled one half of the main town thoroughfare with tables and chairs that quickly became packed with eaters and drinkers. The other half of the road was for the parades that accompanied all of the many Saint's day celebrations; in addition, they had celebration parades heralding the start of spring, summer and autumn, and the longest, shortest and any other day that they felt justified a parade.

On such nights the town square was the centre of the celebrations. At one end of the square, men wearing traditional costume played traditional Spanish music on traditional Spanish guitars. At the other end, budding disc jockeys blasted out pop music on over-amplified speakers. There were two dance areas surrounded by a few hundred chairs occupied by mums, dads, and grandparents. Young children danced, tussled and generally ran amok at the traditional end; teenagers tried to look cool midst the DJ's flashing coloured lights at the other. We attended many of these Arta celebrations over the years that we lived there, often with our own families on their summer holidays, and what really sticks in my memory is that amidst all the noise and laughter, I never saw anyone remotely the worse for drink.

Too many dinners, barbecues and parties are an expatriate's lot, which is fine if you live in an apartment, but it played havoc with my Na Cuberta projects. Not really a problem though, for how could there be a downside to living in a beautiful villa in a country with wall-to-wall sunshine and a host of good friends. Well, in a word, neighbours, or, more specifically, in its singular form, neighbour; the man that owned the next almond-tree field, who had originally sold our land to Magdelena.

I first met him when he drove his tractor up our drive on his way to his field. The right of way for him to gain access to his field was a 2.4-metre strip of land next to our top boundary, which ran behind the original *finca* building and the Mallorcan oven. As the right of way and the entrance to it was first established to provide access for a donkey and cart or a horse-drawn plough, it didn't offer easy access for a large tractor; much easier, therefore, for him to use our entrance and drive. He drove his tractor through our entrance and up our drive as if he had every right to use it in preference to his right-of-way access.

At the time our drive was nothing more than a cart track and the entrance was a hole in the drystone wall, knocked through by the young couple so that delivery vehicles could gain entry. I raised no specific objection to him using it, for it would be a year or more before I began work on the drive and entrance. I had felt that it would have been good manners for him to enquire as to how I felt about him using our entrance, but I had yet to learn that charm and good manners weren't his best qualities.

There was something about the man that irked me. He had that irritating habit of not noticing you when you knew that it was a virtual impossibility for him not to have been aware of your presence; eye-to-eye contact with him was impossible. When he ploughed or hoed his field or harvested the almonds, Jean always offered drinks, accepted with thanks from his helpers, but with little grace from himself. He sometimes acknowledged a wave on his way up our drive, but he never initiated one. Had our paths crossed on a village street, the only way I could have attracted his attention would have been to knock him down.

Whilst I found his behaviour irritating, I could live with it on his five or six visits per year. When I sorted out my drive and fitted some gates, he would have to gain access to his field via the right-of-way route; that would stop him annoying me, I told myself.

Understanding cultural differences or, more to the point, not understanding cultural differences is the root cause of many an expatriate's problems. Mainland dwellers moving in their own country to an offshore island can take time to become accustomed to the ways of the locals. Legislation, as decreed by mainland politicians, often fails to take into account the unique situation of islanders. Small wonder, therefore, that over the years an island's indigenous population tend to display a wary, even suspicious attitude to all imports from the mainland; particularly when the import is people. It therefore follows that expatriates who cannot speak the local language should experience even more integration difficulties.

Having chosen to live on an island 100nm off the mainland, in a small town steeped in historical culture, what chance did we have? Well, as it turned out, a very good one, for Arta had very few foreign settlers and who knows, if that changed into a mass influx the locals may well view things in a different light, but as far as we were concerned the locals were wonderful.

Foreigners who built villas in their village clearly confirmed that Arta was a desirable place to live in. The new settlers provided work for their tradesmen, bought food and hardware from their shops, dined in their restaurants and drank in their bars. In addition, they paid local rates and taxes, but received no services. What's to dislike?

We lived in a beautiful villa, but didn't go out to work; ergo, we were rich. Communication was difficult, because we couldn't speak their language; ergo, we were a bit dim. However, we shopped and dined locally, we smiled and were polite, ergo, all accepted us; with the exception that is, of our neighbour.

I was gathering tools together in preparation to start work on Na Cuberta's entrance; I was going to build stone pillars on which I would hang metal gates. There was some drystone walling to complete and, of course, the right of way to be defined. I wanted there to be no misunderstanding as to which track the farmer could use to access his field.

The car screeched to a halt in front of our courtyard, spraying gravel in all directions. A large man clad in a greenish uniform and large boots laced halfway up his calves accompanied our neighbour. I hadn't seen the uniform before and was unsure which authority he represented. However, his aggressive attitude didn't sit well with me and after he shouted something incomprehensible and prodded me in the ribs a couple of times, I returned the favour. I shouted louder and was no doubt just as incomprehensible as I prodded him in the ribs with increased force. Jean's appearance at the scene prevented what surely would have been at best a scuffle in the gravel.

The claim was that I had reduced the width of the entry to the right of way. I hadn't, of course; for having anticipated such an accusation, I had been meticulous in ensuring that I didn't do so. However, I have to confess that I didn't allow the opening to be as much as one millimetre wider than the stated regulation. How stupid it all was, for I would have given him an extra metre at the entrance had he shown the slightest acknowledgement that our property no longer belonged to him. It was of no consequence how long the land had belonged to his family; he had sold it and you can't have it both ways.

Well that was the start of the nastiness; Bootsy, with the finger-prodding problem, turned out to be our neighbour's cousin, who by virtue of being physically the largest member of the family and a fireman in the Arta Fire Brigade, was accepted as that family's headman. On hearing this information I determined to review my fire-prevention strategy. If having a member of the local fire brigade against me wasn't bad enough, I learned that our neighbour was a personal friend of the current Mayor of Arta.

There followed a series of visits from various town hall-department representatives; always accompanied for some reason by a policeman. Had my neighbour, I wondered, cited the finger-prodding episode with Bootsy the Fireman as some sort of proof that I displayed an aggressive approach towards authority?

The arrival of the police car was a little disturbing; however, both the policeman and the town hall representative were pleasant and polite.

'I'm seeing if you 'ave your paper for knocking down of wall?'

'Err … knocking down of which wall?'

'For knocking down of wall.' He pointed down the drive.

'Oh, that wall, well actually it wasn't me that knocked it down; the previous owner of the land did that. It was like that when I bought it.'

'Is *no problema*,' he smiled, 'you come *mañana Ajuntament D'Arta.* Pay 2,000 pesetas, *no problema.*' He swiped the palms of his hands together, the Mediterranean gesture signifying a job dealt with.

I wasn't going to argue for the sake of £10, so we shook hands and parted the best of friends. Next day, as requested, I presented myself at the town hall to pay my 2000pts. A dark-haired woman behind the counter handed me my bill for 20,000 pesetas. Shit!

It was quite clear that our neighbour was intent on making life difficult for us, so naturally I reciprocated. I extended the walls on each side of the old *finca* buildings to reduce the open area of the right of way. Instead of 28 meters of his right of way being walled, he now had 82 metres of it, all at a width of 2.4 metres measured to the millimetre.

We are talking one very pissed-off neighbour here; there followed two site meetings. The first one was with our neighbour, two town hall representatives and a policeman. The opposition for the second meeting consisted of our neighbour, four town hall representatives, Bootsy and a policeman. The first meeting had been a complete shambles, for the language barrier had proved too strong to breach. The home team for the return match was my interpreter and me. Our supporter's club in the form of Jean was on the terraces. Our interpreter Arrian was a recently met neighbour, who had approached us to see if we were interested in joining a local inhabitants group to lobby for a mains electricity supply, a group I joined with enthusiasm.

Arrian was about 1·7m tall and she had typically Mediterranean features; her black hair and dark eyes seemed to accentuate her strong will and self-assurance. She was in her mid thirties and was married to Bruno, an artist in his early sixties, who worked mainly with mosaics. He had a laid-back air and was happy being artistic, leaving his younger wife to organise everything, which included the total refurbishment of an old Mallorcan farmhouse. The task had given her a healthy dislike of local authority personnel and I suspect that they in turn weren't too enamoured with her. I was delighted to note that some of the town hall team looked a little disconcerted if not dismayed when they recognised Arrian as my interpreter.

She was educated in Switzerland and was fluent in French and English, but having been born in Mallorca she was also fluent in Spanish and Mallorcan. A formidable lady not intimidated by authority, she was the perfect interpreter for my meeting with the town hall representatives. I was very pleased to have her in my corner; this wouldn't be the usual one-sided gathering.

It wasn't just her linguistic skills that were of benefit, it was the fact that having just completed her own building project, she fully understood the problems that I was now experiencing. This was so much so that every time I answered a question, Arrian not only translated it for the gathering, but she also added bits of her own. There were several uncomfortable gentlemen amongst the opposition.

The meeting started with the apparent leader of the town hall team explaining that I didn't have the authority to reduce our neighbour's right of way to below the 2.4-metre width and therefore I would have to take down my newly constructed wall.

I couldn't believe the statement; all our boundary walls were of drystone construction and whilst the surface of such construction was clearly a long way from brickwork accuracy, I had used a measuring stick to ensure that the required dimension was maintained. Who amongst the gathered group, I enquired, had actually measured the clearance?

Arrian asked the question and in classic comedy fashion, everyone looked at each other in the bewildered hope that what they were suspecting wasn't true. Arrian picked up immediately on their embarrassed body language and pitched in with relish.

'You're not telling me that no one from your office has actually been to measure the gap before arranging this meeting?' She repeated the sentence in English for me.

Everyone was talking at once, each no doubt claiming that measuring gaps wasn't within the framework of their job description. There followed a moment of relief when one of the men produced an official-looking form, which was signed by my neighbour asserting that I had reduced his right-of-way access.

Arrian read the form and whilst not able to understand the words, I could easily recognise her derisory tone; she repeated the details for me.

'Yes, it's a nice form, but has anyone from the *Ajuntament* physically measured the gap?'

Strong discriminatory words were being bandied about, the senior man apparently distancing himself from his minions. A question was asked of Arrian, who turned to me.

'They want to know if you have a tape measure they could borrow,' Arrian smiled.

You couldn't make it up; it was like a Laurel and Hardy sketch, but not as believable.

I produced a tape measure from my trouser pocket and after ten minutes of measurement and scrutiny there was a triumphant exclamation. The measurers had found a stone with a pointy bit closing the gap to 2.395 metres. After ten minutes they had found a five-millimetre reduction in the access at a point approximately 1 metre from the ground.

'God almighty!' I exclaimed in exasperation and ran off to my tool shed, returning at speed carrying a large sledgehammer.

Everyone backed away, with Bootsy in the lead. I raised the sledgehammer above my head and smashed it down onto the offending protrusion. A chunk of stone about 30mm thick broke cleanly away.

'Now then,' I proclaimed, 'what do you want me to hit next?'

Arrian told me later that translating the Yorkshire term "now then" posed some difficulty, but she felt that the group had understood without the need for translation.

A couple of the town hall contingent began sidling back down the drive, their body language indicating embarrassment. The leader spoke to our neighbour in less than friendly tones and then after a few words spoken to Arrian and a slight, almost apologetic, nod to me, the site meeting was over.

As the officials departed along with the policeman, Bootsy and his cousin bristling with resentment followed on behind. They had arrived as fully paid-up members of the inner circle and left looking like Billy-no-mates.

I was happy that the right-of-way width matter had been resolved as far as officialdom was concerned, but in the knowledge that I was dealing with a spiteful and resentful pair of small-minded men, I had no doubt that as far as they were concerned, the battle was lost but the war was a long way from being over.

I laboured away, finishing my drive and stone walling with a concrete apron access, and at last fitted my gates. One set for our drive entrance and another for the right-of-way access. I closed the gates with satisfaction at 6.00 p.m. and retired to Tequila Corner, where Jean and I enjoyed our evening sundowners.

When I set off for the bread next morning the gates were on the floor. I fitted metal pegs through the hinge pins, so that the gates couldn't be lifted off. A couple of days later, the gates were damaged. I called the police and they wrote things down, but it was clear that there was little they could do unless they caught the vandals at work.

If I left the gates open they weren't touched, if I closed them they were damaged. I knew of course who was responsible and they knew that I knew, which made keeping calm almost an impossibility. In my daydreams I caught them in the act and my vengeance was so cruel and complete that I felt quite perky for a while. But the reality was that the whole thing was getting to me.

Chapter Twenty-four

It's all been great, but we're ready for home at just the right time. No goodbye from customs.

To say that our embittered neighbour was diminishing our love for the villa would be exaggerating. Na Cuberta still had its serenity and magnificent scenic views, so how could one stupid little man spoil things for us? I say "us", but in truth the problem didn't really get to Jean as it did to me; she viewed the whole thing as more our neighbour's problem than ours.

In rational terms, Jean was correct; the man had sold off a piece of his land and it will have irked him that Magdelena will have made a considerable profit within a year of having bought the land from him. The realisation that he'd missed out big time by selling locally, rather than to outsiders who recognise the value of the location, must have got to him.

It was easy to understand how he had misread the whole situation; it is unlikely that he ever stood back and appreciated the view. In his farmer-oriented mind, he had sold off an unworkable L-shaped piece of land with an assortment of little walled paddocks, an ancient threshing circle and an equally old and derelict *finca*. To his eye, dulled by years of humdrum work association, he had cleverly offloaded this useless plot of land to a young couple, who hadn't realised how out of the way and removed it was from Arta's modern services. Hadn't his great-great grandparents moved from such inconvenient surroundings, to enjoy the advantages that a village rapidly growing into a town could provide? So he'd retained his fields of almond trees that would generate revenue with the minimum of effort and had sold off an idyllic tranquil haven that enjoyed a view to die for.

"In hindsight I was lucky" is an often-heard phrase, or at least it is heard more often than the opposite phrase "in hindsight I got it wrong". I'm quite certain that our neighbour didn't have the mindset to accept that he ever got things wrong, but I know that hindsight eventually led him to realise that he had cocked-up. I have no doubt that his understanding of the subsidy system that the EU formulated, to enable them to generously donate money to the farming communities operating outside the UK, will have been paramount in his decision-making.

However the realisation that telephone-line installations and the imminent provision of power supplies to the area were pushing up land prices to unprecedented levels was probably a shock; he must have been haunted by hindsight. Hindsight was also responsible for the revelation that clarified why my neighbour harboured such hatred of me.

I was intrigued to see three people inspecting one of our neighbour's adjoining fields and after a while, they arrived at our front door. The trio comprised a German couple and an estate agent. Yes, you have guessed correctly, our neighbour had put his land up for sale. Unfortunately, there wasn't sufficient access and neither was there any legal entitlement to entry without our sanction. The trio enquired about the possibility of a shared access. My answer was an emphatic no; it left no room for negotiation. They confirmed that they wouldn't be making an offer for the land and I agreed that they had made a wise decision.

I recognised that our neighbour had left himself few options; well, you can't have too many fewer options than two. He could continue selling almonds and collecting his subsidies or he could sell the land to the only person that could provide the required access: in a word, me.

Our neighbour had blown it big time. By the time he had woken up to that fact, it was too late to recover the situation; clearly, I was the one to blame. No matter that I had nothing to do with him selling off his land in the first place and neither was it my fault that he sold it without securing proper access to his own land. There wasn't anything that would convince him not to view me as the instigator of all his woes.

It could all have been so different; he could have invited Jean and me to dinner and over a glass of brandy discussed proposals that could have benefited us all. Unfortunately, he was a mean-spirited little man destined to a future marred by corrosive thoughts. When I realised just how badly he had screwed up, I did wonder if I should offer him an olive branch; after due consideration I thought – nah.

In my mind, his ultra-aggressive approach towards me was unprovoked and the English trait of compromise tends to lack substance if, hypothetically, negotiations commence with a punch on the nose.

Had I been twenty years younger with an entrepreneurial bent, I would no doubt have borrowed the money to purchase the land and have made a very tidy profit. Regrettably, I wasn't twenty years younger and neither do I possess an entrepreneurial bent. Messrs Sugar and Branson wouldn't have been impressed.

To this day, I still feel an element of antipathy towards my erstwhile neighbour, whilst he never enters into any of Jean's conscious thoughts. She tends to think the best of people and thus, unlike me, she never has to waste time thinking how best to wreak revenge.

I viewed the six days a year when he drove up the track past Na Cuberta as six days too many. The sight of him made my fists clench. Immature I know, but then there are some things that I find difficult to be mature about. Fortunately, Jean has a way of simplifying problems and pointed out that as we had never intended to stay abroad after retirement age, we only had a few years left to enjoy Na Cuberta before we would be returning home to Yorkshire and our family. She intended to enjoy it to the full and was certain that seeing the farmer on a few days each year wouldn't diminish that joy.

She had the full backing of all our family who, whilst loving us very much, thought that we served a far better purpose looking after their holiday home rather than returning to the UK. I found my family's viewpoint somewhat sobering, as I always harboured the thought that the purpose of their annual visits to Na Cuberta was simply to enjoy the company of their parents.

We settled back into an enjoyment-mode lifestyle, but no matter how good our lifestyle, there were times when being far away from our family became almost physically painful and at such times it was harder to resist some of the offers made by those seeking to purchase Na Cuberta. However, our plan was to stay for another two to three years and the enquiries never got further than the "is your villa for sale" stage.

Nonetheless, it didn't stop us discussing the subject of selling Na Cuberta: at which point should we put the property on the market? What about agents? Should we start thinking mains electricity? It would certainly increase the property value by more than the installation costs. These were relaxed conversations, for it would be a while before we would need to take any form of action. So we lounged whilst sipping well-iced gin and tonics and enjoyed the magical view; could we really sell such a property?

* * *

We heard the car coming up our drive; actually, we had heard it well before then, for those sounds that never register in more populated environs were magnified in the silent tranquillity that cloaked Na Cuberta each evening.

It couldn't be any of our friends visiting, for now that we had a telephone they always checked that we were in before driving over. As I made my way around to the drive, the pessimist in me ensured that I readied myself for bad news of some sort. I hadn't built anything recently without permission; surely I couldn't have been denounced again. If my neighbour had started his tricks again I'd … well, I wasn't sure what I'd do, for most of my preferred options would land me in jail; best find out what the problem was first.

The large maroon Audi looked vaguely familiar, as did the middle-aged lady walking towards me with outstretched hand.

'Mr Chappell, my husband and I met you about two years ago, we came with an agent to view your beautiful home.'

I recognised her and remembered that we had met at a time when we were being pestered by so-called estate agents in search of properties for sale. I say so-called, because they weren't in fact bona fide agents but property touts; locals who received a commission from the big Palma estate agencies for advance information on properties that may come up for sale in the future. Even in the cutthroat estate agency business, the touts' approach was at best extremely aggravating.

It may well be that touts are misunderstood beings, but you cannot be a tout and claim the ethical high ground. My mental picture of a tout was of a skinny man, with a thin moustache and a furtive demeanour. Artatout, as we named her, was nothing like that; she was a large, untidy and totally charmless woman with a propensity for being rude.

Our first meeting was when she swept an eager sightseeing entourage of German property-seekers around our swimming pool, with the flamboyance of a tourist guide. I was astonished, astounded, goggle-eyed and thunderstruck; choose any one from four, but none of them gets close to how I felt at the time. In search of a better word I tried an amalgam of all four and finally favoured "gobstoundishstruck".

The woman was totally oblivious to the niceties of general convention; she didn't grasp that establishing whether or not a property was for sale was quite high on the list of things to do first. Even had she cleared that simple hurdle, it was for her an alien concept that the requisite procedure – prior to arriving on a property with a group of would-be purchasers – was to seek the vendor's agreement.

Artatout, could speak no English, which in a market dominated by English speakers must have been a considerable disadvantage. Verbal communication between the two of us was a non-starter. However, being fluent in sign and body language, I had developed a technique that had never failed to alert anyone when I was really pissed off; it was like water off a duck's back to Artatout.

You would have thought that the fact that neither she nor any of her clients ever saw the inside of the villa would have been an indication that Na Cuberta wasn't for sale. As thick skins go, this woman shared all the attributes of an armadillo without its cuddle factor.

Artatout often arrived – always unannounced – with German prospective purchasers and as usual, the majority could speak English. The perception that all Germans are loud and lay claim to choice poolside recliners with draped towels is no truer than the belief that all Englishmen are lager louts. It wasn't surprising, therefore, that whilst Artatout was never embarrassed by her own crass behaviour, her clients never failed to display their discomfort and always apologised profusely when they recognised the embarrassing situation in which they had unwittingly become embroiled.

I remembered that our latest visitor had been one of the German clients who had made such an apology and had been so embarrassed at the time that she and her husband had returned to apologise once again. We had spent a pleasant hour chatting with them over a glass of wine or two and they had left, vowing to have words with the Palma agent about their Arta representative. I doubt that they would have been familiar with the English word "tout", but they clearly understood the concept, for we never saw the awful Artatout woman again.

I wasn't sure why Ursula had come to see us – no, I didn't remember her name, she had to remind me – but I was intrigued and so I invited her to join us for a drink. It turned out that after seeing our property two years earlier, she and her husband had decided to buy a piece of land and have a villa built much in the style of Na Cuberta. They'd bought an apartment at Canamel to use as a base whilst they searched for a plot of land on which to build their dream house.

Sadly, not many weeks after they had found a suitable piece of land, her husband had suffered from a heart attack and had subsequently died. Understandably, she had no desire to continue the building project on her own and eventually she sold off the land.

She had now reached a point in her life where decisions had to be made; now a widow in her mid to late fifties, where was she to spend the rest of her life? There were complications, well aren't there always? Ursula wasn't a German as we had thought, but an Argentinean who had married a German. So, whilst she had lived for some time in Germany, it wasn't her natural home. Her parents had died some years earlier and the Argentinean ties were not now strong enough to draw her back there.

Her apartment in Canamel was comfortable enough, but the area was a summer resort and tended to be deserted in the winter period. Her unmarried daughter had a job that didn't necessitate a domicile in any specific European country, so she dropped in to Mallorca from time to time. However, as Ursula's daughter held the apartment and the area in which it was situated in scant esteem, then popping in was about the best that Ursula could expect from her daughter.

Since first seeing Na Cuberta, Ursula had coveted the property and now not only did she see it as her dream home, but she was also convinced that it would attract her daughter to visit her more regularly and for longer periods. She thought that she might convert the derelict *finca* into a self-contained bungalow for her daughter who might come to view it as a permanent base. More ideas were spilling out as she enthusiastically released the thoughts that she had harboured for such a considerable time. Jean and I felt like a couple of psychiatrists, listening to a tortured soul unburdening her problems. Suddenly, she realised that she was getting ahead of herself, for she was aware that the villa wasn't as yet for sale.

She apologised and explained that she had remembered that we had told her and her husband two years earlier that we didn't intend to stay in Mallorca longer than retirement age. Her request was that when we decided to leave Mallorca, we sell Na Cuberta to her. Oh, and as her daughter was staying with her next week, would it be all right if she brought her over to have a look around?

When Ursula left, Jean and I remained silent, each of us waiting for the other to make some comment and yet both knowing what the other was thinking. We had discussed the future sale of Na Cuberta from time to time, but not the mechanics of the process. We both knew that once

Na Cuberta was listed for sale there would be the usual influx of nosy tyre-kickers to contend with. Plus those irritating punters that didn't have sufficient funds to get anywhere near your asking price, whilst harbouring a belief that their display of disinterested negativity would persuade you to accept their ridiculously derisory offer.

Over the years we had sold three homes and were well aware of the aggravations and disappointments that are part and parcel of the house-selling experience. I'm sure that the majority of you who have experienced the process of selling your home will have a story to tell. It can't be for nothing that selling and moving house is deemed to be one of the most stressful of life's experiences.

Ursula wanted to buy Na Cuberta and was prepared to wait for a time of our choosing; it was a seller's dream scenario. Having a buyer prepared to put down a deposit with no time-limit strings attached was a powerful argument to sell earlier than anticipated; we were now planning our return home.

The biggest job to be tackled before completing the sale was the installation of mains electricity, without which we wouldn't achieve the full value of the property. I had grown accustomed to our thumping great generator, but I have to confess that a mains supply was preferable; unsurprisingly, it was a preference shared by Ursula.

Ursula spoke fluent English and German and being an Argentinean, her native language was Spanish; what a bonus that was. Considering my ineptitude with regard to speaking foreign languages, I sometimes wonder how I came to think that a life abroad would suit me, for I can have communication problems within the UK. I remember having problems in a Troon fish and chip shop; the Scottish lady server was clearly from an alien planet.

In Yorkshire, "fish and chips twice" is the simple phrase that will get you a portion of fish and some chips for two people. I'll rephrase that in case that sounds confusing. Having asked the lady server for "fish and chips twice", she will give you a fish and some chips wrapped in paper, she will then give you another fish and some chips wrapped in a similar fashion; how simple is that. The phrase only differs in that those from a better area would add the word "please" on the end.

I admit that I employed the longer version in Troon, but I don't think that that should have been the cause for any misunderstanding. To this day, I'm not really sure what the lady said to me, but out of the seemingly unintelligible torrent of words "fish supper" seemed to figure strongly. I couldn't believe that the shop was large enough to facilitate the serving of supper; where, for instance, would one sit?

I explained that I was seeking fish and chips twice to take away. There was much confusion, but I eventually I realised that in Scotland, serving fish and chips must be illegal, unless the phrase "fish supper" was included in your order. I like to think that some of my travel experiences will be of some practical assistance to others. My tip of the day to Yorkshire folk about to visit Scotland is to forgo fish and chips for a while and go for sausage and chips or number sixty-two in the local Chinese.

Ursula would have no such problems, for along with her linguistic skills, she was clearly a tough and competent lady; she wouldn't accept waffle from anyone, be they representatives of the local authority, service companies or solicitors.

I began to feel sorry for our neighbour; if he thought that I had been difficult to deal with, he had a big shock coming. I suspect he wouldn't know what had hit him if he started causing Ursula any aggravation. She would definitely retaliate through the legal system and she certainly possessed the appropriate financial clout to do so.

I had regaled Ursula with the details of our neighbour's antics, which she brought up one day during a meeting we had with her solicitor. The solicitor was a local born and bred Arta lady, who confirmed that I'd had the legal right to restrict access to five days per year for my neighbour. Furthermore, if I granted more access permission, a payment could be claimed for each extra day.

The clear and unequivocal advice to anyone thinking of purchasing property in Mallorca and for all I know anywhere else in Spain, is to employ a local solicitor who knows the local laws. When we originally purchased Na Cuberta, my solicitor had super offices in Palma; Ursula's had modest facilities located in the Arta main street; I can tell you that local's best.

Ursula translated the solicitor's view that Germans wouldn't have stood for the treatment we had received from our neighbour; the English, she felt, were a soft touch. I pointed out that whilst that may well be true, we still owned Gibraltar. Jean suggested that Ursula shouldn't translate my statement and Ursula agreed.

'*Si, señor,* you put on other room, is *no problema.*'

'Would we need planning permission, would we need an architect?'

When the vendor looks perplexed, it's time to speak louder and use hands to imitate an architect at a drawing board and to imitate planning department employee stamping approval on architect's drawings by banging fist on palm of hand several times. Then, they clarify the point by repeating fist on palm motion. The vendor is now totally confused and so elaborates on their original statement.

'Is *no problema, contratista local.*' They point towards village, imitate builder laying concrete blocks and then they slap their palms together in a sideways dismissive gesture. 'Is *no problema.*'

The happy couple, having agreed a price and handed over the deposit, set off back to the UK to sort out their affairs; soon, they'll be experiencing the laid-back Mallorcan lifestyle in the sun.

On the UK-bound jet, the husband squeezes his wife's hand.

'I can't wait to get away from the UK, away from the rain and all the petty rules and regulations we have to put up with. Y'see, we couldn't just add an extra room on our house in England without planning permission and form filling. They know how to do it in Spain, it's all different there.' Wrong. Such a statement is almost certain to return and haunt him in the fullness of time.

Well, I can tell you that to purchase Spanish land and build on it can be a bureaucratic nightmare. You require the services of a solicitor, a notary, an agent and permission from Madrid. If you employ a high-flying city solicitor, he is unlikely to know his way around the local by-laws that apply in that delightful out-of-the-way location, where you have chosen to build your dream house. In which case, you will require a local agent, who can speak English well enough to eradicate possible areas of misunderstanding. Hopefully, the local agent will ensure that upon completion, you possess every item of documentation that you may or may not be required to submit for scrutiny at some unspecified date in the future.

Your city solicitor may dismiss the idea that such local documentation is necessary. Don't believe it, for whilst he or she would be pleased to fight your cause in the future should you unfortunately require them to do so, it would prove to be a much costlier exercise. Best that you procure every document that the nit-picking local town hall may demand, regardless of the advice received from the city slickers; it will prevent later hassle from interrupting your sunbathing.

Bearing in mind the Spanish bureaucrat's love of a profusion of seals and stamps on their documentation, the more you have the more comfortable you will feel.

The Spanish building-development and planning-control system mirrors the Spanish trait; it's laid-back. Unfortunately, this national trait is misleading, for you may well live in a property for several years in blissful happiness before the bombshell explodes. No matter how many years the hapless purchaser has lived in that dream house in the sun, sooner or later a gap in the chain of documentation will do for the unwary.

There is no statute of limitation: if it was wrong ten years ago it's still wrong now; if it shouldn't have been built then down it comes. That additional bedroom may well have been built before you purchased the property – but so what. A big fine may sort out the problem; the Spanish are big on fines. If you can escape by paying a fine, you're a winner; better by far than the discovery that the original documentation was so flawed that you don't, nor ever did, own the property you have been living in for the past ten years. It has happened. Retiring to Spain? Keep in mind that age-old adage; buyers beware. Buying a villa or apartment in a well-populated area is, I believe, much safer.

We set about planning our return home with enthusiasm. Some thirteen years earlier we had left England and three children and we were now returning to a somewhat enlarged family; increased by two daughters-in-law, a son-in-law and six grandchildren. Jo and Emma knew Na Cuberta well, whilst Alan, Andrew and Anya's main memories seem to be sunshine and the swimming pool. Amy, our youngest grandchild, is now a tad disgruntled at having to make do with stories of her visits when she was a baby.

One decision we had to make was whether or not to transport back to the UK such furniture and possessions that we had become attached to over the years spent in the Mediterranean. The result of our deliberation on this subject was strongly influenced when we heard of the unfortunate episode in which an acquaintance of our friend Megan had been involved.

A one-man removal company run by an Englishman in Mallorca had become very popular, as his prices were well below the Spanish competition. Unfortunately, at this time, the EU was instigating new border rules and customs officials feared redundancies. The removal man now fell into the category of a non-Spaniard taking a Spaniard's job and as he drove off the ferry at Barcelona he was stopped. The customs men emptied every piece of furniture from his van and left it on the dock in a thunderstorm. The small print on the insurance policy supposedly covering his business was – as often is the case – extremely selective when the claim for damaged furniture was made. The unfortunate man's business went bust and presumably the owner of the furniture wasn't too happy, either. The whole idea of employing a company to return our possessions to the UK lost its appeal.

We decided to take a short break back in the UK and prepare our apartment for our eventual homecoming. Whilst there, we would buy a hatchback and drive back to Na Cuberta, where we would load the vehicle with as many possessions as we could fit in for the journey back home.

There was another reason why I had decided that we would return home by car – I felt that it would be an easier way to smuggle pesetas out of Spain than by air. It was illegal at that time to take Spanish currency out of Spain, so having sold your home, how did you get your peseta-packed carrier bag out of the country?

Changing the cash element of the sale from pesetas into sterling over the counter of a Spanish bank wasn't a good idea; even a dim desk clerk would recognise such an obvious capital gains tax avoidance fiddle. Of course, if you really wanted to be screwed, there were plenty of those shops that offer the best deal in town. The alternative was to pay the capital gains tax, an iniquitous charge based on a formula designed to give the Spanish government a feel-good factor.

If you decided to go down the official route when selling your property, there was no cash payment in the solicitor's office of the difference between the original purchase price and the final selling price. The seller received payment of the original purchase price, plus 60 per cent of the remaining sum. The solicitor passed on the remaining 40 per cent to the Spanish Inland Revenue.

Now here's the rub. It could be that none of the difference between the property's purchase and selling price was in fact profit and if so you shouldn't be paying capital gains tax. You may have purchased a semi-ruin and turned it into a palace and the increased value may actually be equal to the cost of the upgrade; not much profit there. Unfortunately, the Spanish Inland revenue now holds your tax payment and it's your job to prove that it should be paid back. This can be extremely difficult when you have returned to the UK; the claim process can take two years or more to resolve. Naturally, you can forget any claim on the accrued interest gained by the Inland Revenue. It should therefore come as no surprise to anyone, that a system devised by bureaucrats and prejudicially loaded in favour of its own administration turned many hitherto law-abiding UK citizens into money launderers.

Pat and Tina are friends of ours who sold their apartment to live aboard the boat on which Pat was the skipper. After completion of the sale, Tina made two journeys back to the UK wearing knee-length boots stuffed with pesetas. It was the height of summer, but the Spanish airport customs officials saw little amiss with Tina's choice of footwear.

The authorities had the registered land and building costs of Na Cuberta, with the exception of the cash payments made to the builder just prior to his bankruptcy, which unfortunately would show the purchase price as a lower figure than it actually was. The cost of paving, landscaping, wall-building and electricity supply installation, along with kitchen fixtures and fittings, house, garden and patio furniture, all added to a total that would be extremely difficult to evaluate against the final selling price of Na Cuberta; furthermore, how do you evaluate toil and sweat?

If we went down the official route, the chances of recouping our full costs, let alone making a profit, would be doomed; the only winner would be the Inland Revenue with a slice of our money that they were most certainly not entitled to. Needless to say, I wasn't about to hand over our peseta-stuffed carrier bag.

Returning home by car was now our only option, because Jean was displaying an unreasonable reluctance to fly home wearing cash-filled boots.

We drove back from Yorkshire having made preparations for our return home. It was now full steam ahead to complete the sale of Na Cuberta. We were aware that the change in our lifestyle would be huge and yet we could hardly wait to return home. Our family didn't quite view things in the same light, for pleased as they may have been with our imminent return, they were only too aware that their annual holiday costs were about to rocket. I do think, however, that they were more affected by the thought that they would never holiday again in Na Cuberta – which held so many happy memories for them – than they were prepared to admit. Ian, our eldest son, maintained that by selling up we were depriving him of his birthright; he has always favoured the ancient system that decreed that the eldest son inherits everything.

The lack of urgency displayed by the electricity authority in their efforts to complete the installation of Na Cuberta's mains power supply, now made it doubtful that we would meet our agreed completion date.

The electrical contractor, the link between us and the electricity authority, had gone strangely quiet; Ursula being away for a week in Palma didn't help matters. I called into the electrician's office for an update on the work schedule and noticed that his usual "*no problema*" demeanour was missing, replaced by the ubiquitous non-committal, palms-up Mediterranean shoulder shrug. In slowly spoken Yorkshire and much sign language, I reminded him that on his recommendation, I had paid the installation cost upfront, to ensure that the power would be installed before the completion date; I sensed that an element of embarrassment accompanied his shoulder shrug.

My inbuilt wariness of anything slightly out of kilter left me feeling strangely uneasy. I dropped a note through Ursula's letterbox informing her of what I believed could be a pending problem.

We had agreed with Ursula that the completion of sale wouldn't take place until the electricity supply was fully installed. We now had everything to be taken home stacked in the hall ready for loading into the car and our ferry tickets were tucked into my wallet; what we didn't have was electricity and I was nervous.

I confessed to being stunned when Ursula blandly announced that even though the power supply hadn't yet been installed, she was prepared to allow completion to take place if we agreed to a sale price reduction of £20,000. I hesitate to cast aspersions, but the thought ever so slightly crossed my mind that the power connection delay may not totally be down to the electricity authority's ineptitude.

Ursula recognised within seconds of making her offer that it wasn't going to happen and that the sale was about to fall through. On reflection, I suppose that I didn't blame her for trying it on and I confess to an element of admiration for a woman on her own, displaying the toughness of character that such a proposal would demand. However, it worked well for us in that Ursula's realisation that she had been so close to losing Na Cuberta, prompted her to confirm that completion would be finalised with or without the power connection; by now just a simple task requiring one cable connection and the throwing of a switch.

Then came the big plus: it had been agreed that Ursula would purchase Na Cuberta at just above the recorded value and that she would pay the difference between that and the total sale price in cash. However, her bank in Germany had transferred funds to the local bank for the first part of the transaction, but not for the cash payment. Would it be all right, she wondered, if her bank transferred the money directly from Germany into my Guernsey offshore bank account. Well, can a duck swim?

We'd been to several leaving parties over the last two weeks and had shed the inevitable tears. Now, we were ready for the off and the final day dawned cloudless and sunny as usual. The car was packed and waiting; in an hour, the paperwork would be completed and we would be on our way to board the ferry in Palma.

We looked around Na Cuberta for the last time, for although Ursula had said that we would be welcome to call in should we ever return for a holiday in Mallorca, we knew that we would never see Na Cuberta again. We wouldn't want to see it in a better, worse or even altered state. To us, Na Cuberta was perfect and will always be so in our memories. The only acceptable return scenario would be as owners again, but without the assistance of a lottery win, it would never happen.

We drove down the drive without a backward glance; we were going home to our family.

I had no more than twenty to thirty pesetas in my pocket when we approached the Spanish border and I was eager to be stopped and questioned; much in the way you would welcome a police breathalyser test when you haven't consumed alcohol for several days. I imagined being ordered to step out of the car by the border police; they looked mean in their uniforms, dark glasses and highly polished gun belts.

'We 'ave to search for the pesetas, si?'

'You don't scare me, I laugh at your threats; you will never break me down.' I stand tall and match them stare for stare, a slight smile playing about my lips.

When we arrived at the border, the glassed booths weren't manned and all the barriers were open with not a border guard in sight, no one to even to wave us through: Spaniards, eh.

Chapter Twenty-five

The best stories have a happy ending.

Back home we settled into our apartment in Scarcroft, a small village between Leeds and Wetherby. We were happy to settle into the practicality of UK life, such a contrast to the carefree yet short-on-substance world that was the life Mallorca offered the majority of expatriates.

I have to say that life in an apartment didn't fully satisfy me. I started to write this book recounting our Mediterranean adventure, I joined the local golf club and I confirmed my total lack of skill in buying and selling shares on the stock market.

I enjoy listening to music, but if it can't be played loud enough to hear the percussion and base guitar – and in an apartment it can't – then one of life's enjoyments is severely restricted. Considering that, as one grows older, the list of life's enjoyments tends to become ever shorter, one shouldn't indiscriminately throw away those that remain.

So, was I happy? Yes, I was. Was I satisfied? Well no, not really, I wanted to live in a proper house, preferably situated in the less populated area of North Yorkshire.

I knew that when we left England to sail to the Med, the biggest sacrifice for Jean was to leave The Cottage in Boston Spa. She had loved the house for nineteen years and leaving it had been a gut-wrenching ordeal for her. I felt that a similar house in North Yorkshire would erase that particularly sad memory. But whilst we looked at some delightful properties with superb views, Jean wasn't interested. Her point was, and I could see the logic of her argument, that to move to a location that required a car journey for virtually every need was an illogical move for anyone approaching pensionable age.

I did point out that Scarcroft wasn't over-endowed with services; in fact, take away the post office and you were left with none. Our visits to the nearest shopping centre in Wetherby usually included some estate agent window-shopping, but any property in Boston Spa was out. To live in the village and pass the end of the street leading to The Cottage on a regular basis would have been torture for Jean.

Our failure to find a property that really grabbed us defused, to some extent, my desire to leave the apartment and I settled for a life that fell short of what I had envisaged. On the plus side were the relevant economy that living in an apartment offered and the freedom from building maintenance and gardening tasks that are an ever-present demand for the average home owner.

Life as we all know is full of surprises and when Roy, our son-in-law, called for a chat and a cup of tea, he said the magic words.

'Oh, by the way, did you know that The Cottage is up for sale?'

Jean froze. I don't think I've ever seen Jean do that before, but it was an unmistakable freeze. Roy showed us the advert that he had cut out from the newspaper: FOR SALE – THE COTTAGE. BOSTON SPA. I read it and regretfully pointed out to Jean that we couldn't afford it.

'I'm sorry, pet, there's absolutely no way that we can buy it back.'

I have to say that Jean isn't a demanding person. She is happy with her lot and she never craves, as so many do, the possessions or lifestyle of others. But we were talking about The Cottage, which other than the family and me was the love of her life; maybe I promoted myself a bit there.

The tears welled in her eyes and I didn't need to hear how she would never want new clothes and certainly not holidays ever again. No doubt she was sincere albeit unrealistic, but I didn't need to hear such promises, for the tears and the abject expression of disappointment on her face struck me like a blow to the stomach.

Some fifteen years ago she had walked away from the home she loved, all for me. Our adventure had been my dream, not Jean's, and yet never once did she claim to have sacrificed anything on my behalf. Yet, I knew that she had and I realised that to refuse to even consider buying back The Cottage was simply not an option.

As we parked the car in the drive of The Cottage our emotions were working overtime. It had lost none of its welcoming charm in our absence, although the front elevation had altered in that it was displaying much more ivy than stone.

The schoolteacher owners welcomed us in and began showing us around. I have heard it said that you should never buy a house from schoolteachers or the clergy, for it will likely be untidy and badly maintained. I'm only repeating something that I have heard said, not making a pronouncement you understand. Apparently, if you want a property that you could walk into and live in without having to wield so much as a duster, you should purchase a house from a gay couple.

The schoolteachers were a pleasant and friendly couple, but it has to be said that the first part of the above claim couldn't be easily dismissed. Frankly, the condition of our former home was never really an issue, for we knew it inside out and would make an offer whatever state it was in.

We told the couple as we entered the dining room that we had previously lived in the cottage for nineteen years. The admission was prompted by our obvious reaction when we set eyes upon the timber ceiling beams, now painted pale blue. After that I think that they thought that we were there just to have a nosy around and they were duly surprised when I made the offer to pay the asking price. I know how to drive a hard bargain; we shook hands on the deal.

Unfortunately the agent, a tall, well-built, full-of-himself tosspot, wasn't happy that the deal had been concluded without his input. A couple of days later he contacted me to say that there had been a delay in the availability of the property that the present owners were seeking to purchase. Would we be prepared to wait for two months if there was a £1,000 price reduction? Well, we would have waited regardless of the reduction, but we were more than happy to accept the new condition.

Big mistake; the odious one passed the message on that we would accept the delay if there was a price reduction. The owners, thinking that we had reneged on our agreement, accepted the agent's suggestion that The Cottage be put up for auction based on sealed bids; our two days of euphoria came to an abrupt and painful end.

The practice of auction by sealed bids is, to my mind, a particularly loathsome form of selling a property. I had a furious argument on the telephone with the agent, who claimed that he was only working in the best interest of his client.

I rang The Cottage every hour on the hour until the owners returned from work and they agreed to see me. They were understandably a little cool when I arrived.

I confirmed the detail of their agent's telephoned offer to me and whilst they now understood what had transpired, they felt that it was best not to change things again.

'May I make a point here?' This was my last throw of the dice, for whilst it may have been possible that my sealed bid would secure the property we craved, it would be an understatement to admit that I couldn't trust the agent as far as I could throw him.

'As you are aware, I have lived in this house for nineteen years and I can tell you that I know this building inside out. For instance, in 1982, all the windows were due for replacement, but because we were planning to leave, I repaired and repainted every one. Now, seventeen years later, despite the cloaking effect of the ivy, I can tell you that they are the same windows. I know and you know that every one of them needs to be replaced. I also noticed that the garage roof hasn't been replaced, so it still leaks, even if you periodically seal the bad joints. I know which walls have damp problems; just painting the end kitchen and dining room wall won't solve them.

I looked at the rather attractive fireplace display. 'Does the smoke still collect in the roof space when you light a fire? If it does, it will need a class-one liner fitting. Look, I know that all these problems can be put right but at a price.'

I could tell that they were aware of all the defects that I had itemised and I quickly continued, for I felt that I shouldn't encourage any form of discussion.

'I offered you your asking price without a quibble and without it being subject to a building survey report. No one else will offer a sealed bid of any note without first having a building survey and even the laziest surveyor can't fail to pick up on a few of the problems. I'll offer an extra £1,000 to agree a deal now and we're prepared to wait until you sort out your next property. Your solicitor can have a deposit tomorrow. Do we have a deal?'

I think that they were as relieved to accept the offer as I was to have the matter settled; we shook hands and had a cup of tea.

When I returned, Jean was sitting on the bottom step of the staircase in our apartment's foyer. I grinned and nodded my head to her. Jean burst into tears; I was a star!

I now sit typing in my little study in The Cottage, reliving that conversation with a sigh of relief.

Jean's cup is running over, for coming back to The Cottage is the culmination of her dream, the one she'd always had but never mentioned whilst living my dream on our Mediterranean adventure. I realise now that moving back to The Cottage should always have been part of my plan, but had it been so, the feasibility of securing success would have been a worry for me that on reflection I'm glad I didn't have. It's now ten years since we moved back into our family home and Jean's joy at being here never diminishes; I have to admit that I'm not too dissatisfied, either.

My memories of our journey are vivid and I hope that they will always be so. Regrettably, Geoff Hubbard died several years ago and as you may have expected, the church was packed for the funeral ceremony: family, friends, business colleagues, jockeys, racehorse trainers and owners, employees past and present, all were there from all parts of the UK. Some of the soliloquies that referred to several amusing stories and anecdotes about his life had the congregation laughing at times, but there weren't many dry eyes by the end of the service.

Without doubt, our meeting with Geoff Hubbard was central to the success and enjoyment of our adventure. We will always remember him with deep affection and when I finish typing these last few lines, I will go down to the kitchen and pour myself a gin and tonic. With the ice clinking I will walk through to the lounge, but on my way I will stop at the hall mirror and as I often do, I will visualise GA and his beaming smile in its reflection; I'll raise my glass and with no little emotion, I will propose the toast. **'Drink, dear boy?'**